How To Know

THE

TAPEWORMS

How To Know

THE

TAPEWORMS

Gerald D. Schmidt

University of Northern Colorado

WM. C. BROWN COMPANY PUBLISHERS
Dubuque, Iowa

Library of Congress Catalog Card Number: 71-129602

ISBN 0–697–04861–6 (Cloth)
ISBN 0–697–04860–8 (Paper)

THE PICTURED-KEY NATURE SERIES

How To Know The—

AQUATIC PLANTS, Prescott, 1969
BEETLES, Jaques, 1951
BUTTERFLIES, Ehrlich, 1961
CACTI, Dawson, 1963
EASTERN LAND SNAILS, Burch, 1962
ECONOMIC PLANTS, Jaques, 1948, 1958
FALL FLOWERS, Cuthbert, 1948
FRESHWATER ALGAE, Prescott, 1954, 1970
FRESHWATER FISHES, Eddy, 1957, 1969
GRASSES, Pohl, 1953, 1968
GRASSHOPPERS, Helfer, 1963
IMMATURE INSECTS, Chu, 1949
INSECTS, Jaques, 1947
LAND BIRDS, Jaques, 1947
LICHENS, Hale, 1969
LIVING THINGS, Jaques, 1946
MAMMALS, Booth, 1949, 1970
MARINE ISOPOD CRUSTACEANS, Schultz, 1969
MOSSES AND LIVERWORTS, Conard, 1944, 1956
PLANT FAMILIES, Jaques, 1948
POLLEN AND SPORES, Kapp, 1969
PROTOZOA, Jahn, 1949
ROCKS AND MINERALS, Helfer, 1970
SEAWEEDS, Dawson, 1956
SPIDERS, Kaston, 1952
SPRING FLOWERS, Cuthbert, 1943, 1949
TAPEWORMS, Schmidt, 1970
TREMATODES, Schell, 1970
TREES, Jaques, 1946
WATER BIRDS, Jaques-Ollivier, 1960
WEEDS, Jaques, 1959
WESTERN TREES, Baerg, 1955

PREFACE

Tapeworms have long excited in man a sense of bewilderment, and sometimes fear, because they seem to appear spontaneously within a host and, when present, occasionally cause disease. In the last two centuries, even after most scientists accepted the idea that bacteria and other microorganisms were not spontaneously generated, many refused to believe that intestinal worms did not appear *de novo*. How else could they be explained? The pioneering works of Siebold, Küchenmeister, Leuckart, Villot, Braun, and others dispelled superstition forever from scientific thought on these forms and laid the foundation for the modern science of cestodology.

A vast literature has accumulated through the years, describing such aspects as morphology, taxonomy, life cycles, physiology, pathogenesis, and host-relationships of tapeworms. Even so, much remains unknown. In all phases of cestodology we are only on the threshold. This is indeed a fruitful area for research, and there is much promise that exciting discoveries will be made in the years to come.

In this book I have attempted to ease the difficulties of tapeworm identification by providing up-to-date keys, based on morphological features, of the genera of tapeworms of the world. Every effort was made to keep the keys as simple as possible. Whenever feasible, I have not used cryptic characters, such as muscle bundle arrangement and nerve cord location, that necessitates sectioning or dissection of the specimen.

I am well aware that controversy abounds in the systematics of cestodes and that the system I have chosen will not please all workers in the field. Yet, I feel if one can identify an unknown tapeworm to genus with a minimum of difficulty, he is then in a position to judge for himself the merits of higher categories and can select the scheme that best satisfies him.

Many persons contributed advice and effort toward this book. I am especially indebted to Dr. Robert L. Rausch, Dr. H. Harford Williams, Dr. John Mackiewicz, and Dr. Fred Whittaker, who read parts of the manuscript and generously gave me the benefit of their special knowledge of certain groups. Mr. Gary Buhler aided with some of the illustrations. However, all errors still remaining are my sole responsibility.

Most illustrations are adapted from published descriptions. If the source is not cited specifically, the description of the original author was followed. When no author is cited the drawings are original.

In searching the world literature, I have drawn upon hundreds of different journals and monographs. Especially useful have been Yamaguti's *Systema Helminthum*, vol. II, *Cestodes of Vertebrates*, and the classic treatise *The Zoology of Tapeworms* by Wardle and McLeod. These two monographs are highly recommended to the serious student of tapeworms. A list of basic references is included in an appendix.

It has been my intent to provide a low-cost, readily available key to the tapeworms, equally useful for the beginning student and the professional parasitologist. I will welcome suggestions and criticisms from fellow students of this fascinating group of parasites.

The literature search was terminated March 12, 1969.

My greatest thanks go to my wife Andra and my boys Stephen and Jeffrey who gave me the time that was rightfully theirs.

Gerald D. Schmidt
Greeley, Colorado

INTRODUCTION

Tapeworms hold an established and well-recognized place in the hierarchy of the animal kingdom. Their acoelous nature and bilateral symmetry, together with well-organized organ systems, place them in the Phylum Platyhelminthes, along with the Trematoda and Turbellaria. Adaptions to endoparasitism have resulted in complete loss of a digestive system and an increase in reproductive capacity that often staggers the imagination. The unique characters of this group of organisms was recognized by Rudolphi, who in 1809 proposed the class Cestoidea to contain them. The concept still is favored today, although some authorities prefer the name Cestoda.

Nearly every species of vertebrate examined is shown to be host for one or more species of tapeworms. Since there are about 60,000 species of vertebrates, and fewer than 4,000 species of cestodes have been described, it follows that an immense number of species is yet to be found. Unfortunately, comparatively few zoologists are working in the systematics of tapeworms today, partly due to the absence or inaccessability of identification keys. It is hoped that the present book will partly alleviate this problem.

CONTENTS

To Dr. O. Wilford Olsen
scholar, teacher, and friend
this book is dedicated

THE KINGS*

A. D. Hope
Professor, Department of English,
Australian National University, Canberra

The lion in deserts royally takes his prey;
Gaunt crags cast back the hunting eagle's scream.
The King of Parasites, delicate, white and blind,
Ruling his world of fable even as they,
Dreams out his greedy and imperious dream
Immortal in the bellies of mankind.

In a rich bath of pre-digested soup,
Warm in the pulsing bowel, safely shut
From the bright ambient horror of sun and air,
His slender segments ripening loop by loop,
Broods the voluptuous monarch of the gut,
The Tapeworm, the prodigious Solitaire.

Alone among the royal beasts of prey
He takes no partner, no imperial mate
Seeks his embrace and bears his clamorous brood;
Within himself, in soft and passionate play,
Two sexes in their vigour celebrate
The raptures of helminthine solitude.

From the barbed crown that hooks him to his host,
The limbless ribbon, fecund, flat and wet
Sways as the stream's delicious juices move;
And as the ripe joints rupture and are lost,
Quivers in the prolonged, delirious jet
And spasm of unremitting acts of love.

And Nature no less prodigal in birth
In savage profusion spreads his royal sway:
Herds are his nurseries till the mouths of men
At public feasts, or the domestic hearth,
Or by the hands of children at their play,
Transmit his line to human flesh again.

The former times, as emblems of an age,
Graved the gier-eagle's pride, the lion's great heart,
Leviathan sporting in the perilous sea;
Pictured on History's or the Muse's page,
All knew the King, the Hero, set apart
To stand up stiff against calamity,

Breed courage amid a broken nation's groans,
Cherish the will in men about to die,
To chasten with just rule a barbarous tribe
And guard, at last the earth that kept his bones.
And still the Muse, who does not flatter or lie,
Finds for our age a symbol to describe.

The secret life of Technocratic Man,
Abject desire, base fear that shapes his law,
His idols of the cave, the mart, the sty—
No lion at bay for a beleaguered clan,
No eagle with the serpent in his claw,
Nor dragon soter with his searing eye,

But the great, greedy, parasitic worm,
Sucking the life of nations from within
Blind and degenerate, snug in excrement.
'Behold your dream!' she says. 'View here the form
And mirror of Time, the Shape you trusted in
While your world crumbled and my heavens were rent.'

GENERAL MORPHOLOGY OF TAPEWORMS

Although considerable variation of morphology occurs between different orders of tapeworms, there are underlying similarities which unite the orders into the class Cestoda. An understanding of tapeworm anatomy is essential for successful utilization of the keys. The following generalized description is supplemented within the text of this book, especially where specialization has modified the basic pattern.

Tapeworms (Fig. 1) usually consist of a chain of segments called *proglottids,* each of which contains one or more sets of reproductive organs. The proglottids are continuously produced near the anterior end of the animal by a process of asexual budding. Each bud moves toward the posterior end as a new one takes its place, and during the process becomes sexually mature. The gravid or senile, terminal segments detach or disintegrate. The entire body thus formed is called a *strobila,* and a segmented strobila is said to be *polyzoic.* In some groups the strobila consists of a single segment, and is then said to be *monozoic.* If each proglottid overlaps the following one, the strobila is said to be *craspedote;* if not, it is called *acraspedote* (Fig. 2).

Often between the scolex and the first segments of the strobila there is a smooth, undifferentiated zone called the *neck.* This may be long or short, or absent altogether. The neck, or in its absence the posterior part of the scolex, contains germinal cells which have the potential for budding off the segments, a process called *strobilization.*

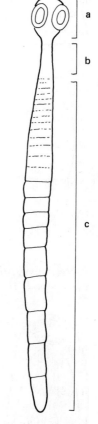

Fig. 1. Generalized tapeworm showing typical morphology. a—Scolex. b—Neck. c—Strobila.

At the anterior end is usually found a holdfast organ or *scolex* which is the principal means of locomotion of these animals. Depending on the group, the scolex may be provided with suckers, grooves, hooks, spines, glandular areas, or combinations of these. In some instances the scolex is quite simple, lacking any of these specializations, or it may be absent altogether. In a few species it is normal for the scolex to be lost and replaced in function by a

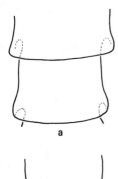

distortion of the anterior end of the strobila. The organ thus produced is called a *pseudoscolex*. A few species are capable of penetrating into the gut wall of the host where the scolex and often a considerable length of strobila are encapsulated by host reactions, while the remainder of the strobila dangles into the lumen of the gut.

Since the taxonomy of tapeworms is based primarily upon the anatomy of the organ systems, an understanding of these systems is essential.

Fig. 2. Craspedote and acraspedote segments. *a.* Craspedote. *b.* Acraspedote.

Nervous system—The structure of the nervous system is poorly understood. It appears to be a modified ladder-type, with a longitudinal cord near each lateral margin and transverse commissures in each segment. The two lateral cords are united in the scolex in a complex arrangement of ganglia and commissures. The nervous system is rarely used as a taxonomic character, although the lateral cords are convenient points of reference for the location of other structures.

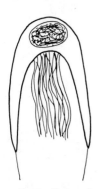

Fig. 3. Flame cell.

Osmoregulatory system—As in other groups of Platyhelminthes, the organ of osmoregulation is the *protonephridium*, or *flame cell* (Fig. 3). These unicellular glands remove excess fluid from the body parenchyma and discharge it from the body by a series of collecting tubules. The largest of these tubules are called the *osmoregulatory canals* (Fig. 4) and are typically of two pairs, one ventrolateral and the other (usually smaller) dorsolateral on each side. These canals may be independent throughout the strobila or may ramify and anastomose in each proglottid. Commonly, a transverse canal near the posterior margin of each segment unites the ventral canals while the dorsal canals remain simple.

The dorsal and ventral canals join in the scolex, usually in association with complex branching. Posteriorly, the two pairs of canals unite into an excretory bladder with a single pore. In polyzoic species this bladder is lost with the detachment of the terminal proglottid and thereafter the canals empty independently at the end of the strobila. In a few instances the major canals also empty through short, lateral ducts.

The major function of the osmoregulatory system seems to be water balance, but some excretion of metabolic wastes also probably occurs. The dorsal canals carry fluid toward the scolex and the ventral canals carry it toward the posterior end. Occasionally the dorsal canals are absent. The arrangement of major canals is of taxonomic importance.

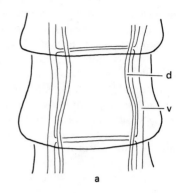

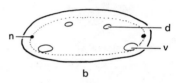

Fig. 4. Osmoregulatory canals. a. Dorsal view. b. Cross section. d—Dorsal vessel. n—lateral nerve cord. v—ventral vessel.

Muscular system—Most tapeworms possess well-defined, longitudinal bundles of muscle fibers and scattered dorsoventral fibers. The scolex is well supplied with muscle fibers, making it extraordinarily motile. In the strobila, the longitudinal muscle bundles are often arranged in a definite layer within the paren-

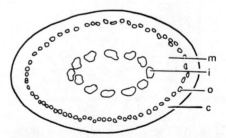

Fig. 5. Muscle bundle arrangement. c—cortex; i—inner muscle bundle. m—medulla. o—outer muscle bundle.

chyma, dividing it into a well-defined cortex and medulla (Fig. 5). The arrangement of these muscles is of taxonomic importance, but since sectioning of the specimen is usually necessary to observe them, their use is omitted from the keys whenever possible.

Reproductive systems—All known tapeworms are *monoecious*, or *hermaphroditic*, with the exception of a few species from birds and one from a stingray, which are *dioecious* or *gonochoristic*. Most commonly, each proglottid contains one complete set each of male and female reproductive organs, although a few species have two complete sets in each segment. A few rare species in birds have one female and two male sets in each proglottid.

As the segment moves toward the rear of the strobila, as described above, the reproductive organs mature and embryonated eggs are formed. Most commonly, the male organs mature first and produce sperm, which are stored until maturation of the ovary. Early maturation of the testes is called *protandry* or *androgyny*, and is used as a taxonomic character. In fewer species the ovaries mature first, a condition known as *protogyny* or *gynandry*. This, too, is used as a taxonomic character.

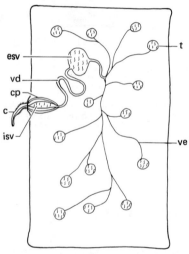

Fig. 6. Proglottid showing male organs. c—cirrus. cp—cirrus pouch. isv—inner seminal vesicle. esv—external seminal vesicle. t—testes. vd—vas deferens. ve—vas efferens.

The *male reproductive system* (Fig. 6) consists of one to many *testes*, each of which has a fine *vas efferens*. The vasa efferentia unite into a common *vas deferens* which drains the sperm toward the genital pore. The vas deferens may dilate into a spheroid *external seminal vesicle* or it may be highly convoluted, the convolutions functioning in sperm storage, or it may be quite simple. Eventually, the vas deferens leads into a *cirrus pouch*, which is a muscular sheath containing the terminal portion of the male system. Inside the cirrus pouch the vas deferens may form a convoluted *ejaculatory duct* or swell into an *internal seminal vesicle*.

Distally, the duct is modified into a muscular *cirrus*, the male copulatory organ. The cirrus may be spinous or not and varies considerably in size between species. The cirrus can invaginate into the cirrus pouch and evaginate through the *cirrus pore*. Often, the male and female genital pores open into a common sunken chamber, the *genital atrium*. This atrium may be simple, or armed with a variety of spines or stylets, or may be glandular or possess accessary pockets. The cirrus pore or the atrial pore may open on the margin or somewhere on a flat surface of the proglottid.

The *female reproductive system* (Fig. 7) consists of a single *ovary*, which may be large or small, compact or diffuse, and may be located anywhere within the proglottid, depending on the genus. Associated with the ovary are *vitelline cells*, or *vitellaria*, which contribute to eggshell formation and perhaps nutrition for the developing embryo. These may be in a single, compact *vitelline gland* or scattered as follicles in various patterns. As ova mature they leave the ovary through a single *oviduct* which may have a controlling sphincter, the *ovicapt*. Fertilization usually occurs in the proximal oviduct. Cells from the vitelline glands pass through

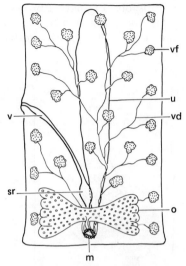

Fig. 7. Proglotted showing female organs. m—Mehlis' gland. o—ovary. u—uterus. v—vagina. vd—vitelline duct. vf—vitelline follicle.

a common *vitelline duct*, sometimes equipped with a small *vitelline reservoir*, and join with the zygote. Together they pass into a zone of the oviduct surrounded by unicellular glands called *Mehlis' glands*. The lumen of this zone is known as the *oötype*. The Mehlis' glands secrete a very thin membrane around the zygote and associated vitelline cells. Eggshell formation is then completed from within by the vitelline cells. Leaving the oötype the embryonating egg passes into the *uterus* where embryonation is completed.

The form of the uterus varies considerably between groups. It may be a simple or convoluted tube, a reticular, lobulated or simple sac, or may be replaced by other structures. In some groups the uterus disappears and the eggs, either singly or in groups, are enclosed within hyaline *egg capsules* imbedded within the parenchyma (Fig. 8). In other

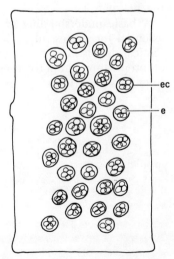

Fig. 8. Proglotted with egg capsules. e—egg. ec—egg capsule.

groups one or more fibro-muscular structures, the *paruterine organs*, form attached to the uterus. In this case the eggs pass from the uterus into the paruterine organs which assume the function

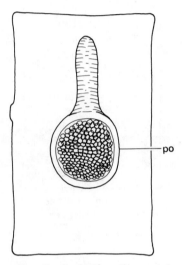

of a uterus (Fig. 9). The uterus then usually degenerates. Eggs are released from the worm through a preformed *uterine pore* in many groups. In others, the proglottid splits or fragments, releasing the eggs. In many *apolytic* species the gravid proglottids detach from the strobila and are passed from the host, where they crawl about on feces or soil scattering eggs as they go. In most *anapolytic* species the eggs are first discharged, then the senile segments are released, either singly or in chains.

The female genital pore, the *vaginal pore,* usually opens near the cirrus pore. The *vagina* may be armed distally with minute spines and may have one or more

Fig. 9. Proglottid with paruterine organ. po—paruterine organ.

sphincters along its length. Near the proximal end there is usually a dilation called the *seminal receptacle* which stores sperm received in copulation. From the seminal receptacle a duct continues into the oötype.

A basic understanding of the general anatomy of tapeworms is essential for successful utilization of the keys. Elucidation of anatomical details of a specimen is dependent upon correct techniques of preparation properly used. A brief discussion of techniques is found on page 13.

BIOLOGY OF TAPEWORMS

Complete life cycles are unknown for most species of tapeworms. In fact, there are several orders in which not a single complete life cycle has been determined. Among the life cycles that are known, considerable variation exists in larval forms and patterns of development. Since these variations are discussed in detail in nearly any text on general parasitology, they need not be considered here, except in a general manner. An excellent source of life cycle information is Olsen's *Animal Parasites, Their Biology and Life Cycles.*

Nearly every tapeworm whose life cycle is known has an *indirect life cycle.* That is, development to sexual maturity occurs in one animal, the *definitive host,* and the larval states occur in a different animal, the *intermediate host.* One notable exception with a *direct life cycle* is *Hymenolepis nana* (Cyclophyllidea, Hymenolepididae), which can complete its larval stages within the definitive host.

Sexually mature tapeworms live in the intestine (or its diverticulae), or rarely in the coelom, of all classes of vertebrates. An exception to this is the genus *Archigetes* (Caryophyllidea, Caryophylliidae) which matures in the coelom of freshwater oligochaetes. Once mature, a worm may live for a few days or up to ten years or more, depending on the species. During their reproductive life, tapeworms produce from a few up to millions of eggs, each containing a larva with the potential of maturing into the adult form. Obviously, the mortality rate of these larvae is high, or we might all be filled to our ears with tapeworms.

Since most tapeworms are hermaphroditic they are capable of fertilizing their own eggs. Sperm transfer can be from the cirrus to the vagina of the same proglottid, or when the opportunity affords, between proglottids of adjacent strobilas. Usually the sperms are deposited within the vagina, but a few species are known in which a vaginal pore is absent. In these cases *hypodermic impregnation* has been observed. Here, the cirrus is plunged through the body wall and the sperms are deposited within the parenchyma. How they find their way into the seminal receptacle is not known.

In some groups mature proglottides detach and lead independent existences within the gut of the host, copulating with each other upon contact. When a segment detaches before the eggs are shed, the species is said to be *apolytic.* When the eggs leave the segment before the segment detaches, it is said to be *anapolytic.*

7

As pointed out above, few species are known to be dioecious. In these cases, both sexes must be present within the definitive host for reproduction to occur, and sperm transfer may be accomplished by copulation or by hypodermic impregnation, according to species.

Indirect Life Cycles

Both invertebrates and vertebrates serve as intermediate hosts of tapeworms. While nearly every group of *invertebrates* has been discovered harboring developing tapeworms, the most common are insects, crustaceans, mites, annelids, and molluscs. As a general rule, when a tapeworm larva is found in an aquatic invertebrate the adult form occurs in an aquatic vertebrate. A similar assumption can be made for terrestrial hosts.

Vertebrate intermediate hosts occur among fishes, amphibians, reptiles and mammals. Tapeworm larvae found in those hosts normally mature within predators whose diet includes the intermediary.

Occasionally, a *paratenic host* occurs in a life cycle. This host is one in which a larval stage can survive but not mature. Often this is the end of the road for the parasite, but when the paratenic is a normal food item of the definitive host, it may provide a useful "ecological bridge" between the small intermediate host and the large definitive host.

Larval Forms

Tapeworm larvae occur in a variety of forms (see *Key to Larval Tapeworms,* Page 18). The following is a list of basic types, with the general groups of intermediate hosts in which they are found. Several of these are divided into subcategories by various authors.

1. *Hexacanth,* or *oncosphere* (Fig. 10a)—the small, spheroid larva that emerges from the egg of any of the Eucestoda. It is characterized by six small hooks which are used to penetrate the gut wall of the intermediate host. In a few species, the hooks are reported not to be present. A hexacanth with a ciliated epithelium is called a *coracidium* (Fig. 10b).

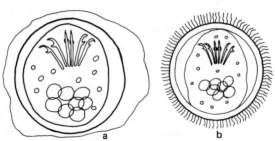

Fig. 10. a. Hexacanth. b. Coracidium.

2. *Decacanth,* or *lycophore* (Fig. 11)—the larva that emerges from the egg in the Cestodaria. Similar to the hexacanth, but with ten hooks.

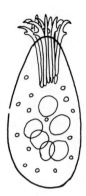

Fig. 11. Lycophore.

3. *Procercoid* (Fig. 12)—a simple, elongated larva, usually with a posterior bulb, the *cercomer,* that bears the hexacanth hooks. The cercomer is often lost before the procercoid is infective to the next host. This stage develops further into a more advanced stage, except in *Archigetes* where by *neoteny* it becomes sexually mature. The procercoid larva is found in several orders of tapeworms, but is absent in the Cyclophyllidea. It develops in arthropods and annelids.

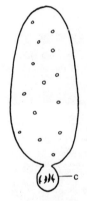

Fig. 12. Procercoid. c—cercomer.

4. *Plerocercoid* (Fig. 13)—derived from a procercoid, this is an elongate, undifferentiated or partially differentiated larva that can mature into an adult if eaten by the definitive host. If the identity of this form is unknown, it is often referred to as a *sparganum.* The body is solid parenchyma. It is sometimes capable of proliferation by asexual budding. It develops in fish, amphibians, reptiles and mammals.

Fig. 13. Plerocercoid.

5. *Plerocercus* (Fig. 14)—a variety of pleurocercoid found in some of the Trypanorhyncha. The posterior end of the body is a bladder, the *blastocyst,* into which the rest of the body can withdraw. They develop in fish.

Fig. 14. Plerocercus.
b—blastocyst.

6. *Cysticercoid* (Fig. 15 a, b, c)—a larval form developing from a hexacanth. The body is solid and there is a formed protoscolex that usually is invaginated into a cavity. There are many varieties of these, of varying shapes and with differing enclosing membranes. They are one of the larval forms of the Cyclophyllidea and develop in arthropods, molluscs, annelids and a few lesser groups.

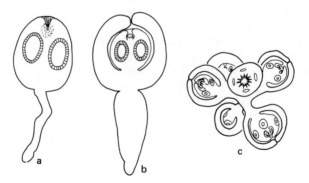

Fig. 15. Typical cysticercoid types. a. Simple, with no enclosing tissues. b. With scolex enclosed. c. Multiple.

7. *Strobilocercoid* (Fig. 16)—a cysticercoid that shows strobilization. It is found in dragonflys.

Fig. 16. Strobilocercoid.

8. *Tetrathyridium* (Fig. 17)—this larval form is known in the cyclophyllidean genus *Mesocestoides*. It is a fairly large cysticercoid that develops in vertebrates which have ingested an earlier cysticercoid in an invertebrate. Some are capable of asexual proliferation. They develop mainly in rodents and lizards, which are then second intermediate hosts.

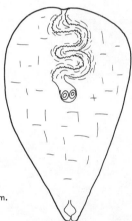

Fig. 17. Tetrathyridium.

9. *Cysticercus*—this is similar to a cysticercoid except that the body is provided with a hollow bladder. They develop in many kinds of mammals, including man. There are several types, as follows:

a. *Simple* (Fig. 18a)—a single protoscolex is present.

b. *Coenurus* (Fig. 18b)—several to many protoscoleces are present, each on a separate stalk invaginated into the common bladder.

c. *Strobilocercus* (Fig. 18c)—this is a simple cysticercus that shows strobilization.

d. *Unilocular hydatid* (Fig. 18d)—up to several million protoscoleces are present. Usually, there is an inner or *endogenous budding* of *daughter cysts*, each with many scoleces or each containing other cysts with protoscoleces inside. Rarely *exogenous budding* occurs, resulting in two or more hydatids. This form may grow very large, sometimes containing several quarts of fluid. Rarely, they are sterile, with no protoscoleces present. Usually, many protoscoleces break free and sink to the bottom of the cyst, forming *hydated sand*. This larval form is known only for the genus *Echinococcus*.

e. *Multilocular*, or *alveolar hydated* (Fig. 18e)—this larval form, known only for *Echinococcus multilocularis*, exhibits extensive exogenous budding, resulting in an infiltration of host tissue by numerous small cysts, each containing many protoscoleces.

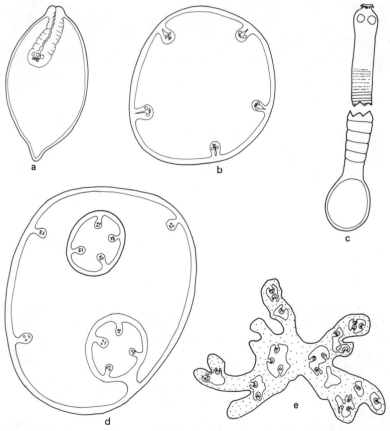

Fig. 18. Cysticercus types. a. Simple. b. Coenurus. c. Strobilocercus. d. Unilocular hydated. e. Multilocular hydatid.

TECHNIQUES OF STUDY

Numerous references are available which expand the following brief account. One very useful manual is Meyer and Penner's, *Laboratory Essentials of Parasitology*.

Obtaining Specimens

Adult tapeworms may be found in literally any species of vertebrate animal, while larval forms are often encountered in a wide variety of vertebrates and invertebrates. Since adults are found most commonly in the intestine and rarely in the coelom, or bile or pancreatic ducts these are the only organs that need be examined. If at all possible, the host should be examined immediately after death, while the tapeworms are still alive. Postmortum changes, including loss of rostellar hooks, often prevent identification of the specimen. Further, if the worm dies within the gut of its host, it usually is contracted such that adequate study of it may be impossible. If it is not feasible to examine the host soon after its death, the viscera should be frozen as quickly as possible and kept until needed.

It is more convenient if the intestine is removed before the search begins, either entire in the case of a small animal or in sections if a larger animal is being examined. If the host was shot, a resulting perforation of the gut sometimes results in tapeworms being discovered in anolomous locations.

For examination, place the intestine in a shallow dish or pan of tap water and carefully cut it open with a pair of sharp, small scissors. Care must be taken to avoid cutting worms present in the lumen. Large forms are easily seen, but a dissecting microscope is often required to find small worms. It is imperative that the scolex is not lost, for the classification depends in large part on the study of its characteristics. Remove the worms that are detached. Immersion of the gut in tap water will paralyze the worms, causing them to release their hold on the host mucosa and allowing relaxation of the strobila. Fixation should not be attempted until the worms do not respond to touch. Place all specimens in tap water at room temperature. (Note: Caryophyllidea are best placed directly in steaming hot formalin).

With large sized intestines or those with abundant contents, it often is best to remove the obvious worms and then gently scrape the mucosa with a scalpel. Remove the gut and pour the remaining material into a graduated cylinder or other tall container, fill with tap water and allow the sediment to sink to the bottom. When

13

this has occurred, pour off the supernatent fluid and replace with clean tap water. Repeat this procedure until the supernatent fluid is clear, then pour a small amount of the sediment at a time into a small dish and examine. With this technique it unlikely that even the smallest worms will be missed.

Fixation

A fixative should preserve the specimen in a life-like condition, with no brittleness or other unfavorable side effects. Unfortunately, the perfect fixative has not yet been discovered. Two widely used fixatives which are good, inexpensive, easily obtainable, and simple to use are AFA, or a solution of 5 per cent formalin. The former is prepared by mixing five parts glacial acetic acid, ten parts formalin, and 85 parts of 85 per cent ethanol. Either fixative should be poured gently over relaxed and extended, large specimens, while small ones may be dropped directly into it. If the tapeworm is not completely relaxed before fixing it will contract at this point and become useless for study. The specimens may be stored up to a year in a fixative or transferred to 70 per cent ethanol with a little glycerine for indefinite storage.

AFA is not recommended for histochemical studies, since it is a coagulative-type fixative. In this case, four per cent formalin or solutions of acrolein or gluteraldehyde are suggested.

Staining

Several stains are satisfactory for the preparation of tapeworms. Probably the two most commonly used for general studies are *hematoxylin* and *carmine*. Since the former is used in an aqueous solution and the latter is prepared in alcohol, the specimens must be passed through a graded series of concentrations of alcohol to the level of the stain. For example, if the worm was fixed in formalin and one wishes to stain it in a carmine-70 per cent alcohol solution, it should be moved through a series of 30 per cent, 50 per cent, and 70 per cent alcohols before placing in the staining solution. The duration in each concentration depends on the size of the specimen, but 15 minutes should be sufficient in most cases. Since hematoxylin has a tendency to fade after a few years, its use should be limited to short-term studies.

The two basic methods of staining are *progressive* and *regressive*. In the former the specimen is placed in the stain solution and left there until the correct definition of internal organs is accomplished. At this point, staining is stopped by placing the worm in plain alcohol. Success of this technique depends upon the skill of the worker, for considerable experience is required to differentiate between proper staining and overstaining.

In the *regressive staining technique,* the worms are first overstained, then destained until proper differentiation is accomplished. This method is easier for the beginner and has the advantage of removing stain from the surface layers, thus making the internal organs more visible. For destaining hemytoxylin, use 5% aqueous hydrochloric acid and for carmine use 5% acidulated 70% alcohol. Counterstaining is not recommended for either method, for it tends to obscure fine structures.

After staining is completed, dehydrate the specimen by passing it through a graded series of alcohol solutions, from 70 per cent through 100 per cent, for about 15 minutes each. The specimens are then cleared in preparation for mounting. Several clearing agents are readily available, such as xylene, oil of wintergreen, oil of cloves, terpincol, cedarwood oil, or beechwood creosote. The last mentioned has the distinct advantage of not causing brittleness of the specimen. Clearing takes only a few minutes; by the time the specimen has sunk to the bottom of the dish maximum clearing has been obtained.

Mounting

Place the specimen from the clearing agent into the mounting medium on a slide. Numerous mountants are available, and most are satisfactory. Canada balsam has the best optical properties for photography but is expensive and tends to become acetic, thus destaining the specimen. (This problem can be avoided by placing a few marble chips in the balsam bottle). Small specimens can be conveniently arranged on a slide, but large specimens must be cut and arranged in rows, or representative sections only may be selected. If a single specimen is mounted, it may be advantageous to support one side of the coverglass with a small glass chip or piece of capillary tubing. If more than one specimen is placed on a slide, they can be arranged to give even support to the coverglass. Place the coverglass carefully, avoiding the capture of air bubbles in the medium. If an insufficient amount of medium was used, more can easily be added by applying it to the underedge of the coverglass, from which it will flow toward the middle.

The mountant should be hardened before concentrated study of the specimen is attempted. Setting the slide in a safe place at room temperature is satisfactory but slow. The process can be speeded up in a drying oven set at about 56° C. As the medium recedes due to evaporation of the solvent, add more to the edge of the coverglass.

Labeling and Storing Slides

Each completed slide must be labeled with collecting data or a code number to avoid later confusion. Much mystery exists in the literature and in private collections due to reporting the incorrect host for a parasite.

Stand slide boxes on end so the slides are horizontal to prevent the specimens from gradually drifting to the edge of the slide.

Before the collection becomes very large, it is well worth the time required to set up a method of cataloging the specimens. This will surely prevent much grief in later years when a certain specimen is needed. A file of three-by-five cards, arranged alphabetically with family indices will serve nicely for several thousand specimens.

How to Use the Keys

The keys in this book are dichotomous; that is, there are two choices at each step. Every attempt was made to avoid ambiguity, but there are often so many exceptions to a general plan within a group that it is possible to make the wrong choice. If the specimen does not key out the first time through, go back to any step where the decision was not clear and run it through the other choice.

One may begin the keys at any level, depending upon how much he knows about the species in question. Thus, if the tapeworm is completely unknown to the worker, he should begin with the key to subclasses, then to orders, then to families and so on. If he knows the order beforehand, he may begin with the key to families within that order, and so on.

After keying the specimen to genus, it is important to compare it with the detailed generic description. There are so many undescribed genera that a new form may be in hand and yet key out to a previously described genus.

If it seems certain that the correct generic designation has been determined, the limit of usefulness of this book has been reached. In a few instances references to keys to the species in the genus are included. Unfortunately, these are woefully few and far between.

If one wishes to identify the tapeworm to species, the method is simple, if somewhat laborious. A complete list of the species in the genus or subgenus must be compiled and the specimen compared with each species. If it matches one of the described species, the work is done; if it matches none of the species, it can only be concluded that the specimens represent a population of organisms that are new to science. It is then the obligation and privilege of the researcher to see that the species is properly described. Since most of the literature on the genus will be in his hands by this point, it is recommended that the worker include in his publication a key to the species in the genus, thus facilitating the efforts of those who subsequently work with this particular group of tapeworms. It must be remembered, however, that variations in morphology within a species often occurs. A long series of specimens is of great advantage in determining whether a specimen represents a new species or is only a variation of an already described form.

To compile the list of species in a genus, one should make use of the *Zoological Record, Biological Abstracts,* and most especially, *Helminthological Abstracts.* This last journal, dating from 1932 to present, is probably the most complete and up to date of the serial abstracts.

The U. S. Department of Agriculture Parasitological Laboratory, Beltsville, Maryland, has compiled a card file on the literature of parasitology that is probably the most extensive in the world. It is called the *Index-Catalogue of Medical and Veterinary Zoology,* and consists of two main parts, an Author Index and a Host-Parasite Index. These indices are available to persons who wish to visit the Beltsville laboratory for this purpose. The Author Index portion has been printed by the U. S. Government Printing Office, and is supplemented each year. Copies of this Index are available to qualified persons and libraries and are extremely useful in systematics work. Each reference cited in this book may be found in the Author Index. At the time of this writing, publication of the Host-Parasite Index is in progress.

The U. S. National Museum Helminthological Collection is also housed at the U.S.D.A. Parasitological Laboratory. Here, many type specimens are available on loan to qualified workers.

A glossary describing the terms used in this text is appended at the end. When in doubt as to the proper meaning of any term, the glossary should be consulted for clarification.

The rest of this book is devoted to the taxonomy of tapeworms. First, there is a key to larval forms, then a series of keys to the adults. I wish you success in your studies of this fascinating group of animals.

KEY TO LARVAL TAPEWORMS

1a. Larva hatching from egg 2
1b. Larva parasitic in a vertebrate or invertebrate 4
2a. Larva with ten small hooks ....*lycophore.*
2b. Larva with six small hooks 3
3a. Larva ciliated ....*coracidium.*
3b. Larva not ciliated .... *hexacanth,* or *oncosphere.*
4a. Larva with fluid-filled bladder 5
4b. Larva with solid structure replacing bladder 10
5a. Parasite of fishes. Scolex with four armed tentacles ....
.... *pleurocercus.*
5b. Parasites of mammals 6
6a. Strobila with evident segmentation ....*strobilocercus.*
6b. No evident segmentation of strobila 7
7a. Single scolex present ....*cysticercus.*
7b. More than one scolex present 8
8a. No exogenous or endogenous budding of daughter cysts ....
....*coenurus.*
8b. Daughter cysts present, formed by exogenous or endogenous budding 9
9a. Budding mainly endogenous ....*unilocular hydatid.*
9b. Budding mainly exogenous ....*multilocular hydatid.*
10a. Larva parasitic in vertebrate 11
10b. Larva parasitic in invertebrate 12
11a. Scolex undifferentiated or with dorsal and ventral bothria, or tentacles .... *pleurocercoid,* or *sparganum.*
11b. Scolex with four suckers ....*tetrathyridium.*
12a. Strobila with evident segmentation ....*strobilocercoid.*
12b. Strobila without evident segmentation 13
13a. Scolex well differentiated, with four suckers and often with armed restellum ....*cysticercoid.*
13b. Scolex undifferentiated. Often with posterior bulb, the cercomer, that bears the hexacanth hooks ....*procercoid.*

Key to the Subclasses of Cestoda

1a. Polyzoic (except orders Caryophyllidea and Spatheboth-riidea), with one or more sets of reproductive systems per proglottid. Scolex present. Shelled embryo with six hooks. Parasites of fishes, amphibians, reptiles, birds and mammals, one genus maturing in coelom of fresh-water oligochaetes ....Eucestoda Southwell, 1930. (P. 19)

18

1b. Monozoic, with single set of reproductive organs. No scolex present. Shelled embryo with ten hooks. Parasites of fishes ....Cestodaria Monticelli, 1891. (P.245)

Key to the Orders in Subclass Eucestoda

1a. Strobila with no internal segmentation. One set of hermaphroditic reproductive organs present ....…..…............
...................................Caryophyllidea Beneden *in* Olsson, 1893.

Diagnosis: Scolex with shallow grooves or loculi, or fimbriated, weakly developed, lacking true suckers. Strobila monozoic. Genital pores mid-ventral. Testes numerous. Ovary posterior. Vitellaria follicular, scattered. Uterus a coiled, median tube opening, often together with vagina, near male pore. Parasites of teleost fishes and aquatic annelids. (P. 24)

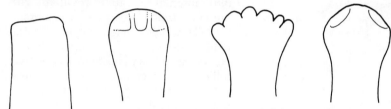

Fig. 19. Typical scoleces of Caryophyllidea.

1b. Strobila with internal segmentation present. More than one set of reproductive organs present 2
2a. Scolex with no true suckers, bothria, bothridia, or tentacles. No external segmentation ....
...........................Spathebothriidea Wardle and McLeod, 1953.

Diagnosis: Scolex feebly developed, undifferentiated or with funnel-shaped apical organ or with one or two hollow, cup-like organs. External metamerism absent, internal metamerism present. Genital pores ventral. Testes in two lateral bands. Ovary dendritic. Vitellaria follicular, lateral or scattered. Uterus coiled, with ventral pore. Parasites of teleost fishes. (P. 42)

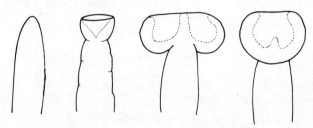

Fig. 20. Typical scoleces of Spathebothriidea.

2b. Scolex with one of the holdfast types listed above (2a). External segmentation usually distinct 3

3a. Scolex with bothridia and four armed proboscides or tentacles ....…..........Trypanorhyncha Diesing, 1863.

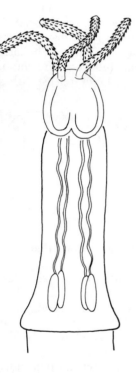

Diagnosis: Scolex elongate, with two or four bothridia, and four eversible (rarely atrophied) tentacles armed with hooks. Each tentacle invaginates into internal sheath provided with muscular bulb. Neck present or absent. Strobila apolytic or anapolytic. Genital pores lateral, rarely ventral. Testes numerous. Ovary posterior. Vitellaria follicular, scattered. Uterine pore present or absent. Parasites of elasmobranchs. (P. 46)

Fig. 21. Typical scolex of Trypanorhyncha.

3b. Scolex with two bothria, tentacles rarely present ....…...............Pseudophyllidea Carus, 1863.

Diagnosis: Scolex with two bothria, with or without hooks. Neck present or absent. Strobila variable. Proglottids anapolytic. Genital pores lateral, dorsal, or ventral. Testes numerous. Ovary posterior. Vitellaria follicular, scattered. Uterine pore present, dorsal or ventral. Egg usually operculate, containing coracidium. Parasites of fish, amphibians, reptiles, birds and mammals. (P. 63)

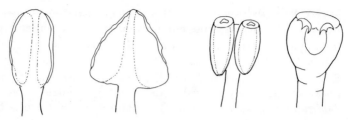

Fig. 22. Typical scoleces of Pseudophyllidea.

3c. Scolex divided into anterior and posterior regions by horizontal groove, sometimes with small suckers or unarmed tentacles ....**Lecanicephalidea Baylis, 1920.**

Diagnosis: Scolex divided into anterior and posterior regions by horizontal groove. Anterior portion cushion-like, or with unarmed tentacles, capable of being withdrawn into posterior portion forming a large sucker-like organ. Posterior portion usually with four suckers. Neck present or absent. Testes numerous. Ovary posterior. Vitellaria follicular, lateral or encircling proglottid. Uterine pore usually present. Parasites of elasmobranchs. (P. 89)

Fig. 23. Typical scoleces of Lecanicephalidea.

3d. Scolex with or without suckers, testes and ovaries without ducts to outside. No external segmentation ....
....**Aporidea Fuhrmann, 1934.**

Diagnosis: Scolex with simple suckers or grooves and armed rostellum. No external metamerism, internal metamerism present or not. Genital ducts and pores, cirrus, oötype and Mehlis' gland absent. Hermaphroditic, rarely gonochoristic. Vitellarian cells mixed with ovary. Parasites of Anseriformes. (P. 95)

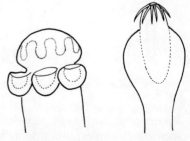

Fig. 24. Types of scoleces found in Aporidea.

3e. Scolex with bothridia 4
3f. Scolex with suckers, and not divided into anterior and pos-
     terior parts. Testes and ovaries with ducts to outside. With
     external segmentation 5
4a. Scolex with two or four bothridia, no armed rostellum. Genital
     pores lateral, rarely ventral. (Also, see Diphyllidea: *Ditrachy-
     bothridium*) ....…......................Tetraphyllidea Carus, 1863.

Diagnosis: Scolex with highly variable bothridia, sometimes also
with hooks, spines or suckers. Myzorhynchus present or absent.
Neck present or absent. Proglottides commonly apolytic. Hermaphroditic, rarely gonochoristic. Genital pores lateral, rarely posterior. Testes numerous. Ovary posterior. Vitellaria follicular
(condensed in *Dioecotaenia*), usually lateral. Uterine pore present
or not. Parasites of elasmobranchs. (P. 96)

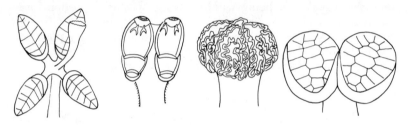

Fig. 25. A few of the varied types of scoleces in Tetraphyllidea.

4b. Scolex with two bothridia, with or without armed rostellum.
     Genital pores ventral ....Diphyllidea Benden *in* Carus, 1863.

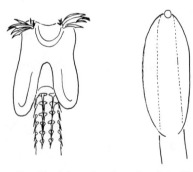

Fig. 26. Types of scoleces found in Diphyllidea.

Diagnosis: Scolex with armed
or unarmed peduncle. Two
spoonshaped bothridia present,
lined with minute spines, sometimes divided by median, longitudinal ridge. Apex of scolex
with insignificant apical organ
or with large rostellum bearing
dorsal and ventral groups of
T-shaped hooks. Strobila cylindrical, acraspedote. Genital
pores posterior, mid-ventral.
Testes numerous, anterior.
Ovary posterior. Vitellaria follicular, lateral or surrounding
segment. Uterine pore absent. Uterus tubular or saccular. Parasites
of elasmobranchs. (P. 115)

5a. Scolex with one apical sucker only 6

5b. Scolex with four or five suckers 7

6a. Scolex a single sucker, followed by several specialized segments cruciform in cross section. Strobila craspedote ....
....Litobothridea Dailey, 1969.

Diagnosis: Scolex a single, well-developed apical sucker. Anterior proglottids modified, cruciform in cross section. Neck absent. Strobila dorso-ventrally flattened, with numerous proglottids, each with single set of medullary reproductive organs. Segments laciniated and craspedote; apolytic or anapolytic. Testes numerous, preovarian. Genital pores lateral. Ovary two- or four-lobed, posterior. Vitellaria follicular, encircling medullary parynchyma. Eggs unembryonated. Parasites of elasmobranchs. (P.116)

Fig. 27. Type of scolex in Litobothridea.

6b. Scolex parenchymatous with single apical sucker. No specialized segments following scolex as described above (6a). Strobila acraspedote ....Nippotaeniidea Yamaguti, 1939.

Diagnosis: Scolex with single sucker at apex, otherwise simple. Neck short or absent. Strobila small. Proglottids each with single set of reproductive organs. Genital pores lateral. Testes anterior. Ovary posterior. Vitelline gland compact, single, between testes and ovary. Osmoregulatory canals reticular. Parasites of teleost fishes. (P.117)

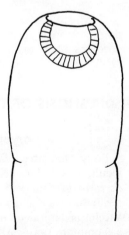

Fig. 28. Type of scolex in Nippotaeniidea.

7a. Scolex with four suckers, sometimes with additional apical sucker or armed rostellum. Vitellaria follicular, usually in lateral margins ....Proteocephalidea Mola, 1928.

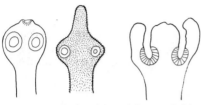

Fig. 29. Typical scoleces of Proteocephalidea.

Diagnosis: Scolex with four suckers, occasionally with apical sucker or armed rostellum. Neck usually present. Metamerism usually distinct. Genital pores lateral. Testes numerous. Ovary posterior. Vitellaria follicular, usually lateral. Uterine pore present or absent. Parasites of fishes, amphibians and reptiles. (P.118)

7b. Scolex with four suckers. Rostellum present or absent. Vitellaria compact, medial, usually postovarian ....Cyclophyllidea Beneden *in* Braun, 1900.

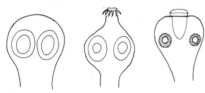

Fig. 30. Typical scoleces of Cyclophyllidea.

Diagnosis: Scolex usually with four suckers, rostellum present or not, armed or not. Neck present or absent. Strobila variable, usually with distinct metamerism, hermaphroditic or rarely gonochoristic. Genital pores lateral (ventral in Mesocestoididae). Vitelline gland single, compact, usually posterior to ovary. Uterus variable. Uterine pore absent. Parasites of amphibians, reptiles, birds and mammals. (P. 131)

DIAGNOSIS OF THE ONLY FAMILY IN CAROPHYLLIDEA

Caryophyllaeidae Leuckart, 1878

Body elongate, oval to flat. Scolex with folds, shallow grooves, loculi, acetabular suckers, or nothing; sometimes with apical sucker or introvert; marked off from body or not. Testes medullary, anterior to ovary and uterus. Cirrus pouch between ovary and testes. Vitellaria lateral or medially arranged. Uterus and vagina sharing a common pore. All gonopores on ventral surface. All known species in freshwater fishes or freshwater oligochaete worms.

Key to the Subfamilies of Caryophyllaeidae

1a. Vitellaria (Fig. 31) entirely cortical ....
....Lytocestinae Hunter, 1927. (P. 25)

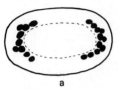 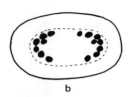 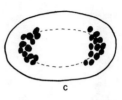

a   b   c

Fig. 31.—Arrangement of vitellaria of subfamilies of Caryophyllidea. a. Lytocestinae.
b. Caryophyllaeinae. c. Capingentinae.

1b. Vitellaria partly or entirely medullary 2

2a. Vitellaria entirely medullary ....
.....................................Caryophyllaeinae Nybelin, 1922. (P. 32)

2b. Vitellaria partly medullary, partly cortical ....
....Capingentinae Hunter, 1930. (P. 39)

Key to the Genera of Lytocestinae

1a. Postovarian vitellaria (Fig. 32) present 2

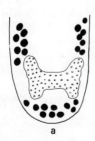 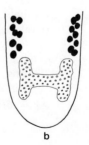

a   b

Fig. 32. a. Postovarian vitellaria present. b. Postovarian vitellaria absent.

1b. Postovarian vitellaria absent 6

2a. **Cirrus and uterovaginal canal open separately** ....
....*Lucknowia* **Gupta, 1961. (Fig. 33)**

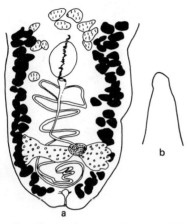

Fig. 33. *Lucknowia fossilisi* Gupta, 1961.
a. Posterior end. b. Scolex.

Diagnosis: Scolex unspecialized, not broader than rest of body. Two gonopores; cirrus sac and uterovaginal canal open separately at beginning of last seventh of body length. Uterine and vaginal pores common. Ovary a transversely elongated band, both medullary and cortical, overlapping vitelline follicles. Vitellaria mostly lateral, from near front end of body to excretory bladder, postovarian follicles present. Seminal receptacle absent. Uterine coils much convoluted, compactly coiled behind ovarian isthmus, not extending anterior to cirrus pouch. Testes medial to vitelline glands, extending from just behind first vitelline follicles to posterior end of cirrus pouch. Eggs thick-shelled, with polar filament at one end. Parasites of freshwater siluroid fishes. India.

Type species: *L. fossilisi* Gupta, 1961

2b. **One gonopore present** 3
3a. **Ovary indistinctly bilobate** ....
....*Lytocestoides* **Baylis, 1928. (Fig. 34)**

Diagnosis: Scolex short, conical, with longitudinal grooves but no loculi. Gonoducts separate? Testes extend between scolex and uterus. Ovary indistinctly bilobate, medullary. Vitellaria extensive, postovarian. Uterus not extending anterior to cirrus pouch. Parasites of cyprinoid fish. Africa.

Type species: *L. tanganyikae* Baylis, 1928.

Fig. 34. *Lytocestoides tanganyikae* Baylis, 1928.

3b. Ovary shaped like an H or an inverted A 4
4a. Ovary shaped like an inverted A ....
.... *Caryophyllaeides* Nybelin, 1922. (Fig. 35)

Diagnosis: Scolex undifferentiated. Cirrus opening into uterovaginal atrium. Cirrus pouch large, oval. External seminal vesicle absent. Testes median, anterior to uterus. Ovary shaped like an inverted A. Postovarian vitellaria present. Uterus extending anterior to cirrus pouch. Parasites of cyprinid fishes. Scandinavia, Europe, Asia.

Type species: C. *fennicus* (Schneider, 1902) Nybelin, 1922.

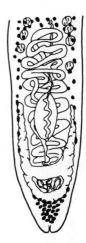

Fig. 35. *Caryophyllaeides fennicus* (Schneider, 1902) Nybelin, 1922. After Mackiewicz (1968).

4b. Ovary H-shaped 5
5a. Scolex broad, flat, fimbriate, not separated from body by a well-defined, constricted neck ....*Khawia* Hsü, 1935. (Fig. 36)

Diagnosis: Scolex lacking loculi, sometimes frilled. One gonopore present. Cirrus pouch well developed. External seminal vesicle absent. Ovary H-shaped, medullary. Vitellaria lateral, with postovarian follicles. Uterus not extending anterior to cirrus pouch. Parasites of cyprinid fishes. Asia, Europe, Japan, U.S.A.

Type species: K. *sinesis* Hsü, 1935.
Key to species: Callentine and Ulmer (1961).

Fig. 36. *Khawia iowensis* Calentine and Ulmer, 1961.

5b. Scolex conical, small, narrower than body and separated from it by well-defined, constricted neck ....
.... *Atractolytocestus* **Anthony, 1958.** (Fig. 37)

Diagnosis: Scolex simple, may possess an apical introvert. Genital pores opening into common atrium. Cirrus pouch round. Outer seminal vesicle not present. Testes medullary, six to 10 in number. Ovary H-shaped, entirely medullary (?). Vitellaria extensive, both cortical and medullary, postovarian follicles present. Uterus not extending anterior to cirrus pouch. Eggs operculate. Parasites of cyprinid fishes. North America.

Type species: *A. huronensis* Anthony, 1958.

Fig. 37. *Atractolyto-cestus huronensis* Anthony, 1958. (Vitellaria omitted.)

6a. Scolex with circular muscular frill ....
.... *Balanotaenia* **Johnston, 1924.**

Diagnosis: Scolex fairly well defined, with frilled, muscular ridges. Two gonopores present. Cirrus pouch and cirrus well developed. External seminal vesicle? Seminal receptacle present. Ovary bilobate, medullary. Vitellaria in testicular zone, with follicles extending lateral to, but not behind, ovary. Uterus mostly postovarian. Parasites of siluroid fish. Australia.

Type species: *B. bancrofti* Johnston, 1924.

6b. Scolex without circular muscular frill 7

7a. Ovarian lobes (Fig. 38) medullary 8

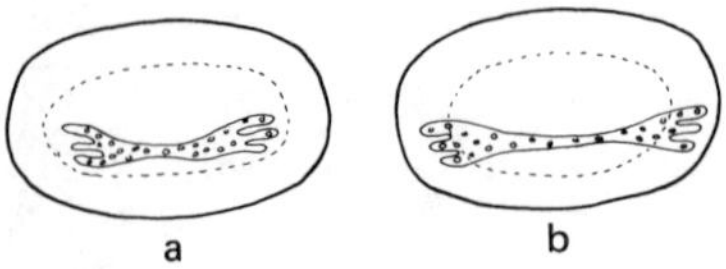

a   b

Fig. 38. a. Ovarian lobes entirely medullary. b. Ovarian lobes partly cortical.

7b. Ovarian lobes cortical 9

8a. Scolex with terminal sucker ....
....*Djombangia* Bovien, 1926. (Fig. 39)

Diagnosis: Scolex nearly spherical, with terminal sucker but no loculi. Well marked neck present. Gonopores separate, in common atrium near posterior end of body. Cirrus pouch not well developed. External seminal vesicle apparently absent. Testes in lateral medulla, from neck to ovary. Ovary bilobed, medullary, at posterior end of body. Vitellaria in testicular zone and lateral, but not behind ovary. Uterus median, nearly reaching neck. Eggs spiny. Parasites of siluroid fish. Java.

Type species: *D. penetrans* Bovien, 1926.

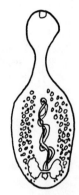

Fig. 39. *Djombangia penetrans* Bovien, 1926.

8b. Scolex undifferentiated ....
...........*Notolytocestus* Johnston and Muirhead, 1950. (Fig. 40)

Diagnosis: Scolex narrow, undifferentiated. Body short, broad. Cirrus opening into uterovaginal canal. Single gonopore present. Testes mainly lateral because of displacement by uterus. Ovary H-shaped, at posterior end of body. Vitellaria mainly lateral, no follicles postovarian. Uterus mainly medial to testes, extending far forward. Parasites of siluroid fishes. Australia.

Type species: *N. major* Johnston and Muirhead, 1950.

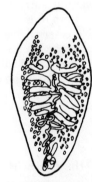

Fig. 40. *Notolytocestus major* Johnston and Muirhead, 1950.

9a. Scolex differentiated 10

9b. Scolex undifferentiated 12

10a. Vitellaria surrounding testes ....
.... *Monobothrioides* **Fuhrmann and Baer, 1925.**

Diagnosis: Scolex with terminal introvert and longitudinal furrows, but no loculi. Gonopores separate. Cirrus pouch well developed. No external seminal vesicle. Seminal receptacle present.
Ovary H-shaped with long, slender, lateral cortical processes and
median, medullary mass of follicles. No postovarian vitellaria.
Uterus not reaching cirrus pouch. Parasites of siluroid fishes. Africa.
Type species: *M. cunningtoni* Fuhrmann and Baer, 1925.

10b. Vitellaria lateral, crescent-shaped in cross section 11

11a. Ovary U-shaped (?) ....*Crescentovitus* **Murhar, 1963.**

Diagnosis: Scolex well differentiated, with shallow bothria on
dorsal and ventral side, and small terminal introvert. Neck separated from scolex by constriction. Genital pores close together on
ventral surface. Vitellaria in lateral cortex, extending to anterior
margin of ovary, none postovarian, crescent-shaped in cross section.
No external seminal vesicle or seminal receptacle. Ovary U-shaped,
arms in lateral cortex and isthmus in medulla. Uterus long. Eight
to ten longitudinal osmoregulatory canals with transverse connec-
tions. Parasites of the coelom of siluroid fishes. India.
Type species: *C. biloculus* Murhar, 1963.

11b. Ovary H-shaped ....*Stocksia* **Woodland, 1937.**

Diagnosis: Scolex flattened, pointed, with apical cushion and
slender longitudinal grooves. Single gonopore present. Cirrus pouch
present. External seminal vesicle apparently absent. Testes median,
anterior to cirrus pouch. Ovary small, H-shaped, at posterior end
of body; lateral lobes in cortex, isthmus in medulla. Vitellaria
lateral, crescent-shaped in cross-section; postovarian follicles absent.
Uterus tightly coiled, anterior to ovary, not extending anterior to
cirrus pouch. Parasites of siluroid fish. Africa.
Type species: *S. pujehuni* Woodland, 1937.

12a. Vitellaria lateral ....*Bovienia* **Fuhrmann, 1931. (Fig. 41)**

Diagnosis: Scolex undifferentiated, or a little hollow, set off from body by a narrow neck. Gonopores separate. Cirrus pouch? Cirrus apparently spined. Seminal receptacle present. Testes median, mostly in anterior half of body. Ovary H-shaped, large, extending to posterior end. Vitellaria lateral, extending from very near anterior end to near ovary. No post-ovarian follicles. Uterus not extending anterior to male gonopore. Parasites of siluroid fish. Java.

Type species: *B. serialis* (Bovien, 1926) Fuhrmann, 1931.

Fig. 41. *Bovienia serialis* (Bovien, 1926) Fuhrmann, 1931. After Mackiewicz (1963).

12b. Vitellaria surrounding testes ....….......................... ....*Lytocestus* **Cohn, 1908. (Fig. 42)**

Diagnosis: Scolex undifferentiated. Gonophores separate. External seminal vesicle absent. Seminal receptacle absent. Ovary bilobed with lateral lobes cortical. Vitellaria in testicular zone, no post-ovarian follicles. Uterus not extending anterior to cirrus pouch. Parasites of mormyrid and siluroid fishes. Hongkong, Burma, India, Africa.

Type species: *L. adhaerens* Cohn, 1908.

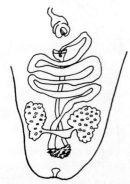

Fig. 42. *Lytocestus indicus* (Moghe, 1925) Moghe, 1931.

Key to the Genera of Caryophyllaeinae

1a. Genital pores in anterior half of body ....
....*Wenyonia* **Woodland, 1923. (Fig. 43)**

Diagnosis: Scolex undifferentiated or with several longitudinal furrows, constricted off from body or not. Two gonopores present in anterior half of body. External seminal vesicle and seminal receptacle absent. Testes anterior. Ovary H-shaped, medullary. Vitellaria lateral, extending to post-ovarian zone. Uterus not extending anterior to genital atrium. Parasites of siluroid fishes. Africa.

Type species: *W. virilis* Woodland, 1923.

Fig. 43. *Wenyonia virilis* Woodland, 1923.

1b. Genital pores in posterior half of body 2
2a. Uterus extending in front of cirrus pouch 3
2b. Uterus entirely behind cirrus pouch 7
3a. Scolex lacking any loculi or folds ....
..................*Paracaryophyllaeus* **Kulakowskaya, 1961. (Fig. 44)**

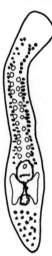

Diagnosis: Scolex slightly widened, without festoons and suckers. Testes in two longitudinal rows. Cirrus pouch rather small. Seminal receptacle present. Ovary H-shaped. Vitellaria begin high and reach to level of ovary. Post-ovarian vitellaria present. Uterus extending anterior to cirrus pouch. Parasites of cyprinoid fish. Russia.

Type species: *P. dubininae* Kulakowskaya, 1961.

Fig. 44. *Paracaryophyllaeus dubininae* Kulakowskaya, 1961.

3b. Scolex with loculi 4

4a. Scolex with three pair of shallow loculi ....
...............................*Hypocaryophyllaeus* **Hunter, 1928.** (Fig. 45)

Diagnosis: Scolex short, wider than anterior body, with three dorsal and three ventral shallow loculi. Gonopores separate. Cirrus pouch small. External seminal vesicle present. Seminal receptacle apparently absent. Ovary H-shaped, medullary. Postovarian vitellaria present. Uterus extending anterior to cirrus pouch. Parasites of catostomid fishes. North America.

Type species: *H. paratarius* Hunter, 1927.

Fig. 45. Hypocaryo-
phyllaeus paratarius
Hunter, 1927. a. Sco-
lex. b. Posterior end.

4b. Scolex with two to six shallow loculi 5

5a. External seminal vesicle absent ....
..............................*Penarchigetes* **Mackiewicz, 1969.** (Fig. 46)

Diagnosis: Scolex with a pair of median bothria, two pairs of lateral loculi, and a small terminal disc. Cirrus joining uterovaginal canal. Ovary H- or dumbbell-shaped. Coils of uterus extending to anterior level of cirrus. Preovarian vitellaria lateral, sometimes continuous with the postovarian vitellaria. External seminal vesicle absent. Parasites of catostomid fishes. North America.

Type species: *P. oklensis* Mackiewicz, 1969.

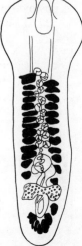

Fig. 46. Penarchige-
tes oklensis Mackie-
wicz, 1969.

5b. External seminal vesicle present 6

6a. Scolex poorly defined. Pre- and postovarian vitellaria continuous ....Archigetes **Leuckart, 1878. (Fig. 47)**

Diagnosis: Scolex not clearly demarcated from body, with up to six shallow loculi. Cercomer with larval hooks sometimes present at posterior end. Single gonopore present, covered by tegument in young specimens. External seminal vesicle present. Seminal receptacle present. Ovary dumbbell-shaped. Vitellaria lateral, continuous in region of ovary, with postovarian follicles. Uterus usually not extending anterior to cirrus sac, but occasionally doing so in gravid specimens. Eggs operculate. Adults in coelom of tubificid oligochaetes (cercomer present) or intestine of freshwater teleosts (cercomer absent), especially cyprinids. Europe, Asia, Japan, England, Africa, North and South America.

Type species: A. *sieboldi* Leuckart, 1878.

Key to species: Kennedy (1965).

Fig. 47. *Archigetes iowensis* Calentine, 1962.

6b. Scolex well defined, with only two loculi. Vitellaria pre- and postovarian but interrupted lateral to ovary .... Biacetabulum **Hunter, 1927. (Fig. 48)**

Diagnosis: Scolex with one dorsal and one ventral loculum. One gonopore present; cirrus opening into uterovaginal canal before reaching atrium. External seminal vesicle present. Seminal receptacle apparently present. Ovary H-shaped, medullary. Some vitelline follicles postovarian. Uterus extending anterior to cirrus pouch. Parasites of catostomid fishes. North America.

Type species: B. *infrequens* Hunter, 1927.

Fig. 48. *Biacetabulum macrocephalum* McCrae, 1962. After Calentine (1965). a. Scolex. b. Posterior end.

7a. Scolex hexagonal, with terminal introvert and six loculi or shallow longitudinal grooves ....
....*Monobothrium* **Diesing, 1863.** (Fig. 49)

Diagnosis: Scolex with terminal introvert and six long shallow loculi. Gonopores separate. Cirrus pouch small. External seminal vesicle present or absent. Testes in median field anterior to cirrus pouch. Ovary H-shaped. Vitellaria in testicular zone, some follicles postovarian or not. Uterus not extending anterior to cirrus sac. Parasites of cyprinid and catostomid fishes. Europe, North America.

Type species: *M. wageneri* Nybelin, 1922.

Key to species: Calentine and Mackiewicz, 1966.

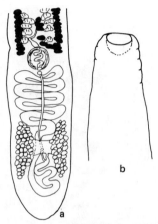

Fig. 49. *Monobothrium ulmeri* Calentine and Mackiewicz, 1966. a. Posterior end. b. Scolex.

7b. Scolex lacking terminal introvert 8

8a. Scolex crenulated, without distinct loculi. No external seminal vesicle ....*Caryophyllaeus* **Mueller, 1787.** (Fig. 50)

Diagnosis: Scolex broad, flattened, lacking loculi, anterior margin frilled. Gonopores separate. External seminal vesicle absent. Cirrus pouch well developed. Seminal receptacle well developed. Ovary H-shaped, medullary. Postovarian vitellaria present. Uterus not extending in front of cirrus pouch. Parasites of cyprinid and catostomid fishes. Europe, North America, Java, Asia, Africa, Japan.

Type species: *C. laticeps* (Pallas, 1781) Mueller, 1787.

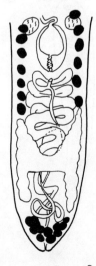

Fig. 50. *Caryophyllaeus laticeps* (Pallas, 1781) Mueller, 1787. After Mackiewicz (1968).

8b. Scolex not as above 9

9a. **Scolex unspecialized, without depressions. Worm always found in pit in gut wall of host** ....
.... *Hunterella* **Mackiewicz and McCrae, 1962. (Fig. 51)**

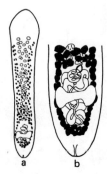

Diagnosis: Scolex not set off from body, a simple, unspecialized rounded or conical enlargement without suckers, loculi or other organs of attachment. Neck absent. Two gonopores; cirrus opens separately, anterior to female gonopore. Testes fill medullary parenchyma from behind scolex to level of cirrus pouch. Cirrus pouch ovoid. External seminal vesicle present. Ovary H-shaped. Coils of uterus not extending anteriorly beyond cirrus pouch. Post-Ovarian vitellaria present. Seminal receptacle present. Eggs operculate, unembryonated. Osmoregulatory canals reticular. Parasites of catostomid fishes, forming nodules on gut wall. North America.

Type species: *H. nodulosa* Mackiewicz and McCrae, 1962.

Fig. 51. *Hunterella nodulosa* Mackiewicz and McCrae, 1962. a. Entire worm. b. Posterior end.

9b. **Scolex provided with one to three pairs of shallow loculi** 10
10a. **Scolex with one pair of loculi** 11
10b. **Scolex with two or three pairs of loculi** 13
11a. **Postovarian vitellaria present** ....
.... *Pliovitellaria* **Fischthal, 1951. (Fig. 52)**

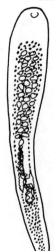

Diagnosis: Scolex not marked off from rest of body. One dorsal and one ventral loculum present. One gonopore present. Cirrus sac post-equatorial. External seminal vesicle present. Testes medullary. Seminal receptacle present. Ovary H-shaped, medullary. Vitellaria medullary, mainly lateral to testes, interrupted lateral to ovary, filling entire medullary space posterior to ovary. Uterus not extending anterior to cirrus sac. Parasites of cyprinid fishes. North America.

Type species: *P. wisconsinensis* Fischthal, 1951.

Fig. 52. *Pliovitellaria wisconsinensis* Fischthal, 1951.

11b. **Postovarian vitellaria absent** 12

12a. Ovary V-shaped ....*Bialovarium* **Fischthal, 1953.**
Diagnosis: Scolex poorly defined, with one dorsal and one ventral loculum. One gonopore. External seminal vesicle present. Cirrus pouch large. Cirrus joins uterovaginal duct in posterior end of cirrus sac. Seminal receptacle present. Ovary V-shaped, medullary. Vitellaria lateral, no follicles postovarian. Uterus not extending anterior to cirrus pouch. Parasites of cyprinid fishes. North America.
Type species: *B. necomis* Fischthal, 1953.

12b. Ovary H-shaped ....
........................*Promonobothrium* **Mackiewicz, 1968.** (Fig. 53)
Diagnosis: Scolex with pair of shallow median loculi, and two small lateral depressions. Cirrus opening separately from uterovaginal canal. Ovary H-shaped. Coils of uterus not extending anteriorly beyond cirrus pouch. Preovarian vitellaria median and lateral; postovarian vitellaria absent. External seminal vesicle present. Parasites of Catostomidae. North America.
Type species: *P. minytremi* Mackiewicz, 1968.

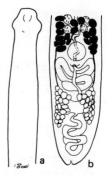

Fig. 53. Promono-
bothrium minytremi
Mackiewicz, 1968. a.
Scolex. b. Posterior
end.

13a. Scolex with two pairs of shallow loculi and an apical disc
...........................*Paraglaridacris* **Janiszewska, 1950.** (Fig. 54)

Diagnosis: Scolex with four loculi and a terminal disc, constricted from rest of body. Gonopore single (?). External seminal vesicle present. Testes medullary, in two lateral rows. Seminal receptacle present. Ovary H-shaped. Vitellaria lateral to testes, postovarian follicles present. Uterus not extending anterior to cirrus pouch. Parasites of Cyprinid fish. Poland. May be synonym of *Archigetes* (see Kennedy, 1965.).
Type species: *P. silesiaca* Janiszewska, 1950.

Fig. 54. Paraglari-
dacris silesiaca Janis-
zewska, 1950.

**13b. Scolex with three pairs of shallow loculi, apical disc present
or absent** 14

14a. Ovary H-shaped. Two gonopores present ....
....….........*Glaridacris* **Cooper, 1920. (Fig. 55)**

Fig. 55. *Glaridacris*
catostomi Cooper, 1920.
After   Mackiewicz
(1965). a. *Scolex.* b.
Posterior end.

Diagnosis: Scolex well defined, with three pairs of loculi. Two gonopores present. Cirrus pouch well developed. Testes median, anterior to cirrus pouch. External seminal vesicle present. Seminal receptacle present. Ovary H-shaped. Vitellaria in testicular zone, some follicles postovarian. Uterus not extending anterior to cirrus pouch. Parasites of catostomid fishes. North America.

Type species: *G. catostomi* Cooper, 1920.

14b. Ovary shaped like an inverted A or H. One gonopore present
.... *Isoglaridacris* **Mackiewicz, 1965. (Fig. 56)**

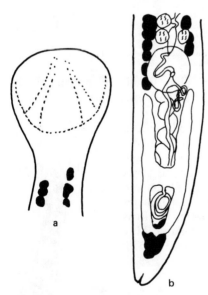

Fig. 56. *Isoglaridacris bulbocirrus* Mackiewicz,
1965. a. Scolex. b. Posterior end.

Diagnosis: Scolex rounded, wider than body, with three dorsal and three ventral shallow loculi. Neck present. Body long, slender. Single gonopore present. Cirrus sac rounded. External seminal vesicle present, inner seminal vesicle absent. Testes begin posterior to first vitelline follicles and extend to cirrus sac. Seminal receptacle weakly developed. Ovary shaped like inverted A; apex of A sometimes not joined. Preovarian vitellaria in lateral rows, not continuous with postovarian vitellaria. Uterus not extending anterior to cirrus pouch. Eggs operculate. Parasite of catostomid fishes. North America.

Type species: *I. bulbocirrus* Mackiewicz, 1965.

Key to the Genera in Capingentinae

1a. Postovarian median vitellaria present 2

1b. Postovarian median vitellaria absent 5

2a. Uterine coils extend anterior to cirrus pouch. Scolex with two large bothria ....*Capingens* Hunter, 1927. (Fig. 57)

Diagnosis: Scolex well defined, one-fifth of body length, with a dorsal and a ventral bothrium. Two gonopores present. Cirrus pouch round, between the two lobes of the ovary. External seminal vesicle present. Testes in wide band anterior to ovary. Ovary dumbbell-shaped, medullary, near posterior end, lateral lobes enclosing cirrus sac. Vitellaria extensive, continuous lateral to ovary, some follicles postovarian. Uterus anterior to cirrus pouch. Parasites of catostomid fishes. North America.

Fig. 57. Capingens singularis Hunter, 1927.

Type species: *C. singularis* Hunter, 1927.

2b. Uterine coils not extending anterior to cirrus pouch. Scolex lacking bothria 3

3a. Ovary shaped like an inverted A ....
....*Adenoscolex* Fotedar, 1958. (Fig. 58)

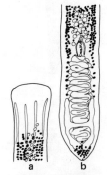

Diagnosis: Scolex smooth, not clearly marked off from rest of body. Neck absent. Two gonopores; cirrus sac and uterovaginal canal open separately at beginning of posterior seventh of body length. External seminal vesicle absent, inner seminal vesicle present. Testes extend from behind scolex to anterior end of cirrus sac. Seminal receptacle present. Ovary entirely medullary, shaped like an inverted A. Postovarian vitellaria present. Uterus never anterior to cirrus sac. Eggs operculated with blunt protuberance near basal end. Parasites of cyprinid fishes. Kashmir.

Type species: *A. oreini* Fotedar, 1958.

Fig. 58. Adenoscolex oreini Fotedar, 1958. a. Scolex. b. Posterior end.

3b. Ovary not as above 4

4a. **Ovary dumbbell-shaped. Scolex quite reduced, anterior margin flattened, neck absent** ....
....*Breviscolex* **Kulakowskaya, 1962. (Fig. 59)**

Diagnosis: Scolex smooth, very short, truncated. Neck absent. Genital apertures not described, apparently opening in common atrium. Cirrus large. External seminal vesicle absent. Testes extend from near anterior end of body to level of cirrus sac. Small seminal receptacle present. Ovary butterfly-shaped, variable. Vitellaria begin a little behind anterior testes, mostly lateral, numerous behind ovary. Uterus not extending anterior to ovary. Parasites of cyprinid fishes. Russia.

Type species: B. *orientalis* Kulakowskaya, 1962.

Fig. 59. *Breviscolex
orientalis* Kulakowska-
ya, 1962.

4b. **Ovary band-shaped. Scolex well developed, neck well marked**
....*Capingentoides* **Gupta, 1961. (Fig. 60)**

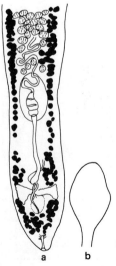

Diagnosis: Scolex smooth, oval, truncated anteriorly and marked off from rest of body. Neck long, narrow. One gonopore; cirrus sac opens into uterovaginal canal at beginning of posterior tenth of body length. Uterine and vaginal pores common. Seminal vesicle present, bell-shaped. Ovary band-shaped or weakly H-shaped. Vitellaria mostly lateral, at level of inner muscular layer; some post-ovarian follicles present. Uterus never anterior to cirrus pouch. Seminal receptacle absent. Eggs non-operculate. Parasites of freshwater siluroids. India.

Type species: C. *batrachii* Gupta, 1961.

Fig. 60. *Capingentoides
batrachii* Gupta, 1961. a.
Posterior end. b. Scolex.

a   b

5a. Uterine coils extending anterior to cirrus pouch. Scolex with three pairs of loculi. Ovary U-shaped ....
....*Spartoides* **Hunter, 1929. (Fig. 61)**

Diagnosis: Scolex well defined, with three pair of loculi. Neck present. Body slender. Gonopores separate. Outer seminal vesicle present. Testes median, anterior to uterine coils. Ovary U-shaped; lateral lobes partly cortical. Vitellaria mostly medullary, in tescular zone, no postovarian follicles present. Uterus extending between testes and posterior end. Parasites of catostomid fishes. North America.

Type species: S. *wardi* Hunter, 1927.

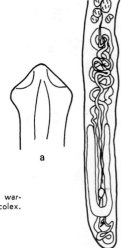

Fig. 61. *Spartoides wardi* Hunter, 1927. a. Scolex. b. Posterior end.

5b. Uterine coils not extending anterior to cirrus pouch. Scolex lacking loculi. Ovary not U-shaped 6

6a. Ovary H-shaped. Neck absent ....
.................................*Pseudolytocestus* **Hunter, 1929. (Fig. 62)**

Diagnosis: Scolex weakly defined, lacking loculi. Gonopores separate. Cirrus pouch well developed. External seminal vesicle present. Testes in broad median field anterior to ovary. Seminal receptacle absent. Ovary H-shaped, mostly medullary, at posterior end of body. Vitellaria in testicular zone; no postovarian follicles. Uterus not extending anterior to cirrus pouch. Parasites of catostomid fishes, North America; siluroid fish, India.

Type species: P. *differtus* Hunter, 1929.

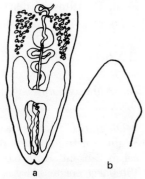

Fig. 62. *Pseudolytocestus differtus* Hunter, 1929. a. Posterior end. b. Scolex.

6b. Ovary band-shaped. Very long neck present ....
.............................*Pseudocaryophyllaeus* **Gupta, 1961. (Fig. 63)**

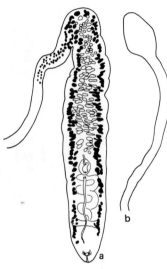

Diagnosis: Scolex smooth, oval, truncated anteriorly, marked off from rest of body by long slender neck. Cirrus pouch and uterovaginal canal open separately. Postovarian median vitellaria absent. Uterus never extends anterior to cirrus pouch. Seminal receptacle absent. Ovary band-shaped. Testes filling most of medullary parenchyma anterior to cirrus pouch. Seminal vesicle present. Eggs non-operculated. Osmoregulatory system with four main canals. Parasites of siluroid fishes. India.

Type species: *P. indica* Gupta, 1961.

Fig. 63. *Pseudocaryophyllaeus indica* Gupta, 1961. a. Body. b. Scolex.

Key to the Families in Spathebothriidae

1a. Scolex with no adhesive organ ....
.................Spathebothriidae **Wardle & McLeod, 1952. (P. 43)**

Diagnosis: Scolex and adhesive organs absent. Strobila slender, with pointed ends. External metamerism lacking. Genital pores irregularly alternating on flat surfaces. Testes lateral. Ovary rosettiform. Parasites of marine teleosts.

Type genus: *Spathebothrium* Linton, 1922.

1b. Scolex with adhesive cup, but not a true, muscular sucker 2

2a. Adhesive cup single, funnel-shaped ....
.................................Cyathocephalidae **Nybelin, 1922. (P. 44)**

Diagnosis: Scolex with funnel-shaped apical adhesive organ. Slight constriction separating scolex from strobila. External metamerism absent, internal metamerism present. Testes medullary. Vitellaria cortical. Eggs operculated. Uterovaginal atrium present, with sphincter. Parasites of freshwater teleosts.

Type genus: *Cyathocephalus* Kessler, 1868.

2b. Adhesive cup double, sometimes partly fused, or completely fused and with ventral septum ....
...................................Diplocotylidae Monticelli, 1892. (P. 44)

Diagnosis: Scolex wih two adhesive cups opening apically, or with a single such cup but with a ventral, vestigial septum. External metamerism absent, internal metamerism present. Genital pores ventral or irregularly alternating dorsal and ventral. Testes lateral, medullary. Cirrus opens anterior to vagina. Ovary bilobed. Vitellaria cortical. Uterus convoluted, anterior and opposite to ovary. Uterine pore anterior to vaginal pore, sometimes in common atrium with it. Eggs operculated. Parasites of teleosts.

Type genus: *Diplocotyle* Krabbe, 1874.

DIAGNOSIS OF THE ONLY GENUS IN SPATHEBOTHRIIDAE

Spathebothrium Linton, 1922 (Fig. 64)

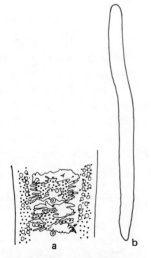

Diagnosis: No indication of scolex or adhesive organs present. Strobila flat, pointed at the ends, especially posterior. External metamerism absent. Internal metamerism present, with up to 36 sets of reproductive organs. No longitudinal muscles. Genital pores alternating irregularly from one flat surface to the other, uterine pore lateral to vaginal pore but rarely on opposite surface from it. No uterovaginal atrium. Testes in two lateral bands, continuous throughout strobila. Cirrus pouch small, anterior to vaginal pore. Ovary rosettiform. Vitellaria lateral. Uterus convoluted, median. Eggs with very large operculum. Parasites of marine teleosts. North Atlantic and North Pacific.

Type species: *S. simplex* Linton, 1922.

Fig. 64. *Spathebothrium simplex* Linton, 1922. *a.* Portion of strobila. After Hart and Guberlet (1936). *b.* Entire worm. After Linton (1922).

DIAGNOSIS OF THE ONLY GENUS IN CYATHOCEPHALIDAE

Cyathocephalus Kessler, 1868 (Fig. 65)

Diagnosis: Scolex with funnel-shaped adhesive organ, separated from strobila by slight constriction. Strobila flat, up to 33 mm long. External metamerism absent, internal metamerism present, with 20 to 45 sets of reproductive organs. Genital pores irregularly alternating from dorsal to ventral surface. Cirrus pouch surounded by prostatic cells. Cirrus opening anterior to uterovaginal atrium. Testes in lateral medulla. Ovary lobated, with broad isthmus, near one surface or the other without regard to genital pore. Vitellaria cortical, surrounding body. Uterus convoluted, medial, antiporal, proximal coils surrounded by great many unicellular glands. Eggs ellipsoidal, with operculum at one end and hooklike knob on the other. Infective embryo lacking hooks. Parasites of freshwater teleosts. Circumboreal.

Fig. 65. *Cyathocephalus truncatus* (Pallas, 1781) Kessler, 1868. After Wisniewski (1933).

Type species: *C. truncatus* (Pallas, 1781) Kessler, 1868.

Key to the Genera in Diplocotylidae

1a. Adhesive cups completely separated by septum 2

1b. Adhesive cups partly or completely fused 3

2a. Scolex with two apical, rounded adhesive cups, dorsal and ventral. Lacking lateral slits. Vitellaria lateral only ....
....*Diplocotyle* Krabbe, 1874. (Fig. 66)

Diagnosis: Scolex with two adhesive cups completely separated by internal septum and with margins entire. Neck absent. Genital pores on ventral surface. Cirrus pouch weakly developed. Testes few, medullary, in two lateral fields. Ovary bilobed, posterior, medullary. Vitellaria cortical, lateral. Uterus strongly convoluted, medullary, with uterine pore anterior to vaginal pore. Eggs operculated. Parasites of marine teleosts. Russia, North Atlantic.

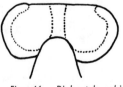

Fig. 66. *Diplocotyle olrikii* Krabbe, 1874. Lateral view.

Type species: *D. olrikii* Krabbe, 1874.

2b. Scolex with cups as above but each with lateral slit. Vitellaria surrounding proglottid ....
....*Schizocotyle* **Akhmerov, 1960. (Fig. 67)**

Diagnosis: Scolex short, rounded, with two cup-shaped adhesive organs separated their entire length by septum and with slit in lateral margin of each. Neck absent. Genital pores ventral. Testes few, medullary, in two lateral fields. Ovary bilobed, medullary, posterior. Vitellaria cortical, surrounding entire proglottid. Uterus rather short, containing large eggs. Parasites of freshwater teleosts. Russia.

Type species: S. *fluviatilis* Akhmerov, 1960.

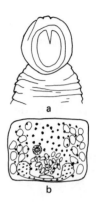

Fig. 67. *Schizocotyle fluviatilis* Akhmerov, 1960. a. Scolex. b. Proglottid.

3a. Adhesive cups partly fused ....*Didymobothrium* **Nybelin, 1922.**

Diagnosis: Very poorly known. Scolex with adhesive cups partly fused. Genital pores irregularly alternating dorsal and ventral. Cirrus pouch muscular. Uterine and vaginal pores in common atrium with sphincter. Parasites of marine teleosts. Mediterranean.

Type species: D. *rudolphii* (Monticelli, 1890) Nybelin, 1922.

3b. Adhesive cups completely fused, but with vestigial septum at bottom ....*Bothrimonus* **Duvernoy, 1842. (Fig. 68)**

Diagnosis: Scolex with adhesive cups completely fused except for vestigial septum on bottom. Genital pores alternating irregularly from top to bottom. Internal metamerism marked. Testes medullary, lateral, intruding into space between two wings of ovary. Cirrus pouch powerful at distal end. Ovary bilobed, each lobe longitudinally elongate. Vitellaria cortical, lateral. Uterine pore and vaginal pore in common, shallow atrium with powerful sphincter. Eggs with large operculum. Parasites of Chondrostei (sturgeons). North America, Rumania, Caspian Sea.

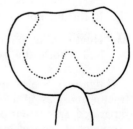

Fig. 68. *Bothrimonus fallax* Lühe, 1900. After Nybelin (1922).

Type species: B. *sturionis* Duvernoy, 1842.

Key to the Suborders of Trypanorhyncha

1a. Pars bothridialis extending farther posteriad than pars vaginalis; pleurocercus without blastocyst (Fig. 69a) ....
....Acystidea Guiart, 1927.

1b. Pars vaginalis extending farther posteriad than pars bothridialis; pleurocercus with blastocyst (Fig. 69 b) ....
....Cystidae Guiart, 1927. (P. 47)

Key to the Families in the Suborder Acystidea

1a. Bothridia each with a pair of ciliated sensory fossettes on the posterior margin. (See also, Octobothriidae in suborder Cystidea) ....…..............Paranybeliniidae Fam. n. (P. 58)

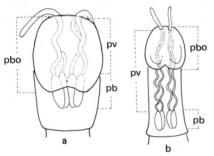

Fig. 69. a. Typical scolex of Acystidea. b. Typical scolex of Cystidea. pb—pars bulbosa. pbo—pars bothridialis. pv—pars vaginalis.

Diagnosis: Scolex short and stout, craspedote. Tentacles armed with ascending spirals of similar hooks. Two bothridia present, longer than pars vaginalis. Each bothridium bears a pair of eversible ciliated fossettes on the posterior border. Known only from larvae dredged up in plankton nets. Hosts unknown.
Type genus: *Paranybelinia* Dollfus, 1966.

1b. Bothridia not as above 2

2a. Hooks solid; tentacle retractor muscle attached to bottom of bulb; bothridia separate ....
......................................Tentaculariidae Poche, 1926. (P. 62)
Diagnosis: Scolex craspedote. Tentacles short and slender. Retractor muscles attached to base of bulb. Bothridia sessile with separated spiny margins. Hooks solid, in even spirals, irregularly arranged at base of tentacle, similar in size and shape. Bulbs ellipsoidal. Proboscis sheaths not twisted or spiral. Proglottids wider than long, anapolytic, acraspedote. Testes medullary, dorsal. Genital pores preequatorial, marginal or submarginal. Cirrus unarmed. Ovary equatorial or more posterior. Parasites of elasmobranchs.
Type genus: *Tentacularia* Bosc, 1797.

2b. Hooks hollow; tentacle retractor muscle not reaching bottom of bulb; bothridia partly or completely fused 3

3a. Mature proglottid with double set of reproductive organs ....
....Hepatoxylidae Dollfus, 1940. (P. 56)
Diagnosis: Scolex large, acraspedote. Tentacles short, broad. Hooks hollow, mostly similar, arranged in regularly alternating longitudinal rows. Retractor muscle attached to top of bulb. Bothridia mostly imbedded in scolex; lateral and sometimes anterior margins of adjacent bothridia fused. Proglottids wider than long, anapolitic, craspedote. Two sets of reproductive organs in each proglottid. Genital pores marginal, preequatorial. Parasites of sharks.
Type genus: *Hepatoxylon* Bosc, 1811.

3b. Mature proglottid with single set of reproductive organs ....
.....................................Sphyriocephalidae Pintner, 1913. (P. 62)
Diagnosis: Scolex short, wide, craspedote. Tentacles cylindrical. Hooks hollow, similar. Retractor muscle attached to anterior end of bulb. Pars vaginalis and pars bulbosa short. Bothridial margins fused, each bothridium forming deep cavity out of which the tentacle emerges. Proglottides craspedote, anapolytic. Genital pores marginal. One set of reproductive organs per proglottid. Parasites of sharks.
Type genus: *Sphyriocephalus* Pintner, 1913.

Key to the Families in the Suborder Cystidea

1a. Each tentacle with externo-lateral longitudinal chainette (Fig. 70 a) or longitudinal band of small hooks (Fig. 70 b) 2

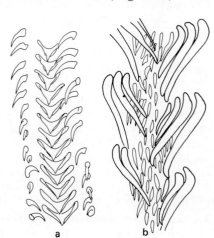

Fig. 70. *a*. Externo-lateral chainette.
b. Externo-lateral band of small hooks.
After Dollfus, (1942).

a   b

1b. Tentacles without chainette or longitudinal band of small hooks 5

2a. Scolex with two bothridia 3

2b. Scolex with four bothridia 4

3a. Scolex craspedote J .....Dasyrhynchidae Dollfus, 1935, (P. 50)
Diagnosis: Scolex long, craspedote. Tentacles cylindrical, with chainette. Pars vaginalis long; tentacle sheath coiled. Pars bulbosa long; retractor muscles inserted in anterior end of bulb. Two prominent bothridia, each with distinct posterior notch. Proglottides acraspedote, anapolytic, posterior ones longer than wide. Single set of reproductive organs in each proglottid. Genital pores marginal, equatorial or postequatorial. Parasites of sharks.
Type genus: *Dasyrhynchus* Pintner, 1928.

3b. Scolex acraspedote.....Lacistorhynchidae Guiart, 1927. (P. 57)
Diagnosis: Scolex long, spinous, acraspedote. Tentacles with oblique rows of differing hollow hooks and a single or double chainette. Two bothridia present. Tentacle retractor muscle inserted at posterior end of bulb or preequatorial. Pars bulbosa often followed by a swollen region, homologous to appendix of plerocercus. Proglottids acraspedote, apolytic, usually spinous. Genital pores marginal, postequatorial, with muscular pad before and behind or surrounded by sucker. Parasites of elasmobranchs.
Type genus: *Lacistorhynchus* Pintner, 1913.

4a. Bothridia on short stalks, located on apex of scolex ....
.....................................Pterobothriidae Pintner, 1931. (P. 61)
Diagnosis: Scolex long, slender, acraspedote, pars bulbosa usually swollen. Pars postbulbosa present. Tentacles with hooks of differing types and chainette of V-shaped hooks. Bothridia pedunculate, mobile, four in number. Tentacle sheaths spiral or not. Proglottides acraspedote, apolytic. Genital pores marginal, postequatorial. Parasites of elasmobranchs.
Type genus: *Pterobothrium* Pintner, 1931.

4b. Bothridia without stalks, located on dorsal and ventral surfaces of scolex ....Gymnorhynchidae Dollfus, 1935. (P. 55)
Diagnosis: Scolex acraspedote: pars vaginalis longer than pars bothridialis. Pars postbulbosa present. Four sessile bothridia present, with anterior margins fused to scolex and other margins free. Tentacles with ascending spirals of falciform hooks and a double chainette or longitudinal band of very small hooks. Known only from plerocercus with large blastocyst, encysted in marine teleosts. Adult unknown, presumably in elasmobranchs.
Type genus: *Gymnorhynchus* Rudlophi, 1819.

5a. Lateral or posterior margins of bothridia with two eversible ciliated pits ....Otobothriidae Dollfus, 1942. (P. 59)

Diagnosis: Scolex craspedote, rather short. Tentacles shorter than sheaths, armed with oblique rows of large hooks from inner face to middle line of outer face and more numerous rows of smaller hooks over rest of tentacle. Chainette absent. Bothridia wide, shallow, sometimes notched on posterior margin, with two eversible ciliated pits on lateral or posterior margins. Proglottides acraspedote, apolytic. Genital pores marginal, equatorial or post-equatorial.

Type genus: *Otobothrium* Linton, 1890.

5b. No eversible ciliated pits on bothridia 6

6a. Scolex with four bothridia ....
....**Gilquiniidae Dollfus, 1942. (P. 54)**

Diagnosis: Scolex acraspedote, marked off from the body by a constriction. Tentacles short, with similar hooks evenly distributed in spirals or quincunxes; or the tentacles may be vestigial or lacking, in which case the bulbs are still present. Four bothridia with inner margins fused to scolex. Proglottids acraspedote, apolytic or anapolytic. Genital pores marginal, preequatorial. Parasites of elasmobranchs.

Type genus: *Gilquinia* Guiart, 1927.

6b. Scolex with two bothridia 7

7a. Testes overreaching osmoregulatory canals; no vitelline follicles behind ovary ....**Eutetrarhynchidae Guiart, 1927. (P. 51)**

Diagnosis: Scolex long, acraspedote. Tentacles long, cyclindrical, hooks on inner surface of different size than those of outer surface. Two wide, flattened bothridia each with distinct notch on posterior surface. Proglottides acraspedote, apolytic. Testes numerous, crossing osmoregulatory canals laterally. No postovarian vitellaria. Parasites of elasmobranchs.

Type genus: *Eutetrarhynchus* Pintner, 1913.

7b. Testes not overreaching osmoregulatory canals; some vitelline follicles behind ovary ....
....**Hornelliellidae Yamaguti, 1954. (P. 56)**

Diagnosis: Scolex rather long, lacking pars postbulbosa; followed by unsegmented neck. Tentacles long and stout, armed with hooks of varying sizes and shapes. Two bothridia present, each wtih thickened, elevated borders. Proglottides apolytic, acraspedote. Genital pores marginal. Parasites of elasmobranchs.

Type genus: *Hornelliella* Yamaguti, 1954.

Key to the Genera in Dasyrhynchidae

1a. Base of scolex expanded ....
....……....*Dasyrhynchus* **Pintner, 1928.** (Fig. 71)

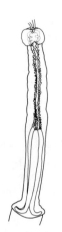

Diagnosis: Scolex long, slender, swollen at base, slightly craspedote. Tentacles long, slender, emerging near tip of scolex, armed with one or two chainettes and intercalary rows of small hooks as well as varying sizes and shapes of other hooks. Tentacular sheaths coiled or spiral; bulbs long and slender. Bothridia fused, each fused pair with deep posterior notch. Proglottides acraspedote. Gravid proglottids as long as wide. Genital pores irregularly alternating. Cirrus pouch oval. Cirrus unarmed. Testes very numerous, filling all available space between osmoregulatory canals. Vagina posterior to cirrus pouch, opening into common atrium with cirrus. Ovary rather small, bilobed, near posterior margin of proglottid. Vitellaria encircling proglottid, cortical. Gravid uterus saccular. Parasites of selachians. Atlantic and Pacific oceans.

Fig. 71. Dasy-rhynchus talis-mani Dollfus, 1935.

Type species: *D. variouncinatum* (Pintner, 1913).
Key to species: Wardle and McCleod (1952).

1b. Base of scolex not expanded 2

2a. Chainette hooks with basal wings (Fig. 70a) ....
.... *Floriceps* **Cuvier, 1817.** (Fig. 72)

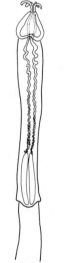

Diagnosis: Scolex long, slightly craspedote. Tentacles emerging near apex of scolex, each with chainette flanked by satellite hooks. Chainette hooks each biwinged. Pars vaginalis long. Bothridia two, reverse heart-shaped. Tentacle sheaths sinuous. Bulbs much longer than wide. Strobila acraspedote. Genital pores irregularly alternating. Cirrus unarmed. Osmoregulatory canals dorsal to cirrus pouch and vagina. Base of cirrus pouch directed anteriomedially in gravid proglottids. Testes filling field between osmoregulatory canals. Vagina opens anterior to cirrus pouch. Seminal receptacle present. Ovary X-shaped in cross section. Vitellaria lateral to muscle bundles, in lateral, interrupted fields. Uterine pore anteriomedian. Parasites of elasmobranchs. Atlantic and Pacific.

Fig. 72. Floriceps sac-catus Cuvier, 1817. After Dollfus (1942).

Type species: *F. saccatus* Cuvier, 1817.
Key to species: Wardle and McCleod (1952).

2b. Chainette hooks without basal wings ....
.... *Callitetrarhynchus* **Pintner, 1931.** (Fig. 73)

Diagnosis: Scolex long, very weakly craspedote. Tentacles emerging from anterior margin of bothridia. Pars vaginalis long, glandular; tentacle sheaths sinuous. Bulbs about three times longer than wide. Bothridia two, nearly round, with strong notch in posterior margin. Chainette hooks lacking lateral wings; satellite hooks present. Strobila thin, acraspedote. Genital pore in middle third of margin. Cirrus pouch pyriform. Testes small, partly post-ovarian. Vagina is behind cirrus pouch. Ovary bilobed, about one-fifth from posterior end of proglottid. Vitellaria in lateral cortex. Parasites of selachians. Cosmopolitan.

Type species: C. *gracilis* (Rudolphi, 1819) Pintner, 1931.

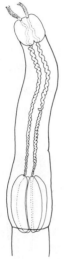

Fig. 73. *Callitetrarhynchus gracilis* (Rudolphi, 1819) Pintner, 1931. After Dollfus (1942).

Key to the Genera in Eutetrarhynchidae

1a. Strobila with no more than six proglottids ....
....*Christianella* **Guiart, 1931.**

Diagnosis: Scolex acraspedote. Bulbs long, narrow. Two bothridia, each strongly notched on posterior border. Tentacles very long, heteroacanthous, with spiral half turns of similar hooks. Strobila acraspedote, apolytic, consisting of only 3 to 6 proglottids. Genital pore in posterior quarter of lateral margin. Cirrus pouch large, reaching median line of proglottid. Cirrus long, unarmed. Testes filling preovarian, intervascular area. Ovary bilobed, posterior. Vitellaria encircling testicular zone. Uterus saccular. Parasites of selachians. Atlantic, Pacific, Mediterranean, Indian Ocean.

Type species: C. *minuta* (Beneden, 1849) Guiart, 1931.

1b. Strobila with more than six proglottids 2

2a. Hooks arranged in continuous rows ....
     ....*Eutetrarhynchus* Pintner, 1913. (Fig. 74)

Fig. 74. *Eutetrarhyn-chus lineatus* (Linton, 1909) Pintner, 1913. After Dollfus (1942).

Diagnosis: Scolex long, acraspedote, covered with very small spines. Pars vaginalis longer than pars bothridialis and pars bulbosa. Pars postbulbosa small. Tentacle sheaths sinuous, with small red organ of unknown nature at posterior end of each. Bulbs always much longer than wide. Two bothridia, with free posterior and lateral borders. Tentacles emerging from near apex of scolex. Armature hetero-acanthous, external hooks with toe and heel, internal hooks without toe and heel. Strobila anapolytic, slightly craspedote or not, according to species. Genital pores irregularly alternating, postequatorial. Cirrus pouch pyriform, transverse. Testes large, numerous, preovarian. Vagina ventral to cirrus pouch, provided with a distal sphincter. Ovary bilobed, wide. Vitellaria surrounding testicular area. Uterus reaching near anterior end of proglottid, with lateral branches. Parasites of selachians. Atlantic, Mediterranean, Indian Ocean.

Type species: *E. ruficollis* (Eysenhardt, 1829) Pintner, 1913.

Key to species: Wardle and McCleod, (1952.)

2b. Hooks arranged in half-rows, ascending obliquely from mid-line of internal surface of tentacle 3

3a. First hooks in ascending rows large, decreasing in size throughout length of row ....
     ....*Parachristianella* Dollfus, 1946. (Fig. 75)

Diagnosis: Scolex slender, acraspedote, pars bulbosa and pars vaginalis each longer than pars bothridialis. Bulbs much longer than wide. Tentacle sheaths slightly sinuous but not spiral. Bothridia two, rounded, not contiguous apically. Retractors inserted in posterior ends of bulbs. Prebulbar organ distinct. Tentacles moderately long. Armature heteroacanthous, consisting of ascending spiral rows beginning with two large triangular hooks at middle of internal surface, remaining hooks decreasing in size as row ends near middle of external surface. Strobila unknown. Parasites of Batoidea. France, California.

Type species: *P. trygonis* Dollfus, 1946.

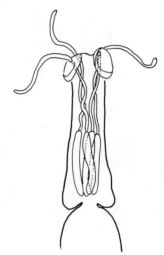

Fig. 75. *Parachristianella trygonis* Dollfus, 1946.

3b. First hooks in ascending rows small, increasing in size near middle of row, then decreasing toward end of row ....
.. *Prochristianella* Dollfus, 1946.

Diagnosis: Scolex long, slender, acraspedote. Pars bulbosa and pars vaginalis both longer than pars bothridialis. Pars bulbosa swollen. Tentacle sheaths sinuous, not spiral. Prebulbar organs not seen. Bulbs 6 or 7 times longer than wide. Retractors inserted at posterior ends of bulbs. Bothridia two, rounded, not contiguous apically. Tentacles emerging near apex of scolex. Armature heteroacanthous, complex. First hooks in each ascending diagonal row small, enlarging towards middle of row then decreasing in size toward end of row. Strobila known only from subadult. Acraspedote. Genital pore immediately postequatorial. Testes in two longitudinal rows of 29 to 32 each; no testes postovarian. Ovary occupies the last one-seventh of proglottid. Parasites of Batoidea. France.

Type species: *P. trygonicola Dollfus*, 1946.

Key to the Genera in Gilquiniidae

1a. Well-developed tentacles present ....
....*Gilquinia* **Guiart, 1927.** (Fig. 76)

Diagnosis: Scolex acraspedote, pars vaginalis longer than pars bothridialis and pars bulbosa. Tentacle sheaths sinuous. Bulbs elliptical. Bothridia four. Tentacles emerging from notches in anterior margin of bothridia. Armature homeoacanthous. Strobila acraspedote. Genital pores irregularly alternating, preequatorial. Vagina ventral to cirrus. Zerney's vesicle well developed. Testes pre- and postovarian. Ovary bilobed, separated from posterior end of proglottid by testes. Vitellaria completely encircling medulla. Uterus extending to near level of genital pore, filling most of proglottid when gravid. Parasites of Squalii. Atlantic, Mediterranean, Pacific.

Fig. 76. *Gilguinia squali* (Fabricius, 1794) Guiart, 1927. After Hart (1936).

Type species G. *squali* (Fabricius, 1794) Guiart, 1927.

1b. **Tentacles missing, although tentacle sheaths may be present** ....*Aporhynchus* **Nybelin, 1918.** (Fig. 77)

Diagnosis: Scolex acraspedote, long. Four bothridia with free lateroposterior margins. Tentacles not present; tentacle sheaths and bulbs present. Strobila apolytic, acraspedote. Neck present. Genital pores muscular, irregularly alternating, preequatorial. Zerney's vesicle and external seminal vesicle present. Cirrus pouch extends to ventral osmoregulatory canal. Testes numerous, in pre- and postovarian fields. Vagina opens posterior to cirrus. Ovary bilobed, separated from posterior end of proglottid by testes. Vitellaria encircling entire proglottid. Uterine pore present. Parasites of Squalii. North Atlantic, Scandinavia.

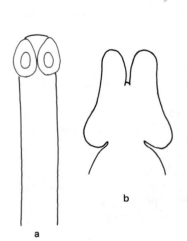

Fig. 77. *Aporhynchus norvegicum* (Olsson, 1868) Nybelin, 1918. After Rees (1941). a. Scolex. b. Longitudinal section of scolex.

Type species: A. *norvegicum* (Olsson, 1866) Nybelin, 1918.

Key to the Genera in Gymnorhynchidae

1a. **Tentacles with double chainette; incomplete ring of very large hooks at base of armed portion** ....
..............................._Gymnorhynchus_ **Rudolphi, 1819. (Fig. 78)**

Diagnosis: Scolex acraspedote, pars bothridialis shorter than pars vaginalis and pars bulbosa. Bothridia four, anterior and medial margins fused with scolex, other margins free. Tentacles emerging near apex of scolex. Armature poeciloacanthous, with double chainette; incomplete ring of very large hooks separating armed portion from unarmed portion. Adult anatomy unknown. Pleurocercus known from several marine teleosts. Atlantic, Mediterranean.

Fig. 78. *Gymnorhynchus gigas* (Cuvier, 1817) Rudolphi, 1819. After Dollfus (1942).

Type species: *G. gigas* (Cuvier, 1817) Rudolphi, 1819.

1b. **Tentacles without chainettes; complete ring of very large hooks at base of armed portion** ....
..............................._Molicola_ **Dollfus, 1935. (Fig. 79)**

Diagnosis: Scolex acraspedote. Retractors attached to bases of bulbs. Bothridia four, comma-shaped, anterior ends fused to scolex. Tentacles emerging from near apex of scolex. Armature poecilacanthous, chainettes replaced by longitudinal band of small hooks on external surface of tentacle. Complete ring of large hooks separating armed from unarmed portions of tentacles. Strobila acraspedote, apolytic. Genital pores irregularly alternating, preequatorial on lateral margin. Cirrus pouch pyriform, thin-walled. Cirrus long. External seminal vesicle present. Testes numerous, in intervascular medulla. Vagina with distal sphincter, opening into atrium ventral to cirrus. Ovary bilobed, separated from posterior end of proglottid by several testes. Vitellaria surrounding medulla. Uterus elongate, with a ventral, poral outpocketing. Parasites of selachians. Atlantic, Pacific.

Type species: *M. horridus* (Goodsir, 1841) Dollfus, 1935.

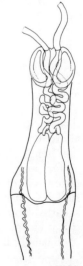

Fig. 79. *Molicola horridus* (Goodsir, 1841) Dollfus, 1935.

DIAGNOSIS OF THE ONLY GENUS IN HEPATOXYLIDAE
Hepatoxylon Bosc, 1811 (Fig. 80)

Diagnosis: Scolex wrinkled, acraspedote. Bothridia separated by narrow partition; each bothridium in form of narrow slit. Tentacles short, globular or truncated. Hooks similar, in spiral longitudinal rows, decreasing in size posteriad. Tentacle retractors not inserted on base of sheath. Bulbs ellipsoid to comma-shaped. Proglottids much wider than long. Two sets of genitalia per proglottid, each with a ventral uterine pore. Cirrus unarmed. Testes median to osmoregulatory canals. Ovaries compact, near posterior margin of proglottid. Vitellaria cortical, encircling proglottid. Vagina posterior to cirrus, with outer and inner sphincters. Parasites of selachians. Cosmopolitan.

Type species: *H. squali* (Martin, 1797) Bosc, 1811.

Fig. 80. *Hepatoxylon trichiuri* (Holten, 1802) Dollfus, 1942.

DIAGNOSIS OF THE ONLY GENUS IN HORNELLIELLIDAE
Hornelliella Yamaguti, 1954

Diagnosis: Scolex long, stout. Pars bulbosa and pars vaginalis long, pars postbulbosa absent. Tentacle sheaths provided with muscular rings. Bothridia two, large, lacking posterior margin. Tentacles emerge from anterior margin of bothridia, heteroacanthous. Strobila acraspedote, apolytic. Genital pores irregularly alternating. Genital ducts opening into common muscular pouch, the hermaphroditic organ. Testes numerous, intervascular, none as far posterior as ovary. Ovary four-winged, separated from posterior end of proglottid by transverse band of vitellaria. Vitelline follicles profuse, between transverse and longitudinal muscle sheaths. Uterus ventromedian, extending to anterior end of proglottid; preformed uterine pore present. Eggs nonoperculate. Parasites of elasmobranchs. Mediterranean.

Type species: *H. annandalei* (Hornell, 1912) Yamaguti, 1954.

Key to the Genera in Lacistorhynchidae

1a. Bothridia not notched posteriorly ....
......................................*Eulacistorhynchus* **Subhapradha, 1957.**

Diagnosis: Scolex fairly long, acraspedote. Bulbs long; retractor muscles attached to bases of bulbs. Bothridia two, oval or rounded, lacking posterior notch. Tentacles long, poeciloacanthus; double chainette present. Strobila acraspedote, mature proglottids much longer than wide. Genital pore lateral, in posterior third of proglottid. Cirrus pouch oval, cirrus armed. Testes in single field medial to vitellaria. Ovary compactly lobated, near posterior end of proglottid. Vitellaria lateral. Parasites of sharks. India.

Type species: *E. chiloscyllius* Subhapradha, 1957.

1b. Bothridia notched posteriorly 2

2a. Bulbs very long .... *Grillotia* **Guiart, 1927.** (**Fig. 81**)

Diagnosis: Scolex acraspedote, long, slender, with the tentacles emerging from anterior margins of bothridia. Pars vaginalis long; tentacle sheaths not spiral. Retractor muscles inserted in posterior ends of bulbs. Pars postbulbosa short. Bothridia two, nearly rounded, with small notch in posterior margin. Tentacles poeciloacanthous with hollow hooks of several types. Midline of external surface with longitudinal band of small hooks arranged in sinusoidal pattern, in place of chainette. Midline of internal surface lacking hooks. Strobila acraspedote, apolytic. Genital atrium in posterior half of proglottid margin, irregularly alternating. Cirrus pouch ovoid, nearly one-fourth width of proglottid. Cirrus unarmed. Testes numerous, some usually postovarian. Vagina ventral to cirrus pouch. Seminal receptacle present. Ovary bilobed, somewhat anterior to posterior end of proglottid. Uterus with lateral branches, extending nearly whole length of proglottid. Vitellaria lateral, mostly medullary. Parasites of elasmobranchs. Cosmopolitan.

Fig. 81. *Grillotia* sp.
After Hart (1936).

Type species: *G. erinaceus* (Beneden, 1858) Guiart, 1927.

Key to species: Wardle and McCleod, (1952).

2b. **Bulbs short** ....*Lacistorhynchus* **Pintner, 1913. (Fig. 82)**

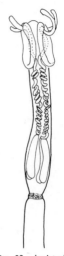

Diagnosis: Scolex craspedote, long, pars vaginalis very long. Tentacle sheaths spiral. Pars bulbosa rather short, slightly swollen. Bothridia two, rounded, slightly notched on posterior margin. Tentacles emerging from anterior edge of bothridia. Poeciloacanthous, with simple chainette. Strobila acraspedote, slender. Genital atria irregularly alternating, with muscular pad before and after. Cirrus pouch pyriform. Testes very numerous, filling entire intervascular field, some postovarian. Vagina posterior to cirrus pouch. Ovary four-lobed in cross section, separated from posterior end of proglottid by several testes. Vitellaria lateral. Uterus median, long. Parasites of selachians. Atlantic and Pacific.

Type species: *L. tenuis* (Beneden, 1858) Pintner, 1913.

Fig. 82. *Lacistorhynchus tenuis* (Beneden, 1858) Pintner, 1913.

Key to the Genera in Paranybeliniidae Fam. N.

1a. **Bulbs of pars bulbosa about three times longer than wide, hooks each with ventral tooth** ....
................................*Pseudonybelinia* **Dollfus, 1966. (Fig. 83)**

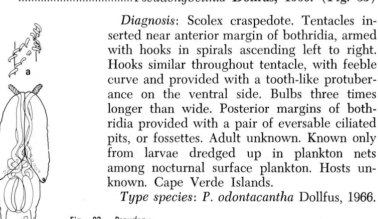

Diagnosis: Scolex craspedote. Tentacles inserted near anterior margin of bothridia, armed with hooks in spirals ascending left to right. Hooks similar throughout tentacle, with feeble curve and provided with a tooth-like protuberance on the ventral side. Bulbs three times longer than wide. Posterior margins of bothridia provided with a pair of eversable ciliated pits, or fossettes. Adult unknown. Known only from larvae dredged up in plankton nets among nocturnal surface plankton. Hosts unknown. Cape Verde Islands.

Type species: *P. odontacantha* Dollfus, 1966.

Fig. 83. *Pseudonybelinia odontacantha* Dollfus, 1966. a. Portion of tentacle, with typical hooks. b. Entire juvenile.

1b. **Bulbs of pars bulbosa about twice longer than wide, hooks lacking ventral tooth** ....
...............................*Paranybelinia* **Dollfus, 1966. (Fig. 84)**

Diagnosis: Scolex craspedote. Tentacles inserted near anterior margins of bothridia, armed with hooks in spirals ascending left to right. Hooks all similar, arcuate, lacking ventral tooth-like projection. Bulbs twice longer than wide. Posterior margins of bothridia provided with a pair of eversable ciliated pits. Adult unknown. Known only from larvae found with nocturnal surface plankton dredged up in nets. Hosts unknown. Cape Verde Islands.

Type species: *P. otobothrioides* Dollfus, 1966.

Fig. 84. Paranybelinia otobothrioides Dollfus, 1966.

Key to the Genera in Otobothriidae

1a. **Two complete sets of reproductive organs per segment** ....
..............................*Diplootobothrium* **Chandler, 1942. (Fig. 85)**

Diagnosis: Scolex long, craspedote. Tentacle sheaths sinuous, longer than tentacles. Bulbs 7-8 times longer than wide. Retractors inserted near anterior ends of bulbs. Bothridia two, each with two lateral ciliated sensory pits. Tentacle armature heteroacanthous, hooks in diagonal rows of 9 or 10. Neck present. Strobila acraspedote. Two sets of reproductive organs in each proglottid. Genital pores equatorial in mature segments, postequatorial in gravid ones. Cirrus pouch oval, small. Testes not described. Vagina posterior to cirrus pouch. Ovaries bilobed, midway between median line and lateral margin. Uteri nearly touching. Vitellaria not described. Parasites of Selachii. Florida.

Type species: *D. springeri* Chandler, 1942.

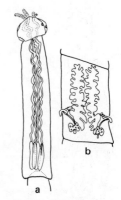

Fig. 85. Diplootobothrium springeri Chandler, 1942. a. Scolex. b. Proglottid.

1b. **One complete set of reproductive organs per segment** 2

2a. **Tentacle sheaths strongly convoluted. Plerocercus with short, rounded appendix** ....*Otobothrium* **Linton, 1890. (Fig. 86)**

Fig. 86. Generalized *Otobothrium.* After Dollfus (1942).

Diagnosis: Scolex long or short, craspedote. Tentacle sheaths spiral. Retractor muscles inserted at or near anterior end of bulb. Pars bulbosa swollen. Bothridia two, often with posterior notch, each side with a ciliated, eversable sensory pit. Tentacles emerging from anterior margins of bothridia, shorter than their sheaths. Armature heteroacanthous. Strobila acraspedote, apolytic. Genital pores postequatorial. Cirrus pouch small, oval, directed somewhat forward. Cirrus unarmed. Testes numerous, in intervascular field, some postovarian. Ovary bilobed, somewhat removed from posterior margin of proglottid. Vagina and vitellaria not described. Uterus extending to near anterior end of proglottid, no uterine pore. Parasites of selachians. Cosmopolitan.

Type species: *O. crenacolle* Linton, 1890. (Fig. 86)

2b. **Tentacle sheaths scarcely convoluted. Plerocercus with very long, narrow appendix** ....
.................................*Poecilancistrum* **Dollfus, 1929. (Fig. 87)**

Fig. 87. *Poecilanstrum* sp. After Dollfus (1942).

Diagnosis: Scolex acraspedote, pars vaginalis short, bulbs longer than wide. Pars bulbosa not swollen. Bothridia two, rounded, each with a ciliated, protrusable sensory pit on each lateral margin. Tentacles emerge from anterior margins of bothridia. Armature heteroacanthous. Strobila acraspedote, apolytic. Neck present. Genital pores in postequatorial lateral margin of proglottid. Cirrus pouch oval, containing long cirrus. External seminal vesicle present. Testes numerous, in entire proglottid between osmoregulatory canals. Vagina opens posterior to cirrus. Seminal receptacle present. Ovary bilobed. Uterus reaches near to anterior end of proglottid. Parasites of Squalii. Brazil, India, Texas.

Type species: *P. caryophyllum* (Diesing, 1850) Dollfus, 1929.

Key to the Genera in Pterobothriidae

1a. External surface of tentacles with chainette of V-shaped hooks
.....................................*Halysiorhynchus* Pintner, 1913. (Fig. 88)

Diagnosis: Scolex long, acraspedote. Tentacle sheaths spiral. Retractors inserted in bases of bulbs. Bothridia four, small, on short stalks arising from apex of scolex. Tentacles with poecilacanthous armature, each external surface bearing a chainette of V-shaped hooks. Strobila acraspedote, apolytic, flattened anteriorly, subcylindrical posteriorly. Genital pores irregularly alternating, near posterior margin of proglottid. Cirrus pouch extending to midline of proglottid. Cirrus unarmed. Testes in two lateral fields anterior to ovary. Ovary bilobed, posterior. Cortical vitellaria encircling entire proglottid. Uterus median, with posterior pore. Parasites of Batoidea. Ceylon.

Type species: *H. macrocephalus* (Shipley and Hornell, 1906) Pintner, 1913.

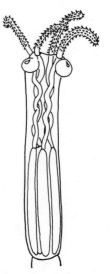

Fig. 88. *Halysiorhynchus macrocephalus* (Shipley and Hornell, 1906) Pintner, 1913. After Southwell (1930).

1b. External surface of tentacles with longitudinal band of small hooks which are not V-shaped ...*Pterobothrium* Diesing, 1850.

Diagnosis: Scolex long, slender, acraspedote. Tentacle sheaths spiral. Pars bulbosa somewhat swollen. Retractors attached at differing levels, according to species. Bothridia four, each on a short, motile stalk, the lateral pairs of which are connected by a thin membrane. Pars postbulbosa always present. Tentacle hooks poecilacanthous, each external surface with a band of small hooks. Unsegmented neck absent. Strobila acraspedote, apolytic. Genital pores irregularly alternating, in posterior half of margin. Cirrus pouch thick-walled. Testes numerous, in intervascular field. Vagina ventral to cirrus pouch. Ovary bilobed, near posterior border of proglottid. Vitellaria lateral. Uterine pore anterior. Parasites of Selachii. Cosmopolitan.

Type species: *P. macrourum* (Rudolphi, 1819) Diesing, 1850.

DIAGNOSIS OF THE ONLY GENUS IN SPHYRIOCEPHALIDAE

Sphyriocephalus Pintner, 1913 (Fig. 89)

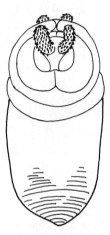

Diagnosis: Scolex thicker than wide. Tentacles arising from within bothridial cavities. Hooks hollow, similar, in regularly alternating longitudinal rows. Tentacle sheath and bulb short. Retractor not entering bulb. Bothridia fused, with longitudinal ridge on median side of bottom of deep bothridial cavity. Notch present on posterior margin of each set of fused bothridia. Proglottides wider than long. Genital pores irregularly alternating. Cirrus pouch slender. Cirrus unarmed. Testes in medulla between osmoregulatory canals. Vagina posterior to cirrus pouch, with distal sphincter. Ovary posterior, bilobed. Vitellaria encircling proglottid in cortex. Uterus saccular, with submedian pore. Parasites of selachians. Atlantic, Pacific, Mediterranean.

Fig. 89. *Sphyriocephalus tergestinus* Pintner, 1913. After Dollfus (1930).

Type species: *S. viridis* (Wagener, 1854) Pintner, 1913.

Key to the Genera in Tentaculariidae

1a. Scolex long; bothridia without free borders ....
....*Tentacularia* Bosc, 1797. (Fig. 90)

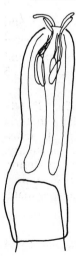

Diagnosis: Scolex long, craspedote, subcylindrical. Bothridia separated, without free borders, spinous. Tentacles short, slender, armed with solid hooks in spirals, similar except at base of tentacle. Tentacle sheaths not twisted. Bulbs ellipsoidal. Proglottids acraspedote, anapolytic. Genital pores irregularly alternating, ventromarginal. Cirrus unarmed. Testes numerous, filling dorsal medulla between outer osmoregulatory canals. Seminal receptacle sometimes present. Ovary bilobed in frontal section, X-shaped in cross section. Parasites of elasmobranchs. Cosmopolitan.

Type species: *T. coryphaenae* Bosc, 1797.

Fig. 90. *Tentacularia coryphaenae* Bosc, 1797. After Yamaguti (1934).

1b. Scolex short; bothridia with free borders ....
.................…...................................*Nybelinia* **Poche, 1926. (Fig. 91)**

Diagnosis: Scolex short, craspedote. Bothridia separate, with free boarders. Tentacles cylindrical, armed with solid, similar hooks in quincunxes. Proglottids craspedote or not, anapolytic. Genital pores irregularly alternating, ventromarginal. Testes medullary, numerous. Cirrus pouch long. Cirrus unarmed. Internal seminal vesicle present or not. Ovary X-shaped in cross section. Vitellaria in whole cortex except in region of wings of ovary. Parasites of elasmobranchs. Cosmopolitan.

Type species: *N. lingualis* (Cuvier, 1817) Poche, 1926.

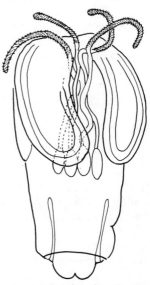

Fig. 91. *Nybelinia lingualis* (Cuvier, 1817) Poche, 1926. After Dollfus (1942).

Key to the Families of Pseudophyllidea

1a. Vagina and cirrus pouch opening medial on flat surface 2

1b. Vagina and cirrus pouch opening marginal or submarginal, not medial 6

2a. Uterine pore on same surface as those of cirrus pouch and vagina ....…..3

2b. Uterine pore on surface opposite those of cirrus pouch and vagina 5

3a. Cirrus pouch absent ....
..........................Cephalochlamydidae Yamaguti, 1959. (P. 66)
Diagnosis: Scolex triangular, with two wide, shallow bothria united at the apex. Neck present. Strobila small, proglottids acraspedote. Genital atrium median, anterior. Testes few, medullary, in two submedian fields anterior to ovary. Ovary bilobed, posterior. Vitellaria follicular, in two lateral cortical fields. Uterus winding broadly, opening posterior to genital atrium. Eggs anoperculate, embryonated. Parasites of amphibians.
Type genus: *Cephalochlamys* Blanchard, 1908.

3b. Cirrus pouch present 4

4a. **Adult up to 110 mm long: External metamerism anterior only. Vitellaria medullary. Plerocercoid with four retractable tentacles** ....Haplobothriidae Meggitt, 1924. (P. 67)

Diagnosis: Plerocercoid (in liver of freshwater teleosts) with four tentacle-like outgrowths on scolex. Plerocercoid may attain length of 90 mm in definitive host and show distinct segmentation: Each segment shows secondary segmentation beginning at anterior end.

Type genus: *Haplobothrium* Cooper, 1914.

4b. **Adult usually over 110 mm long. External metamerism usually complete. Vitellaria cortical. Plerocercoid without tentacles** ....
....Diphyllobothriidae Lühe, 1910. (P. 67)

Diagnosis: Scolex variable in shape, usually bilaterally compressed, bearing two bothria, sometimes covered with fine spines, rarely with lobated apical cap. Neck conspicuous or not. External metamerism usually distinct, usually acraspedote. Strobila anapolytic. One to 14 sets of reproductive organs per proglottid. Genital pores ventral, median, independent or together in common atrium. Testes numerous, mostly medullary. External seminal vesicle present. Ovary posterior, bialate, medullary, ventral. Vitellaria follicular, cortical, often in two lateral bands joining in front of genital pores. Uterus spiral, expanded distally, opening ventrally posterior to vaginal pore. Eggs operculate, unembryonated when laid. Parasites of fishes, reptiles, birds and mammals.

Type genus: *Diphyllobothrium* Cobbold, 1858.

5a. **Bothria deep, with inrolled margins. Eggs anoperculate, embryonated** ....Ptychobothriidae Lühe, 1902. (P. 75)

Diagnosis: Scolex bilaterally compressed, rounded apically, with deep bothria having rolled edges. Neck absent. Proglottids acraspedote. Genital atrium opens middorsally. Testes in dorsal medulla, in two lateral fields. Ovary posterior, median, transversely elongated. Vitellaria usually in two lateral, cortical fields. Uterus sinuous, medullary, opening on midventral surface. Eggs anoperculate, embryonated when laid. Parasites of marine teleosts and birds.

Type genus: *Ptychobothrium* Lönnberg, 1889.

5b. **Bothria deep, shallow, or absent, but lacking inrolled margins. Eggs operculate, unembryonated** ....
...............................Bothriocephalidae Blanchard, 1849. (P. 78)

Diagnosis: Scolex variable, usually with apical disk bearing dorsal and ventral notches, and occasionally marginal spines. Bothria deep, shallow, or absent, elongate when present. Neck absent. Metamerism distinct (except *Anatrum*), occasionally with secondary segmentation. Proglottides usually craspedote, with median

dorsal and ventral furrows. Genital atrium dorsal, median. Cirrus
pouch round, median. Testes medullary in two lateral fields. Seminal receptacle present or not. Ovary posterior, in ventral medulla.
Vitellaria usually cortical, sometimes medullary. Uterus sinuous,
with rounded uterine sac. Uterine pore ventral, median. Eggs operculate, unembryonated. Parasites of teleosts.
Type genus: Bothriocephalus Rudolphi, 1808.

6a. **Cirrus distinctly protrusible, with large spines. Two sets of
reproductive organs per segment** ....
...............................**Echinophallidae Schumacher, 1914. (P. 80)**
Diagnosis: Scolex on young forms with inconspicuous apical disk
and shallow, oval bothria. Adult forms with scolex replaced by
pseudoscolex shaped like four-sided truncated pyramid or trape-
zoid, occasionally funnel-shaped. Neck absent. Proglottids strongly
craspedote, with lateral margins swollen. Two sets of reproductive
organs per proglottid. Genital pores dorsal, submarginal. Cirrus
pouch well developed. Cirrus with large spines near base. Testes
medullary, mostly postequatorial. Ovary lobated, posterior. Vitellaria filling most of cortex. Uterine pore median, ventral. Parasites
of marine teleosts.
Type genus: Echinophallus Schumacher, 1914.

6b. **Cirrus not distinctly protrusible nor spined. One set of reproductive organs per segment** 7

7a. **Eggs anoperculate, embryonated. Scolex unarmed. Uterine
pore dorsal or ventral**.....**Amphicotylidae Ariola, 1899. (P. 81)**
Diagnosis: Scolex unarmed, may be replaced by pseudoscolex;
bothria distinct. Neck present or absent. Metamerism distinct,
strobila serrate or not. Genital pores marginal, usually irregularly
alternating. External seminal vesicle absent. Cirrus unarmed. Testes
medullary, numerous. Ovary ventral, medullary. Vitellaria variable.
Uterus saclike, with rudimentary opening usually ventral, occasionally dorsal. Eggs anoperculate, embryonated. Parasites of
teleosts.
Type genus: Amphicotyle Diesing, 1863.

7b. **Eggs operculate, embryonated or not. Scolex armed or not.
Uterine pore ventral** 8

8a. **Scolex cuboidal, commonly armed, with rounded, shallow
bothria, rarely replaced by pseudoscolex. Genital pores marginal. Eggs embryonated or not** ....
.............................**Triaenophoridae Lönnberg, 1889. (P. 85)**
Diagnosis: Scolex stout, cuboidal or pyramidal, usually with
apical disk, usually armed. May be replaced by pseudoscolex in
Fistulicola. Bothria shallow, rounded. Neck absent. Metamerism

distinct or not. One set of reproductive organs per proglottid. Genital atrium marginal, irregularly alternating. Testes medullary. Ovary usually posterior, bilobed. Vitellaria cortical or medullary. Uterus greatly coiled; uterine sac small. Uterine pore ventral, median, anterior to level of genital atrium. Eggs operculate, embryonated or not. Parasites of teleosts.

Type genus: Triaenophorus Rudolphi, 1793.

8b. Scolex elongated, with elongated bothria, or replaced by pseudoscolex. Genital pores dorsosubmarginal, rarely marginal. Eggs unembryonated ....
...................**Parabothriocephalidae Yamaguti, 1959. (P. 87)**

Diagnosis: Scolex elongated, with shallow bothria, occasionally replaced by pseudoscolex. Neck absent. Proglottids elongate, craspedote, secondary external metamerism sometimes present. One set of reproductive organs per proglottid. Genital atrium marginal or dorsosubmarginal. Cirrus pouch obliquely transverse. Cirrus armed. Testes numerous, medullary, some follicles postovarian or not. Ovary posterior, medullary. Vitellaria cortical or medullary. Uterus with median sac. Uterine pore ventral, median, anterior. Eggs operculate, embryonated. Parasites of marine teleosts.

Type genus: Parabothriocephalus Yamaguti, 1934.

DIAGNOSIS OF THE ONLY GENUS IN CEPHALOCHLAMYDIDAE
Cephalochlamys Blanchard, 1908 (Fig. 92)

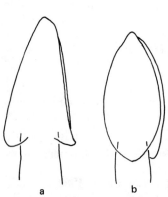

a　　　　b

Fig. 92. *Cephalochlamys namaquensis* (Cohn, 1906) Blanchard, 1908. After Thurston (1967). a. Lateral view. b. Dorsal view.

Diagnosis: Bothria broad and flat. Neck present. Genital atrium medioventral, at anterior end of proglottid. Cirrus long and thin. Testes in two lateral fields, 3 to 23 total. Seminal receptacle present. Ovary transversely elongated, posterior. Vitellaria lateral and/or ventral to osmoregulatory canals, no postovarian follicles. Uterus with broad loops overlapping testes; no uterine sac. Uterine pore midventral, immediately behind genital pore. Eggs anoperculate, embryonated. Parasites of clawed toads. Africa.

Type species: C. namaquensis (Cohn, 1906) Blanchard, 1908.

DIAGNOSIS OF THE ONLY GENUS IN HAPLOBOTHRIIDAE
Haplobothrium Cooper, 1914 (Fig. 93)

Primary segments separate and become adult strobilas up to 119 mm long, independent of one another. Adult holdfast with fine spines and shallow dorsal and ventral depressions, presumably bothria. Adult strobila: segmented at anterior end only; one set of genitalia per segment. Genital pores midventral. External seminal vesicle present. Testes in two bands in lateral medulla. Cirrus pouch median, anterior. Cirrus armed. Seminal receptacle present, well developed. Ovary medullary, posterior. Vitellaria lateral,

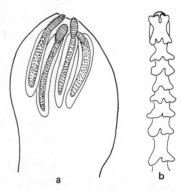

Fig. 93. *Haplobothrium bistrobilae* Premvati, 1969. a. Primary scolex. b. Pseudoscolex of secondary strobila.

medullary. Uterus with convoluted proximal duct and large distal sac. One large median and two smaller lateral osmoregulatory canals. Parasites of *Amia calva* (Osteichthyes). North America. (Considered to represent a separate order by Joyeux and Baer (1961)).

Type species: H. globuliforme Cooper, 1914.

Key to the Genera in Diphyllobothriidae

1a. Parasites of reptiles 2

1b. Parasites of birds 5

1c. Parasites of mammals 8

2a. Large sucker-like structure at apex of scolex. Bothria rudimentary ....*Scyphocephalus* Riggenbach, 1898.

Diagnosis: Scolex with deep suckerlike apical organ; bothria short, shallow, occupying only last fourth of scolex. Neck absent. Proglottids wider than long. Genital atrium midventral, preequatorial. Cirrus pouch occupying entire thickness of medulla. Testes numerous, meeting near anterior and posterior ends of proglottid. Ovary bilobed, posterior. Seminal receptacle present. Vitellaria cortical, surrounding proglottid. Uterus with only 2 or 3 loops. Parasites of varanid lizards. Java, Philippines.

Type species: S. bisulcatus Riggenbach, 1898.

2b. Scolex not as above, bothria well developed 3

3a. **Bothria with fused edges, forming two tubes** ....
....*Bothridium* **Blainville, 1824.** (**Fig. 94**)

Diagnosis: Bothria fused along margins to form tubelike structures with sphincters at front and rear ends; frilled or slit-like openings present at front end. Proglottids wider than long, proterogynous. Testes in lateral fields. Seminal receptacle present. Genital atrium medioventral, anterior to uterine pore. Cirrus pouch preequatorial, in dorsoventral plane. Ovary bilobed, postequatorial. Vitellaria surrounding inner muscular layer, interrupted in median field. Uterus with thick duct and dorsal sac. Uterine pore ventromedian, posterior to genital pore. Parasites of boid snakes and varanid lizards. Africa, Ceylon, Philippines, India, Australia, Asia.

Fig. 94. *Bothridium pythonis* Blainville, 1824.

Type species: *B. pithonis* Blainville, 1824.

3b. **Bothria not fused at edges** 4

4a. **Scolex broad, fan-like; bothria directed somewhat anteriad, sometimes with basal aperture** ....
....*Duthiersia* **Perrier, 1873.** (**Fig. 95**)

Diagnosis: Scolex bilaterally compressed so that it appears triangular or fan-like. Bothria deep, with frilled or crenulated margins; posterior aperture present in some species. Neck absent. Genital pore median, anterior to uterine pore. Cirrus pouch large, near anterior end of proglottid. Testes numerous, surrounding median genitalia. Vagina with distal sphincter, opening posterior to cirrus pouch. Seminal receptacle present. Ovary bilobed, postequatorial. Vitellaria cortical, in longitudinal lateral bands. Uterus looped. Uterine pore midventral, posterior to cirrus pouch. Parasites of varanid lizards. Africa, Sarawak, Maluccas.

Fig. 95. *Duthiersia fimbriata* Diesing, 1854. After Woodland (1938).

Type species:D. expansa Perrier, 1873.

4b. Scolex spoon- or finger-shaped; bothria broad and shallow ....*Lueheella* **Baer, 1924. (Syn:** *Spirometra*). **(Fig. 96)**

Diagnosis: Scolex elongate, somewhat bilaterally flattened, finger- or spoon-shaped in lateral view. Bothria broad and shallow. Neck slender. Most proglottids wider than long. Vagina opening immediately behind cirrus, both medioventral, preequatorial. Testes numerous, in two lateral fields which may join in front of genital pores or not, according to species. Ovary bilobed, posterior. Vitellaria continuous in cortex except interrupted over and under median genitalia. Uterus a simple spiral. Uterine pore midventral, posterior to vaginal pore. Parasites of reptiles, birds and mammals. Cosmopolitan.

Fig. 96. *Lueheella mansoni* (Cobbold, 1883) Rêgo. 1961. After Joyeux (1927).

Type species: *L. praetoriensis* Baer, 1924.

5a. Two sets of reproductive organs in each proglottid ....*Digramma* **Cholodkovsky, 1915.**

Diagnosis: Scolex small, triangular, not set off from rest of body. Bothria are short grooves connected apically. Neck absent. Each flat surface with two parallel, longitudinal grooves; ventral surface with a third median groove. Two sets of reproductive organs per proglottid. Genital pores in ventral surface with a third median groove. Two sets of reproductive organs per proglottid. Genital pores in ventral submedian grooves. Testes in dorsal medulla, interrupted in submedian fields. Ovaries in submedian fields. Vitellaria cortical. Uterus dorsal to vagina, coiled. Parasites of piscivorous birds. Japan, Europe.

Type species: *D. alternans* (Rudolphi, 1810) Cholodkovsky, 1915.

5b. One set of reproductive organs per proglottid 6

6a. **External metamerism only at anterior end; acraspedote** ....
....*Ligula* **Bloch, 1782. (Fig. 97)**

Diagnosis: Scolex small, triangular. Bothria each a shallow groove. Neck absent. Strobila with median groove on dorsal and ventral surfaces. External metamerism on anterior portion only; rest with numerous wrinkles. Genital atrium midventral. Testes in single layer in dorsal medulla. Seminal receptacle present. Ovary posterior. Vitellaria cortical. Uterus coiled, in median area. Uterine pore midventral, posterior to genital atrium. Parasites of piscivorous birds. Circumboreal.

Fig. 97. *Ligula intestinalis* (Linnaeus, 1758) Bloch, 1782. After Cooper (1918).

Type species: *L. intestinalis* (Linnaeus, 1758) Bloch, 1782.

6b. **External metamerism over entire strobila** 7

7a. **Scolex small, triangular. Bothria shallow, connected by groove over apex** .... *Schistocephalus* **Creplin, 1829.**

Diagnosis: Scolex small, triangular. Bothria are shallow grooves, connected apically. Neck absent. External metamerism complete. Proglottids craspedote, wider than long, greatest width preequatorial. Genital atrium midventral, preequatorial. Cirrus pouch subspherical. Testes numerous, in single layer in dorsal medulla. External seminal vesicle present. Ovary bilobed, posterior. Vitellaria cortical, continuous, absent in median area. Uterus submedian, regularly alternating. Uterine pore posterior to genital atrium, submedian, regularly alternating. Parasites of piscivorous birds. Circumboreal.

Type species: *S. solidus* (Mueller, 1776) Creplin, 1829.

7b. **Scolex distinct. Bothria narrow, deep, not connected by apical groove** .... *Diphyllobothrium* **Cobbold, 1858. (Fig. 98)**

Diagnosis: Scolex variable in shape. Bothria distinct, narrow, deep, not connected by apical groove. Neck present, sometimes quite short. Strobila often very long, with longitudinal grooves on flat surfaces. Proglottids craspedote, usually wider than long. Genital atrium medioventral, preequatorial, surrounded by small papillae. Testes very numerous, in single layer, continuous across proglottid except in zone of median genitalia. External seminal vesicle present, muscular. Ovary bilobed, posterior. Vitellaria very numerous, in single layer, continuous across proglottid except in zone of median genitalia. Uterus with parallel lateral loops, or rosette-shaped. Uterine pore posterior to genital pore. Parasites of marine and terrestrial mammals and birds. Cosmopolitan.

Type species: *D. stemmacephalum* Cobbold, 1858.

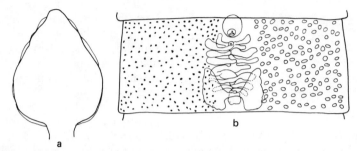

Fig. 98. *Diphyllobothrium alascense* Rausch and Williamson, 1958. a. Scolex. b. Proglottid.

8a. Two sets of reproductive organs in each proglottid 9

8b. One set of reproductive organs in each proglottid 11

8c. More than two sets of reproductive organs in each proglottid 15

9a. Osmoregulatory canals numerous (35-70), anastomosing, confined to medulla ....*Multiductus* Clarke, 1962. (Fig. 99)

Diagnosis: Scolex globular with deep bothria; posterior region overlaps first four proglottids. Neck absent. Strobila long (18 meters); proglottids craspedote. Double set of reproductive organs in each segment. Genital atria at same transverse level. Cirrus, vagina

Fig. 99. *Multiductus physeteris* Clarke, 1962. Apical view of scolex.

and uterus opening into shallow atrium. Cirrus not described. Cirrus pouch very muscular, ventral to seminal vesicle. Testes numerous, in several layers in medulla. Vagina with strong sphincter near pore, opening behind cirrus. Vitellaria in one median and two lateral fields, between two longitudinal muscle layers. Uterus sac-like. Ovary lacking isthmus; located in ventroposterior region of proglottid. Eggs operculate, with thick shells. Two layers of longitudinal cortical muscle bundles. Excretory system consists of 35 to 70 longitudinal canals, with numerous anastomoses, all in medulla. Sperm whale. Antarctica.

Type species: *M. physeteris* Clarke, 1962.

9b. Osmoregulatory canals not so numerous, cortical 10

10a. Genital pores at same level ....
................................*Diplogonoporus* **Lönnberg, 1892. (Fig. 100)**

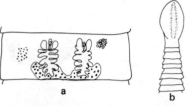

Fig. 100. *Diplogonoporus tetrapterus* (Siebold, 1848) Lönnberg, 1892. After Rausch (1964). a. Proglottid (testes and vitellaria not filled in). b. Scolex.

Diagnosis: *Scolex* short, bilaterally compressed. Bothria deep, slit-like. Neck absent. Proglottids first arising as primary segments which then subdivide into secondary and tertiary segments. Proglottids short, wide. Two sets of reproductive organs per proglottid. Genital pores ventral, submedian. Testes in median and lateral fields. External seminal vesicle present. Ovary transversely elongated, lobated, posterior. Vitellaria in median and lateral fields. Uterine coils parallel or rosette-shaped. Uterine pores posterior to genital pores. Parasites of baleen whales, seals, sea otter, man. Circumboreal.

Type species: *D. balaenopterae* Lönnberg, 1892.

10b. One set of genital pores more anterior than the other ....
....*Baylisia* **Markowski, 1952. (Fig. 101)**

Fig. 101. *Baylisia baylisi* Markowski, 1952.

Diagnosis: Scolex short. Bothria cup-shaped. Neck absent. External metamerism not corresponding to internal metamerism. Two sets of reproductive organs per proglottid. Genital pores ventral, set into longitudinal furrows, alternating in position so that they are at different levels from one another. Testes in single layer in two lateral fields. External seminal vesicle present. Ovary composed of compact central part giving off branches along the uterine coils; V-shaped in sagittal section. Vitellaria cortical, in continuous sheath interrupted by osmoregulatory canals. Uterus comprising a few horizontal coils in central part of proglottid. Uterine pores posteromedial to genital pores. Parasites of seals. Antarctica.

Type species: *B. baylisi* Markowski, 1952.

11a. Bothria intensely crenulated to form flower-like scolex 12

11b. Scolex otherwise 13

12a. Bothria with margins infolded to form cauliflower-like apical organ on scolex. Vitellaria in ventral cortex ....
.....................*Pyramicocephalus* **Monticelli, 1890. (Fig. 102)**

Diagnosis: Bothria with anterior margins folded to form flower-like apical organ on scolex. Strobila wrinkled, external metamerism lacking. Genital pore medioventral. Cirrus pouch well developed. Testes numerous. Ovary posterior, bilobed. Vitellaria in ventral cortex. Uterus median, sinuous. Parasites of seals. Circumboreal.

Type species: *P. anthocephalus* (Fabricius, 1780) Monticelli, 1890.

Fig. 102. *Pyramicocephalus anthocephalus* (Fabricius, 1790) Monticelli, 1890. After Ariola (1900).

12b. Anterior half of bothria as above, posterior half well-developed. Vitellaria in cortex surrounding entire proglottid ....*Baylisiella* **Markowski, 1952. (Fig. 103)**

Diagnosis: Scolex imbeds deep into intestinal wall. Bothria powerful, foleaceous at anterior margins. Neck absent. Strobila thick, tapering toward posterior end. Proglottids short, wide. Genital atrium midventral, surrounded by numerous papillae. External seminal vesicle present. Testes medullary, in two or three layers. Ovary posterior, transversely elongate. Vitellaria cortical, surrounding entire proglottid except at genital pore. Uterus comprised of a few irregular transverse coils. Uterine pore posterior to genital pore. Eggs operculate. Osmoregulatory canals

Fig. 103. *Baylisiella tecta* (Linstow, 1892) Markowski, 1952.

cortical, around 100 in number. Parasites of elephant seals. Antarctica.

Type species: *B. tecta* (Linstow, 1892) Markowski, 1952.

13a. Testes intermingled with inner longitudinal muscle bundles
....*Glandicephalus* Fuhrmann, 1920. (Fig. 104)

Diagnosis: Scolex cylindroid, bluntly pointed apically. Bothria wide apically, lips overlapping posteriorly. Bothrial cavities lined with unicellular glands. Short neck present. Strobila thick, external metamerism well marked. Proglottids shorter than wide, craspedote. Genital atrium midventral. Testes intermingled with inner longitudinal muscle bundles. Ovary ventral, interjected among muscle bundles. Vitellaria cortical, in single layer. Uterus median, with narrow lateral loops surrounded by gland cells. Parasites of seals. Antarctica.

Type species: *G. antarcticus* (Baird, 1853) Fuhrmann, 1920.

Fig. 104. *Glandicephalus antarcticus* (Baird, 1853) Fuhrmann, 1920. After Markowski (1952).

13b. Testes not intermingled with longitudinal muscle bundles ..14

14a. Cirrus and vagina opening into common atrium. Gravid uterus with broad horizontal loops lending rosette-like appearance ....*Diphyllobothrium* Cobbold, 1858.
(See page 70)

14b. Cirrus and vagina opening separately. Gravid uterus a close spiral of coils, not rosette-like ....*Lueheella* Baer, 1924.
(See page 69)

15a. Four complete sets of reproductive organs per segment ......
................................*Tetragonoporus* Skrjabin, 1961. (Fig. 105)

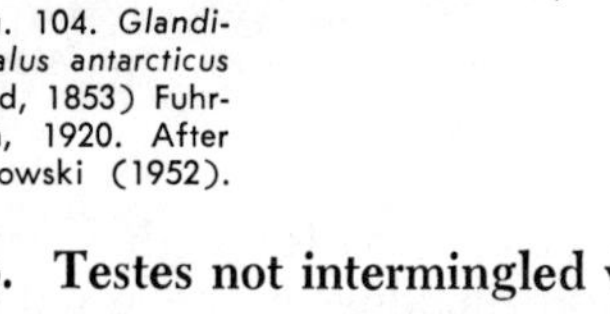

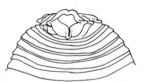

Diagnosis: Scolex capped with a 12-lobed, fleshy structure, 6 lobes in each half. Two short, fleshy, bothria present, narrow at bottom, wide at top. Neck absent. Proglottids numerous (45,000), wider than long. Genital pores ventral. Four complete sets of

Fig. 105. *Tetragonoporus calyptocephalus* Skrjabin, 1961.

reproductive organs in most segments, arranged in submedian pairs. Testes medullary, between and lateral to uteri. Ovary transversely elongated, posterior. Vitelline follicles cortical, continuous, external seminal vesicle present. Eggs operculate. Parasites of bile duct of sperm whale. Kurile Islands.

Type species: *T. calyptocephalus* Skrjabin, 1961.

15b. Five to 14 complete sets of reproductive organs per segment
.............................*Polygonoporus* **Skrjabin, 1967. (Fig. 106)**

Diagnosis: Scolex terminated with a 12-lobed, fleshy cap; with 3 lobes in each quadrant; two bothria present. Neck absent. Strobila immediately behind scolex expanded into "spoon-like" shape with jagged edges. Strobila large (30 meters).

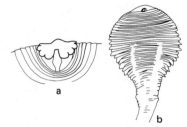

Fig. 106. *Polygonoporus giganticus* Skrjabin, 1967. *a.* Scolex. *b.* Anterior portion of strobila.

Proglottids much wider than long, each with 5 to 14 complete sets of reproductive organs. Genital pores ventral. Testes numerous, mainly medullary. External seminal vesicle present. Ovary transversely elongated, posterior. Vitelline follicles cortical, in two fields flanking genital pores. Eggs operculate. Parasites of sperm whale. Antarctica.

Type species: *P. giganticus* Skrjabin, 1967.

Key to the Genera in Ptychobothriidae

1a. Scolex armed 2
1b. Scolex unarmed 3
2a. Hooks arranged in two semicircles ....
....*Senga* **Dollfus, 1934. (Fig. 107)**

Diagnosis: Scolex rectangular, with bilobed apical disk bearing hooks on the margins. Bothria wide and shallow with thick margins. Neck absent. Strobila short. External metamerism incomplete. Proglottids acraspedote, apolytic or pseudapolytic. Genital atrium middorsal, slightly postequatorial. Male reproductive system not described. Ovary posterior, not bilobed.

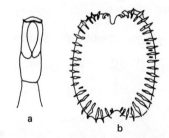

Fig. 107. *Senga besnardi* Dollfus, 1934. *a.* Scolex. *b.* Apical disk.

Vitellaria in complete cortical layer around proglottid. Uterine duct extending forward past genital atrium, expanding into uterine sac with ventral, median pore near anterior margin of proglottid. Eggs anoperculate, not embryonated. Parasites of freshwater teleosts. Asia.

Type species: *S. besnardi* Dollfus, 1934.
Key to Species: Fernando and Furtado (1963).

2b. Hooks arranged in four quadrants ....
...................................*Polyoncobothrium* **Diesing, 1854.** (**Fig. 108**)

Diagnosis: Scolex nearly rectangular, with apical disk bearing hooks in four quadrants. Neck absent. Strobila weakly segmented. Genital atrium middorsal, preequatorial. Testes medullary, lateral to ovary. Ovary in posterior medulla. Vitellaria cortical, in two dorsal and two ventral bands. Uterus winding, opening midventrally near anterior margin of proglottid. Eggs anoperculate, unembryonated. Parasites of freshwater fishes. Africa.

Type species: P. polypteri (Leydig, 1853) Lühe, 1900.

Fig. 108. Polyon-cobothrium polyp-teri (Leydig, 1853) Lühe, 1900. After Janicki (1926).

3a. Vitellaria continuous around proglottid ....
....*Clestobothrium* **Lühe, 1899.**

Diagnosis: Scolex spheroid, with deep bothria. Bothrial margins fused except for anterior aperture; bothria connected by apical groove. Neck absent. Metamerism complete. Margins of strobila serrated. Genital atrium middorsal, equatorial or postequatorial. Testes medullary, in two lateral fields. Ovary transversely elongated, in ventral medulla. Vagina with small seminal receptacle. Vitellaria continuous in cortex, surrounding proglottid. Uterine sac large, opening midventrally. Eggs anoperculate. Parasites of marine teleosts. Mediterranean, Atlantic.

Type species: C. crassiceps (Rudolphi, 1819) Lühe, 1899.

3b. Vitellaria not continuous around proglottid 4

4a. Vitellaria dorsolateral, free from muscle bundles ....
....*Ptychobothrioides* **Yamaguti, 1959.**

Diagnosis: Scolex longer than broad. Bothria well developed, with margins inrolled. Neck present. Genital atrium middorsal. Cirrus pouch containing winding ejaculatory duct. Testes numerous, in two lateral fields of medulla. Seminal receptacle apparently absent. Ovary posterior, transversely elongated, in ventral medulla. Vitellaria in two dorsolateral cortical fields, not intruding into intermuscular space. Uterus sinuous in medulla, with distal sac provided with longitudinal muscle just before opening outside. Uterine pore submedian, anterior to level of genital atrium. Eggs subglobular. Parasites of hawks. Abyssinia.

Type species: P. spiraliceps (Volz, 1900) Yamaguti, 1959.

4b. Vitellaria lateral, infiltrating longitudinal muscle bundles 5

5a. Genital pore anterior to midlevel of proglottid. Uterine pore alternating, on left and right sides of midline ....
................................*Ptychobothrium* Lönnberg, 1889. (Fig. 109)

Diagnosis: Scolex flattened, unarmed, heart-shaped in lateral view, lacking terminal disk. Bothria well developed. Neck absent. External metamerism incomplete. Genital atrium dorsal. Cirrus pouch thin-walled, lacking prostate cells around proximal end. Testes lateral, in dorsal medulla. Vagina with seminal receptacle. Ovary compact, posterior. Vitellaria intermingled with longitudinal muscle bundles. Uterine sac opening submedian, alternating sides of median line, near anterior margin of proglottid. Eggs oval, thin-shelled. Parasites of marine teleosts. Atlantic, Pacific.

Type species: *P. belones* (Dujardin, 1845) Lönnberg, 1889.

Fig. 109. *Ptychobothrium belones* (Dujardin, 1845) Lönnberg, 1889. After Janicki (1926).

5b. Genital pore posterior to midlevel of proglottid. Uterine pore midventral ....
............*Plicatobothrium* Cable and Michaelis, 1967. (Fig. 110)

Diagnosis: Scolex triangular to fan-shaped, lacking apical organ or hooks. Bothria deep, open their entire lengths; not connected apically, lined with minute, hair-like spines. Neck probably absent. Proglottids acraspedote; strobila distinctly segmented only at intervals. Genital pore dorsal, median, posterior to midlevel of proglottid. Uterine pore midventral. Testes in lateral medullary parenchyma. Ovary median, at extreme posterior end of proglottid, flanked by arms of Y-shaped uterus of succeeding segment. Vitellaria densest laterally, but encompassing medullary parenchyma except in vicinity of genital pores; follicles between conspicuous layers of longitudinal muscle fibers that are not grouped into distinct bundles. Eggs thin-shelled, anoperculate. Parasites of marine teleosts. Curaçao.

Type species: *P. cypseluri* Cable and Michaelis, 1967.

Fig. 110. *Plicatobothrium cypseluri* Cable and Michaelis, 1967.

Key to the Genera in Bothriocephalidae

1a. Holdfast bilaterally flattened, armed with hooks ....
.... *Oncodiscus* Yamaguti, 1934. (Fig. 111)

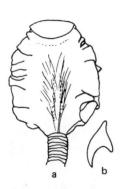

Fig. 111. *Oncodiscus sauridae* Yamaguti, 1934. a. Scolex. b. Hook.

Diagnosis: Scolex strongly compressed laterally, with median furrow on each side. Bothria with crenulated borders. Apex disk-like, with minute hooks along margin. Neck absent. Metamerism complete. Proglottids craspedote, with median notch on posterior border. Genital atrium middorsal, postequatorial. Cirrus pouch with thin walls, lacking prostatic cells. Testes in lateral medulla. Vagina greatly enlarged, muscular distally. No seminal receptacle. Ovary compact, lobulated, ventral, posterior. Vitellaria very numerous, cortical. Uterine duct coiling forward in median field, expanding into very large uterine sac. Uterine pore midventral, equatorial. Eggs operculate, unembryonated. Parasites of marine teleosts. Japan, India.
Type species: *O. sauridae* Yamaguti, 1934.

1b. Holdfast not flattened, unarmed 2

2a. Vitellaria medullary ....*Taphrobothrium* Lühe, 1899. (Fig. 112)

Fig. 112. *Taphrobothrium japonense* Lühe, 1899. After Yamaguti (1934).

Diagnosis: Scolex elongate, with prominent apical disk. Bothria long, slender and shallow. Neck absent. External metamerism incomplete at irregular intervals. Genital atrium middorsal. Cirrus pouch muscular, elliptical. Testes medullary, in two lateral fields. Seminal receptacle absent. Ovary median, transversely elongated, with ends directed dorsolaterally. Vitellaria medullary, scattered among testes. Uterus sigmoid, with terminal sac. Uterine pore ventral, submedian, irregularly alternating. Eggs operculated, embryonated. Parasites of marine teleosts. Japan.
Type species: *T. japonense* Lühe, 1899.

2b. Vitellaria cortical 3

3a. Scolex with apical disk ....
.... *Bothriocephalus* Rudolphi, 1808. (Fig. 113)

Diagnosis: Scolex elongate, with apical disk bearing indentations on bothrial margins that may be connected by apical groove. Marginal surfaces of scolex concave or convex, may bear longitudinal grooves. Bothria variable. Neck absent. External metamerism complete; secondary pseudometamerism sometimes present on older proglottids. Proglottids acraspedote, anapolytic. Genital atrium dorsomedial. Testes in lateral medulla. Seminal receptacle absent. Ovary posterior, transversely elongate, in ventral medulla. Vitellaria cortical. Uterus and uterine sac median or alternating submedian. Uterine pore median, anterior to genital atrium. Eggs operculate, unembryonated. Parasites of marine and freshwater fishes. Cosmopolitan.

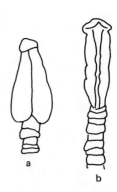

Fig. 113. *Bothriocephalus cuspidatus* Cooper, 1917. After Cooper. (1918). *a*. Lateral view. *b*. Dorsal view.

Type species: *B. scorpii* (Mueller, 1776) Rudolphi, 1808.

3b. Scolex lacking apical disk 4

4a. Two smooth bothria and neck present ....
...................................*Penetrocephalus* **Rao, 1960.** (Fig. 114)

Diagnosis: Two smooth bothria, like those of *Diphyllobothrium*. No apical disk on scolex. Neck absent. Segmentation prominent, proglottids very craspedote. Cirrovaginal pore dorsal, immediately before ovary. Uterine pore median, ventral. Oval cirrus pouch, slightly right or left of middorsal line. Cirrus prominent. Testes in two lateral fields, continuous between segments, about 60 per proglottid in older worms.

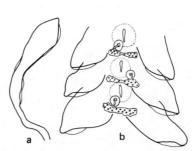

Fig. 114. *Penetrocephalus ganapati* Rao, 1960. *a*. Scolex. *b*. Portion of strobila.

Ovary bilobed, transversely elongated, near posterior margin of proglottid. Vagina opens into atrium. Seminal receptacle present. Vitellaria in lateral fields. Uterus developing into spherical median sac. Parasites of marine teleosts. India.

Type species: *P. ganapati* Rao, 1960.

4b. Bothria and neck absent ....*Anatrum* **Overstreet, 1968.**

Diagnosis: Scolex elongate, clavate, lacking bothria, apical disc or armature, unsegmented neck present. External metamerism lacking, interior metamerism evident. Proglottids wider than long.

Testes in lateral medulla. Cirrus pouch oval, at right angles to dorsal surface. Cirro-vaginal atrium dorsal, median. Ovary bilobed, in ventral, median, central medulla. Seminal receptacle present. Vitellaria cortical. Uterus with distal sac. Uterine pore ventral, irregularly alternating from one side of median line to the other. Eggs thin-shelled, operculate, unembryonated when laid.

    Type species: *A. tortum* (Linton, 1905) Overstreet, 1968.

Key to the Genera in Echinophallidae

1a. **Minute spines on posterior margins of proglottids. Holdfast funnel-like** .... *Atelemerus* **Guiart, 1935.**
    Diagnosis: Scolex funnel-like. Strobila short, external metamerism incomplete. Posterior border of proglottids covered with minute spines. Two sets of reproductive organs per segment. Genital pores dorsal, close to lateral margin. Cirrus pouch cylindrical, equatorial. Cirrus armed. Testes and ovary not described. Uterus in anterior third of proglottid. Uterine pore ventral, anterior. Eggs anoperculate (?). Parasites of marine teleosts. Azores.

    Type species: *A acanthodes* Guiart, 1935.

1b. **No spines on posterior margins of proglottids. Holdfast with weak dorsal and ventral sucker-like depressions** ....
.... *Echinophallus* **Schumacher, 1914. (Fig. 115)**

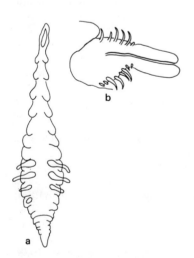

    Diagnosis: Pseudoscolex present, poorly developed, with shallow bothria. Neck absent. Posterior borders of proglottids unarmed, thickened into lobes. Two sets of reproductive organs per segment. Genital pores dorsal, close to lateral margins. Cirrus pouch large. Cirrus with large spines on base. Testes in two submedian fields median to ovaries, mostly postequatorial. Ovary lobated, posterior. Vitellaria extensive, mostly cortical. Uterus strongly coiled, with weak sac, median to ovary. Uterine pore submedian, near anterior end of proglottid. Eggs operculate. Parasites of marine teleosts. Mediterranean, Japan.

Fig. 115. *Echinophallus japonicus* Yamaguti, 1934. a. Entire worm. b. Cirrus.

    Type species: *E. wageneri* (Monticelli, 1890) Schumacher, 1914.

Key to the Subfamilies of Amphicotylidae

1a. Vitellaria cortical ....Amphicotylinae Lühe, 1902. (P. 81)

1b. Vitellaria medullary 2

2a. Vitellaria in two lateral fields ....
....Abothriinae Nybelin, 1922. (P. 82)

2b. Vitellaria continuous around proglottid 3

3a. Small sucker at rear border of bothrium ....
...................................Bothriocotylinae Yamaguti, 1959. (P. 83)

3b. No sucker at rear border of bothrium ....
.................................Marispometrinae Cooper, 1917. (P. 84)

Key to the Genera in Amphicotylinae

1a. Bothria divided into loculi by transverse grooves ....
.................................Pseudamphicotyla Yamaguti, 1959.

Diagnosis: Scolex with apical disk and elongate surfacial bothria, each of which is divided into loculi by transverse septal grooves. Neck absent. External metamerism distinct anteriorly, indistinct posteriorly. Genital pore marginal, irregularly alternating. Cirrus pouch club-shaped. Cirrus armed. Testes numerous, in single broad field. Vagina muscular. Ovary two-winged, poral. Vitellaria mostly cortical, encircling proglottid. Uterus wide, median, with median terminal sac. Uterine pore ventromedian. Eggs anoperculate. Parasites of marine teleosts. Japan.

Type species: *P. quinquarii* (Yamaguti, 1952) Yamaguti, 1959.

1b. **Bothria not divided into loculi by transverse grooves** 2

2a. **Bothria with posterior accessory sucker. Uterine pore dorsal**
....*Amphicotyle* **Diesing, 1863.**

Diagnosis: Scolex with apical disk and rounded bothria, each with posterior partition forming an accessory sucker. External metamerism well marked anteriorly, obscured posteriorly by secondary wrinkles. Proglottids anapolytic. Genital atrium marginal, irregularly alternating. Cirrus pouch large, weakly muscular. Cirrus unarmed. Testes in two lateral fields. Seminal vesicles absent. Ovary asymmetrical, antiporal. Vitellaria cortical, scattered. Uterus simple, with terminal sac. Uterine pore dorsal. Parasites of marine teleosts. Mediterranean.

Type species: *A. heteropleura* (Diesing, 1850) Lühe, 1902.

2b. Bothria without accessory sucker. Uterine pore ventral ....
....*Eubothrium* **Nybelin, 1922. (Fig. 116)**

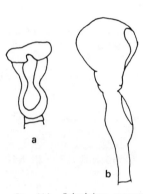

Fig. 116. *Eubothrium rugosum* (Batsch, 1786) Nybelin, 1922. After Ekbaum (1933). a. Typical scolex. b. Deformed scolex.

Diagnosis: Scolex with apical disk and simple bothria, sometimes deformed. Neck absent. Strobila usually with distinct external metamerism; dorsomedial longitudinal furrows present. Testes medial to nerve trunks, in two lateral fields, sometimes almost continuous. Genital atrium marginal, irregularly alternating. Cirrus pouch medium sized. Vagina opens anterior to cirrus. Ovary reniform, median or poral. Vitellaria cortical in two lateral zones. Uterine pore ventral. Parasites of marine and freshwater teleosts. Circumboreal.

Type species: *E. rugosum* (Batsch, 1786) Nybelin, 1922.

Key to the Genera in Abothriinae

1a. Scolex normal. Vitellaria only in lateral medulla ....
....*Bathybothrium* **Lühe, 1902. (Fig. 117)**

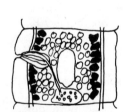

Fig. 117. *Bathybothrium rectangulum* (Bloch, 1782) Lühe, 1902. After Nybelin (1922).

Diagnosis: Scolex normal, lacking apical disk. Neck? External metamerism indistinct. Median groove present on ventral surface. Genital atrium lateral. Cirrus pouch pyriform, small. Testes numerous, in single field anterior and lateral to uterus. External seminal vesicle present. Ovary thick, posterior, compact. Vitellaria few, in lateral medulla. Uterine sac with lateral outpocketings. Uterine pore ventromedian or slightly aporal. Parasites of cyprinid fishes. Europe.

Type species: *B. rectangulum* (Bloch, 1782) Lühe, 1902.

1b. Scolex deformed. Vitellaria not as above 2

2a. Vitellaria interspersed with testes ....
....*Abothrium* **Beneden, 1871. (Fig. 118)**

Diagnosis: Scolex deformed. Neck present. Strobila thick. Genital atrium lateral. Cirrus pouch small. Testes numerous, in two lateral fields. Ovary posterior, compact, transversely elongated. Vitellaria intermingled with testes. Uterus sac-like. Uterine pore ventral. Inner longitudinal muscle bundles strongly developed. Eggs thin-shelled. Parasites of marine teleosts. Atlantic, Pacific.

Type species: *A. gadi* Beneden, 1871.

Fig. 118. *Abothrium gadi* Beneden, 1871. After Nybelin (1922).

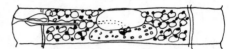

2b. **Vitellaria not interspersed with testes** ....
....*Parabothrium* **Nybelin, 1922.** (Fig. 119)

Diagnosis: Scolex deformed. Genital atrium lateral. Cirrus pouch large, elongated, muscular. Testes numerous, in two fields lateral to ovary and uterus. Vagina with terminal sphincter. Ovary in posterior medulla. Vitellaria posterior, ventral to testes, extending laterally beyond nerve trunks. Uterine sac opening funnel-like in ventromedial region of proglottid. Eggs round, with thin shell. Parasites of marine teleosts (Gadidae). Europe, North America.

Type species: *P. bulbiferum* Nybelin, 1922.

Fig. 119. *Parabothrium bulbiferum* Nybelin, 1922.

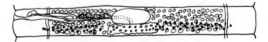

DIAGNOSIS OF THE ONLY GENUS IN BOTHRIOCOTYLINAE
Bothriocotyle Ariola, 1900 (Fig. 120)

Diagnosis: Scolex conical, lacking apical disk. Bothria shallow, with small distinct sucker at posterior margin of each. Neck absent. Strobila spiral, concave ventrally, external metamerism distinct, lacking accessory wrinkles. Proglottids broader than long. Genital atrium dorsal, submedian, irregularly alternating. Cirrus pouch large. Cirrus armed. Testes in single broad medullary layer, extending lateral to nerve trunks. Ovary bilobed, in aporal medulla. Vitellaria medullary, ventral. Uterus with long narrow duct and small sac. Uterine pore midventral. Eggs anoperculate, thin-shelled. Parasites of marine teleosts. Mediterranean.

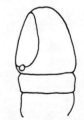

Fig. 120. *Bothriocotyle solinosomum* Ariola, 1900. After Schumacher (1913).

Type species: *B. solinosomum* Ariola, 1900.

Key to the Genera in Marsipometrinae

1a. Scolex in shape of truncated pyramid, with well-defined apical disk ....*Marsipometra* **Cooper, 1917.** (Fig. 121)

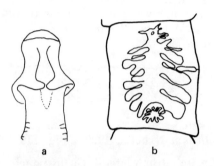

Fig. 121. *Marsipometra confusa* Simer, 1930. After Beaver and Simer (1940). a. Scolex. b. Proglottid.

Diagnosis: Scolex in shape of truncated pyramid; apical disk present. Constriction often present between apex and base of scolex. Neck present or absent. External metamerism well marked. Genital atrium marginal, equatorial. Cirrus unarmed. Testes numerous, lateral, may extend anterior to uterus and posterior to ovary. Ovary posterior, may be separated from posterior margin of proglottid by testes or vitellaria. Seminal receptacle present. Vitellaria usually ventral, medullary, lateral to ovary but confluent anterior and posterior to it. Uterine sac central, with many radial branches. Eggs small, thin-shelled. Parasites of freshwater Chondrostei (Polyodontidae). United States.

Type species: M. *hastata* (Linton, 1897) Cooper, 1917.

1b. Scolex rounded, lacking apical disk ....
.................................*Fissurobothrium* **Roitman, 1965.** (Fig. 122)

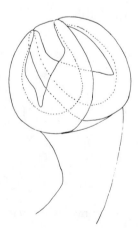

Fig. 122. *Fissurobothrium unicum* Roitman, 1965.

Diagnosis: Scolex lacking apical disk. Bothria deep, with very muscular walls, giving a sucker-like appearance. Neck present. Proglottids wider than long. Genital pores lateral, slightly preequatorial, surrounded by sphincter. Cirrus pouch cylindrical, containing seminal vesicle and unarmed cirrus. Small external seminal vesicle present. Testes numerous, in two lateral fields. Vagina posterior to cirrus pouch. Large seminal receptacle present. Ovary posterior, with two multilobed wings. Vitellaria medullary. Uterus with several large, lateral branches. Eggs anoperculate. Parasites of cyprinid fishes. Russia.

Type species: F. *unicum* Roitman, 1965.

Key to the Genera in Triaenophoridae

1a. Scolex armed 2

1b. Scolex unarmed 3

2a. Scolex with many small hooks. Vitellaria in lateral medulla
and dorsal cortex ....
.... *Ancistrocephalus* Monticelli, 1890. (Fig. 123)
Diagnosis: Scolex with apical disk armed
with several alternating rows of small hooks,
most numerous on bothrial surfaces. Neck absent. External metamerism distinct, proglottids
wider than long. Genital pores marginal, irregularly alternating. Testes in two lateral
fields which unite at posterior end of proglottid. Ovary lobulated, posterior. Vitellaria mainly in two lateral fields. Uterus narrow, coiled,
with expanded terminal end. Uterine pore
opening ventrosubmarginal, irregularly alternating without regard to position of genital
pores. Eggs operculate, unembryonated. Parasites of ocean sunfish. Atlantic, Pacific, Mediterranean.

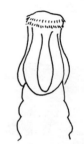

Fig. 123. *Ancistro-
cephalus microcephalus*
(Rudolphi, 1819) Mon-
ticelli, 1890. After
Wagner (1854).

Type species: *A. microcephalus* (Rudolphi,
1819) Monticelli, 1890.

2b. Scolex with two dorsal and two ventral trident hooks. Vitellaria cortical, diffuse ....
.... *Triaenophorus* Rudolphi, 1793. (Fig. 124)
Diagnosis: Scolex with apical disk armed
with dorsal and ventral pairs of trident-
shaped hooks. Bothria rounded, shallow.
Neck absent. External metamerism absent;
strobila with transverse wrinkles. Genital
atrium marginal, irregularly alternating.
Cirrus pouch transverse. Testes numerous,
in single medullary field. Ovary bilobed,
posterior, slightly poral. Vitellaria cortical,
diffuse. Uterus weakly coiled, with terminal sac. Uterine pore ventral, slightly poral,
anterior to level of genital pores. Eggs
operculate. Parasites of teleosts. Circumboreal.

Fig. 124. *Triaenophorus
crassus* Forel, 1868. After
Miller (1945). a. Trident
hook. b. Scolex.

Type species: *T. lucii* (Mueller, 1776)
Rudolphi, 1793.

3a. Vitellaria medullary, ventral to testes ....
....Anoncocephalus Lühe, 1902. (Fig. 125)

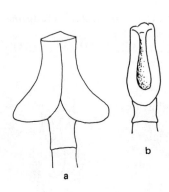

Fig. 125. *Anoncocephalus chilensis*
(Riggenbach, 1896) Lühe, 1902. a.
Dorsal view. b. Lateral view.

Diagnosis: Scolex unarmed, truncated apically, arrowhead-shaped in lateral view, bilaterally compressed. Bothria narrow, deep. Neck absent. External segmentation present. Proglottids wider than long. Genital atrium marginal, postequatorial, irregularly alternating. Cirrus armed. Cirrus pouch pyriform. Testes in two dorsal, lateral fields, united at posterior end of proglottid. Ovary compact, posterior, poral. Vitellaria medullary, ventral to testes. Uterus coiled, narrow, with large, muscular terminal sack. Osmoregulatory canals numerous, anastomosing. Parasites of marine teleosts. Chile.

Type species: A. *chilensis* (Riggenbach, 1896) Lühe, 1902.

3b. Vitellaria cortical 4

4a. Testes in two lateral fields, medial to nerve trunks ....
....Eubothrioides Yamaguti, 1952.

Diagnosis: Scolex unarmed, bilaterally compressed, arrowhead-shaped in lateral view, lacking apical disk. Bothria elongate, prominent. Neck absent. Strobila with dorsal and ventral longitudinal grooves. Proglottids broader than long, craspedote. Genital atrium marginal, irregularly alternating. Cirrus pouch small, cortical. Testes few, in two lateral fields medial to nerve trunks. Ovary transversely elongated, posterior, poral. Seminal receptacle absent. Vitellaria cortical, diffuse. Uterus convoluted in median field, with small distal uterine sac. Uterine pore midventral near anterior end of proglottid. Eggs operculate. Parasites of marine teleosts. Japan.

Type species: E. *lamellatum* Yamaguti, 1952.

4b. Testes in one continuous field, partly exceeding nerve trunks
...............................*Fistulicola* **Lühe, 1899. (Fig. 126)**

Diagnosis: Scolex arrowhead-shaped in lateral view, with unarmed apical disk. Bothria wide, shallow. Scolex sometimes replaced with pseudosolex. Neck absent. External metamerism evident. Proglottids much wider than long, with leaf-like expansions on lateral margins. Genital pores marginal, irregularly alternating. Testes medullary, in one continuous field, partly exceeding nerve trunks. Ovary poral, ventral. Vitellaria cortical, continuous around proglottid. Uterus wide, strongly coiled, with muscular distal portion. Eggs operculate, embryonated. Parasites of marine teleosts. Atlantic, Pacific, Mediterranean.

Type species: *F. plicatus* (Rudolphi, 1819) Lühe, 1899.

Fig. 126. *Fistulicola plicatus* (Rudolphi, 1819) Lühe, 1899.

Key to the Genera in Parabothriocephalidae

1a. Cirrus pore marginal. Linguiform fluted projection at base of each bothrium ......*Glossobothrium* **Yamaguti, 1952. (Fig. 127)**

Diagnosis: Scolex elongate, with unarmed apical disk. Linguiform fluted appendage projecting from base of each bothrium. Neck absent. Proglottids short. Genital atrium marginal, irregularly alternating. Cirrus pouch claviform, covered with layer of gland-like cells. Cirrus armed with minute spines. Testes numerous, medullary, medial to osmoregulatory canals with a few postovarian. Vagina forming a fusiform muscular swelling anterior to ovarian isthmus. Ovary bilobed, posterior, slightly poral. Vitellaria diffuse, cortical. Uterus S-shaped, with distal sac. Uterine pore ventral, median, near anterior margin of proglottid. Egg operculate, unembryonated. Parasites of marine teleosts. Japan.

Type species: *G. nipponicum* Yamaguti, 1952.

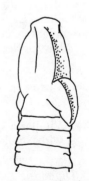

Fig. 127. *Glossobothrium nipponicum* Yamaguti, 1952.

1b. Cirrus pore dorsal, near lateral margin. No linguiform projections near bothria **2**

2a. Cirrus unarmed. Egg with conspicuous lateral swelling ....
..........*Neobothriocephalus* **Mateo and Bullock, 1966. (Fig. 128)**

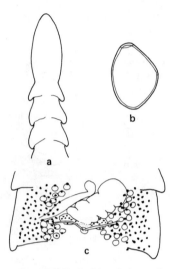

Fig. 128. *Neobothriocephalus aspinosus* Mateo and Bullock, 1966. *a.* Scolex. *b.* Egg. *c.* Proglottid.

Diagnosis: Scolex ovoid, with long, shallow, surficial bothria. Neck absent. Strobila tapered at both ends, most apparently at anterior end. Proglottids slightly craspedote, wider than long except at extreme posterior end. Genital pore dorsal, near lateral margin, irregularly alternating left and right. Genital atrium anterior to vagina. Cirrus pouch large, muscular, with conspicuous swelling at its base; obliquely oriented with basal end at anterior margin of proglottid. Cirrus unarmed. Testes few (25-60), medullary, in two lateral fields, continuous between segments. Vagina with prominent sphincter short distance from genital pore. Small seminal receptacle present. Ovary bilobed, submedian, slightly poral, near posterior margin of proglottid. Vitellaria in two wide lateral bands, mostly cortical but some follicles medullary. Uterus a prominent sac protruding into preceding segment. Eggs thin-shelled, operculate, unembryonated, with prominent lateral swelling. Parasites of marine teleosts. Peru.

Type species: *N. aspinosus* Mateo and Bullock, 1966.

2b. Cirrus spined. Egg lacking lateral swelling 3

3a. Vitellaria cortical. Scolex lacking, replaced with pseudoscolex with shallow depressions ....
....................................*Parabothriocephaloides* **Yamaguti, 1934.**

Diagnosis: Scolex replaced by conical pseudoscolex bearing depressions on surface. Neck absent. Strobila pointed at both ends, broadest near anterior end. Proglottids with swollen posterior margins. Genital atrium equatorial, dorsosubmarginal, irregularly alternating. Cirrus pouch large. Cirrus armed. Testes medullary, between osmoregulatory canals. Vagina with well-developed sphincter, opening behind cirrus. Seminal receptacle present. Ovary posterior, bilobed, slightly poral. Vitellaria diffuse, cortical. Uterus S-shaped, median, with large sac invading preceding segment.

Uterine pore midventral, at anterior end of proglottid. Eggs operculated, unembryonated. Parasites of marine teleosts. Japan.
Type species: *P. segmentatus* Yamaguti, 1934.

3b. Vitellaria medullary. Scolex present, small ....
.... *Parabothriocephalus* **Yamaguti, 1934.**

Diagnosis: Scolex long, small, lacking apical disk. Neck absent. Strobila slender, filiform near anterior end. Anterior proglottids longer than broad, with salient posterior margins. Genital atrium dorsosubmarginal, postequatorial. Convoluted vas deferens in front of base of cirrus pouch. Cirrus armed. Testes medullary, medial to nerve trunks. Vagina with narrow proximal duct and expanded distal sac with spinose base, opening posterior to cirrus. Ovary bilobed, posterior, poral. Vitellaria diffuse, cortical. Uterus sigmoid, with median sac invading preceding proglottid. Eggs operculate, unembryonated. Parasites of marine teleosts.
Type species: *P. gracilis* Yamaguti, 1934.

Key to the Families in Lecanicephalidea

1a. Paired hooks associated with four suckers on anterior half of scolex ....**Balanobothriidae Pintner, 1928. (P. 90)**

Diagnosis: Scolex egg-shaped. Anterior portion with four small suckers; each sucker anterior to two small, double-pronged hooks. Posterior portion of scolex surrounded by membranous collar. Neck present. Genital atrium lateral. Testes in single preovarian field. Vitellaria lateral. Ovary posterior. Parasites of elasmobranches.
Type genus: *Balanobothrium* Hornell, 1912.

1b. No hooks on scolex **2**

2a. No suckers on scolex ....
.......................**Disculicepitidae Joyeux and Baer, 1935. (P. 91)**

Diagnosis: Scolex lacking hooks or suckers of any kind, divided into anterior, flattened portion of variable shape, and posterior, rounded, corrugated portion. Neck present. Proglottids rectangular to square. Genital pores ventro-submarginal. Testes in irregular clusters, preovarian. Ovary posterior, bilobed. Vitellaria an irregular, postovarian mass (?). Uterus median. Parasites of elasmobranches.
Type genus: *Disculiceps* Joyeux and Baer, 1935.

2b. Suckers present on anterior or posterior portions of scolex, or both **3**

3a. Large, cup-like apical sucker on scolex, may be protruded into cushion-like structure. Tentacles present or not ....
...................................Lecanicephalidae Braun, 1900. (P. 92)

Diagnosis: Scolex with large apical organ which may be retracted to form a sucker-like structure, or protracted to form a cushion-like structure; may be in the form of tentacles. Remainder of scolex with four small, rounded suckers. Neck present or absent. Genital atrium lateral. Testes in single preovarian field. Vitellaria lateral or encircling proglottid. Parasites of elasmobranchs.

Type genus: *Lecanicephalum* Linton, 1890.

3b. No suckers or tentacles on anterior half of scolex ....
...................................Adelobothriidae Yamaguti, 1959. (P. 91)

Diagnosis: Anterior portion of scolex massive, simple; posterior portion membranous, collar-like, bearing four small, rounded suckers. Proglottids craspedote. Testes in single, large, preovarian field. Vitellaria cortical, encircling entire proglottid. Parasites of elasmobranchs.

Type genus: *Adelobothrium* Shipley, 1900.

DIAGNOSIS OF THE ONLY GENUS IN BALANOBOTHRIIDAE

Balanobothrium Hornell, 1912 (Fig. 129)

Fig. 129. *Balanobothrium parvum* Southwell, 1925.

Diagnosis: *Scolex* egg-shaped, with membranous collar around base. Anterior portion with four small suckers, each anterior to two small, double-pronged hooks. Entire scolex embedded in gut wall of host. Neck present. Proglottids wider than long. Genital atrium lateral, preequatorial, irregularly alternating. Cirrus pouch entirely poral. Cirrus armed, posterior to vaginal pore. Testes very numerous, in single field anterior to ovary. External seminal vesicle absent. Ovary bilobed, posterior. Vitellaria in two or more lateral rows. Vagina anterior to cirrus pouch. Uterine pore midventral. Uterus median. Parasites of elasmobranchs. Indian Ocean, Pacific.

Type species: *B. tenax* Hornell, 1912.

DIAGNOSIS OF THE ONLY GENUS
IN DISCULICEPITIDAE
Disculiceps Joyeux and Baer, 1935 (Fig. 130)

Diagnosis: Scolex with large anterior, flattened, cushion-like portion, variable in shape according to state of contraction. Posterior portion globular, corrugated: both portions lacking hooks or suckers. Neck present. Proglottids acraspedote, rectangular. Genital atrium ventro-submarginal. Cirrus unarmed, opening posterior

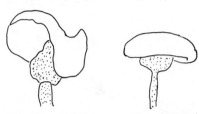

Fig. 130. *Disculiceps* sp. After Southwell (1925). Two typical forms of the scolex.

to vagina. Testes in irregular clusters, preovarian. Ovary bilobed, posterior. Ovary an irregular mass, postovarian (?). Vagina opens anterior to cirrus. Seminal receptacle absent. Uterus median with lateral branches. Osmoregulatory canals reticular. Parasites of elasmobranchs. North America, Bermuda, France, India.

Type species: D. *pileatus* (Linton, 1890) Joyeux and Baer, 1935.

DIAGNOSIS OF THE ONLY GENUS
IN ADELOBOTHRIIDAE
Adelobothrium Shipley, 1900 (Fig. 131)

Diagnosis: Anterior portion of scolex massive, variably conical. Posterior portion membranous, collar-like, with four small suckers. Neck absent. Proglottids cylindrical, craspedote. Genital pores irregularly alternating. Cirrus pouch oval. Cirrus unarmed. Testes numerous, in entire intervascular, preovarian field. External seminal vesicle present. Ovary bilobed, posterior. Vitellaria cortical, encircling entire proglottid when mature. Vagina opens ventral to cirrus pouch. Seminal receptacle present. Gravid uterus median, sac-like, filling most of medulla. Egg with polar filaments. Parasites of elasmobranchs. Ceylon, Loyalty Islands, Tortugas.

Type species: A *aetiobatidis* Shipley, 1900.

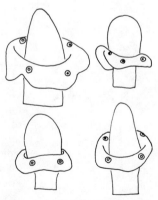

Fig. 131. *Adelobothrium aetiobatidis* Shipley, 1900. After Southwell (1925). Various shapes of scoleces.

Key to the Genera in Lecanicephalidae

1a. Scolex with unarmed tentacles 2
1b. Scolex without tentacles 3
2a. Tentacles originating on anterior half of scolex ....
.... *Polypocephalus* **Braun, 1878. (Fig. 132)**

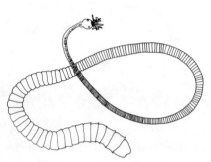

Diagnosis: Scolex divided into two portions. Anterior portion composed of 14 to 16 simple or feather-like retractable tentacles. Posterior portion cushion-like, with four simple suckers. Neck present or not. Proglottids craspedote or not. Genital pores irregularly alternating. Cirrus armed. Testes few, large. Cirrus pouch pyriform. Ovary bilobed, posterior. Vitellaria in bilateral fields, composed of a few large acini. Vagina posterior to cirrus pouch. Small seminal receptacle present. Uterus median. Parasites of elasmobranchs. India, Ceylon, North America.

Fig. 132. *Polypocephalus radiatus* Braun, 1878. After Southwell (1925).

Type species: *P. radiatus* Braun, 1878.

2b. **Tentacles arising on posterior half of scolex** ....
.............................*Calycobothrium* **Southwell, 1911. (Fig. 133)**

Diagnosis: Scolex divided into two portions. Anterior portion cushion-like, with two or four small suckers. Posterior portion with 14 short, hollow tentacles arranged around the base of the anterior portion like the petals of a flower. Neck present. Proglottids acraspedote, longer than wide. Genital pores marginal, irregularly alternating. Cirrus pouch extending to midline of proglottid. Cirrus armed. Testes numerous, in single intervascular, preovarian field. Small internal seminal vesicle present. Ovary compact, posterior. Vitellaria in bilateral fields. Vagina opens anterior to cirrus. Small seminal receptacle present. Uterus unknown. Parasites of elasmobranchs. Celyon.

Fig. 133. *Calycobothrium typicum* (Southwell, 1911) Southwell, 1911. After Southwell (1925).

Type species: *C. typicum* (Southwell, 1911) Southwell, 1911.

3a. **Anterior portion of scolex reduced to small papilla. Posterior portion with four large, pedunculated suckers** ....
............*Staurobothrium* **Shipley and Hornell, 1905.** (Fig. 134)

Diagnosis: Anterior portion of scolex represented by a small, unarmed papilla. Posterior portion of scolex with four large, powerful, pedunculated papillae arranged like a Maltese cross. Neck absent. Proglottids craspedote. Genital pores irregularly alternating. Cirrus pouch pyriform, bent posteriad. Cirrus unarmed. Testes few (24) large, first appearing as central mass, then spreading evenly throughout preovarian field in mature proglottid. Ovary posterior, bilobed. Vitellaria few, large, in lateral fields that join anteriorly. Vagina opens anterior to cirrus. Very large seminal receptacle present. Uterus median. Parasites of elasmobranchs. Ceylon.

Type species: *S. aetobatidis* Shipley and Hornell, 1905.

Fig. 134. *Staurobothrium aetobatidis* Shipley and Hornell, 1905.

3b. **Anterior portion of scolex well-developed, may be retractile** .4

4a. **Six osmoregulatory canals present. Scolex rectangular in cross section** ....*Hexacanalis* **Perrenoud, 1931.** (Fig. 135)

Diagnosis: Scolex rectangular in cross-section. Anterior region bulbous, non-glandular, retractable. Posterior portion simple, with four suckers. Neck long. Proglottids craspedote. Genital pores irregularly alternating. Cirrus pouch reaches median line. Cirrus unarmed. Testes numerous, anterior to ovary, none anterior to cirrus pouch. Ovary bilobed, about one-fourth from posterior end. Vitellaria in bilateral fields, absent anterior to cirrus pouch on poral side. Vagina opens posterior to cirrus pouch. Uterus saccular, median. Osmoregulatory system with six major anastomosing trunks. Parasites of elasmobranchs. Ceylon.

Type species: *H. abruptus* (Southwell, 1911) Perrenoud, 1931.

Fig. 135. *Hexacanalis abruptus* (Southwell, 1911) Perrenoud, 1931.

4b. **Two or four osmoregulatory canals present. Scolex rounded in cross section** 5

5a. Anterior portion of scolex large, globular, covered with minute spines ....
........*Tetragonicephalum* **Shipley and Hornell, 1905. (Fig. 136)**

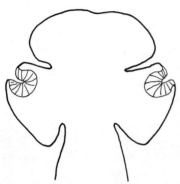

Fig. 136. *Tetragonicephalum trygonis* Shipley and Hornell, 1905. After Southwell (1925).

Diagnosis: Scolex divided into two parts: anterior portion large, cushion-like, covered with minute spines; posterior portion with four suckers. Neck short. Strobila long, slender. Genital atrium enlarged, with frilled margin, irregularly alternating. Cirrus pouch not fully developed until uterus contains eggs. Cirrus long, unarmed. External seminal vesicle present. Testes few (7-12), anterior to level of genital pore, disappearing early. Ovary posterior, present only in same segments as testes. Vitellaria arising postovarian, extending along lateral margins in mature proglottids. Vagina opens posterior to cirrus. Large seminal receptacle present. Uterus median, saccular. Parasites of elasmobranchs. Indian Ocean.

Type species: *T. trygonis* Shipley and Hornell, 1905.

5b. Anterior portion of scolex quite variable in appearance, from flattened to globular, often with gland cells but not spinulate (Fig. 137) .... *Lecanicephalum* **Linton, 1890.**

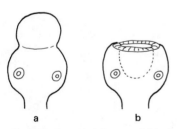

Fig. 137. *Lecanicephalum* sp. Original.
a. Anterior portion of scolex extruded.
b. Anterior portion of scolex withdrawn.

Diagnosis: Scolex variable, but clearly divided into two portions. Posterior portion rounded or depressed, with four simple suckers. Anterior portion massive, globular or flattened, lacking cuticular spines, often with glandular cells in its wall, retractable into posterior portion. When retracted, the resulting depression appears as a large apical sucker. Neck usually present. Proglottids craspedote or not. Genital pores marginal, irregularly alternating. Cirrus pouch variable with the species. Cirrus armed or not. Testes usually numerous, in preovarian intervascular field. Ovary two-winged, posterior. Vitellaria bilateral, usually with some postovarian follicles. Vagina opening into atrium posterior to cirrus. Seminal receptacle usually present, often very large. Uterus median, saccular when gravid. One or two pairs of osmoregulatory canals. Parasites of elasmobranchs. Cosmopolitan.

Type species: *L. peltatum* Linton, 1890.

DIAGNOSIS OF THE ONLY FAMILY IN APORIDEA
Nematoparataeniidae Poche, 1926 (P. 95)

Diagnosis: Scolex armed, with or without suckers, or with grooves. External metamerism absent; internal metamerism present or absent. Genital pores absent. Cirrus, cirrus pouch, Mehlis' gland, and oötype absent. Testes follicular. Ovary and vitellaria follicular, surrounding testes. Protandrous. Parasites of birds.

Type genus: *Nematoparataenia* Maplestone and Southwell, 1922.

Key to the Genera in Nematoparataeniidae

1a. **Suckers present on scolex. Huge, glandular rostellum present, with undulating row of hundreds of tiny hooks** .... *Nematoparataenia* **Maplestone and Southwell, 1922.** (Fig. 138)

Diagnosis: Scolex with four large, forwardly-directed suckers and a huge, glandular rostellum armed with an undulating row of about 1000 very small hooks. Short neck present. Strobila cylindrical, up to 10 mm long, with a longitudinal groove on one side. External and internal metamerism lacking. Testes follicular, filling most of medulla, degenerating posteriad. Ovary only in midregion of body, follicular, surrounding testes except in region of lateral groove. Vitellaria follicular, mixed with ovarian cells. Ovarian and vitelline cells in hindbody replaced with eggs. Eggs with two membranes, in clusters in membranous capsules. Two pairs of osmoregulatory canals. Parasites of birds. Australia, Sweden.

Type species: *N. paradoxa* Maplestone and Southwell, 1922.

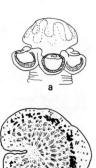

Fig. 138. *Nemato-parataenia southwelli* Fuhrmann, 1933. *a*. Scolex. *b*. Cross-section of strobila, showing longitudinal groove.

1b. **Suckers absent. Small rostellum present, with 10 hooks** 2

2a. Scolex with four narrow grooves ....
....*Apora* **Ginetsinskaya, 1944.** (**Fig. 139**)

Diagnosis: Scolex with four narrow grooves and rostellum armed with 10 hooks. Stobila cylindrical, with longitudinal groove on one side. External and internal matamerism lacking. Testes follicular, medullary, arranged in semicircle in cross section. Vasa efferentia converging toward longitudinal groove but joining together without opening to outside. Ovary follicular, surrounding testes in semicircle. Vitellaria follicular, mixed with ovarian cells. Posteriorly, the ovarian and vitelline cells are replaced with eggs enclosed in membranous capsules. One pair of longitudinal osmoregulatory canals. Parasites under the koilon of anatid birds. Russia.

Fig. 139. *Apora dogieli* Ginetsinskaya, 1944. Cross-section of strobila.

Type species: *A. dogieli* Ginetsinskaya, 1944.

2b. Scolex without grooves or sucking devices ....
.................................*Gastrotaenia* **Wolffhügel, 1938.** (**Fig. 140**)

Diagnosis: Scolex rounded, lacking suckers or grooves, with rostellum bearing 10 hymenolepid-type hooks. Neck long. Strobila cylindrical, lacking longitudinal groove. External metamerism lacking, internal metamerism evident. Testes horseshoe-shaped, in intervascular field, with open end directed toward ovary. Ovary follicular, increasing in size to enclose testes. Vitellaria compact, next to ovary. Two pairs of osmoregulatory canals. Some specimens lacking female organs.

Fig. 140. *Gastrotaenia cygni* Wolffhügel, 1938.

Gravid specimens not yet reported. (This worm may be a cysticercoid of a hymenolepid cestode). Parasitic under the koilon of anatid birds. North and South America.

Type species: *G. cygni* Wolffhügel, 1938.

Key to the Families in Tetraphyllidea

1a. Dioecious forms ....Dioecotaeniidae Schmidt, 1969 (P. 98)

Diagnosis: Scolex with four bothridia, each with surficial loculi. Myzorhynchus, hooks, and suckers absent. Neck present. Proglottids acraspedote. Testes arranged in circle in two layers. Male genital pore lateral. Cirrus pouch with large internal seminal vesicle. External seminal vesicle absent. Ovary transversely elongated, containing seminal receptacle in one lobe. Vagina median, convoluted, lacking external pore. Vitelline glands condensed on posterolateral surfaces of lobes of ovary. Uterus a bilobed, transverse sac. Uterine pore ventral. Dorsomedian sheath contains injected cirri, continuous from level of first vagina to posterior end. Osmoregulatory canals with six major vessels, lateral ones with ducts to margins of each segment. Parasites of rays (Myliobatidae). North America.

Type genus: *Dioecotaenia* Schmidt, 1969.

1b. Monoecious forms **2**

2a. Each bothridium divided into three loculi arranged in a triangle. Genital pores at terminal end of mature proglottid ......
....................................**Triloculariidae Yamaguti, 1959. (P. 98)**

Diagnosis: Scolex unarmed, with four sessile bothridia, each divided into three sucker-like loculi arranged in a triangle. Myzorhynchus absent or rudimentary. Long neck present. Free proglottids spinose anteriorly. Genital pores near median at extreme posterior end of proglottid. Parasites of elasmobranchs.

Type genus: *Trilocularia* Olsson, 1867.

2b. Bothridia otherwise. Genital pores marginal **3**

3a. Scolex unarmed ....**Phyllobothriidae Braun, 1900 (P. 99)**

Diagnosis: Scolex unarmed. Bothridia variable, sessile or pedunculated, commonly folded, crumpled or loculate, sometimes simple. Accessory suckers present. Myzorhynchus usually present. Genital pores marginal. Parasites of elasmobranchs.

Type genus: *Phyllobothrium* Beneden, 1849.

3b. Scolex armed ....**Oncobothriidae Braun, 1900 (P. 109)**

Diagnosis: Scolex armed with simple or branched hooks or hooklike horns. Bothridia usually sessile, simple or divided into loculi. Accessory suckers present or not. Myzorhynchus absent. Neck present or absent. Genital pores marginal. Parasites of elasmobranchs.

Type genus: *Oncobothrium* Blainville, 1828.

DIAGNOSIS OF THE ONLY GENUS
IN DIOECOTAENIIDAE
Dioecotaenia Schmidt, 1969 (Fig. 141)

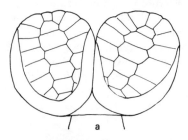

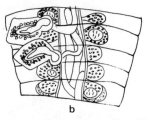

Fig. 141. *Dioecotaenia cancellata* (Linton, 1890) Schmidt, 1969. a. Scolex. b. Portion of female proglottid, with two male proglottids engaged in hypodermic impregnation.

Sexes completely separate, each lacking even accessory genital organs of the other. Sexual dimorphism of size and shape apparent. Scolex with four bothridia on short peduncles, each divided into 21 loculi. External segmentation feeble, proglottids acraspedote. Male genital pore lateral, irregularly alternating. Testes medullary, in two layers, arranged in a circle on both sides of cirrus pouch. Cirrus pouch muscular, large, containing internal seminal vesicle. Cirrus long, armed at base with large hooks; the remainder covered with minute, deciduous spines. Ovary bilobed, medullary. Vagina median, convoluted. Vaginal pore absent. Seminal receptacle imbedded in substance of one lobe of ovary, irregularly alternating sides. Vitelline glands two, compact, surrounding posterolateral margins of both lobes of ovary. Uterus a bilobed, transverse sac arising anterior to ovary. Uterine pore preformed, medioventral, near posterior margin of proglottid. Medullary, continuous, dorsomedian sheath containing injected cirri present in female. Sperm transfer by hypodermic impregnation. Parasites of cow-nosed ray. Chesapeake Bay.

Type species: *D. cancellata* (Linton, 1890) Schmidt, 1969.

DIAGNOSIS OF THE ONLY GENUS
IN TRILOCULARIIDAE
Trilocularia Olsson, 1867 (Fig. 142)

Diagnosis: Scolex with four sessile, triangular bothridia, each with three loculi arranged in triangle. No suckers or myzorhynchus. Neck present. Free proglottids with anterior spines. Genital pore and cirrus pouch median near posterior end of proglottid. Testes anterior to ovary. Vagina ventral to cirrus. Ovary posterior, U-shaped with wings median to vitellaria. Vitellaria in lateral medullary fields. Uterus with dorsal duct and ventral elongate uterine sac with 10-15 lateral branches on each side. No preformed uterine pore. Parasites of sharks. Scandinavia, Britain. Mediterranean.

Type species: *T. gracilis* Olsson, 1867.

Fig. 142. *Trilocularia gracilis* Olsson, 1867. After Linton (1924).

Key to the Genera in Phyllobothriidae

1a. Myzorhynchus with four suckers ....

Myzophyllobothrium Shipley and Hornell, 1906. (Fig. 143)

Diagnosis: Scolex with prominent myzorhynchus bearing four suckers. Bothridia leaf-like, attached at base, with smooth edges. Neck short. Genital pores marginal, equatorial. Cirrus pouch thin walled. Cirrus well developed, unarmed. Testes numerous, in entire intervitelline field anterior to ovary. Vagina anterior to cirrus pouch. Ovary posterior, with broad lateral wings. Vitellaria in complete lateral fields. Uterus median, extending to level of cirrus pouch. Parasites of elasmobranchs. Ceylon.

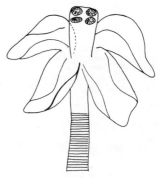

Fig. 143. *Myzophyllobothrium rubrum* Shipley and Hornell, 1906.

Type species: *M. rubrum* Shipley and Hornell, 1906.

1b. Myzorhynchus without suckers, or absent 2

2a. Bothridia approximately cylindrical, open at both ends ....

..............................*Pithophorus* Southwell, 1925. (Fig. 144)

Diagnosis: Scolex with four globular or cylindrical hollow bothridia; each opens at both anterior and posterior ends. Myzorhynchus present or absent (?). Neck present. Genital pores near equator, irregularly alternating. Cirrus pouch very large, swollen, extending to median line. Cirrus armed at tip in mature proglottids only. Testes numerous in two lateral fields medial to vitellaria. Vagina anterior to cirrus sac. Ovary with two large lobes. Vitellaria lateral. Uterus median, extending nearly entire length of proglottid. Parasite of elasmobranchs. Ceylon, Japan.

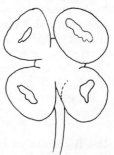

Fig. 144. *Pithophorus tetraglobus* (Southwell, 1911) Southwell, 1925.

Type species: *P. tetraglobus* (Southwell, 1911) Southwell, 1925.

2b. Bothridia hollow, open at one end only 3

2c. Bothridia not as above 7

3a. **Bothridia spherical** ....
.........................*Scyphophyllidium* **Woodland, 1927. (Fig. 145)**

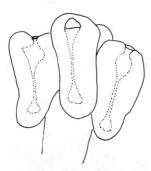

Fig. 145. *Scyphophyllidium gi-ganteum* (Beneden, 1858) Wood-land, 1927. After Euzet (1959).

Diagnosis: Scolex with four globular, sucker-like bothridia, each with irregular, anterior opening. Myzorhynchus and accessory suckers absent. Neck very long. Genital pores in anterior third of proglottid margin, irregularly alternating. All proglottids broader than long. Testes numerous, occupying entire intervitelline field anterior to ovary. Vagina anterior to cirrus pouch. Ovary posterior, bilobed. Vitellaria in two wide lateral fields. Uterus median, somewhat convoluted. Parasite of elasmobranchs. Europe, North America.

Type species: S. *giganteum* (Beneden, 1858) Woodland, 1927.

3b. **Bothridia not spherical** 4

4a. **Submarginal accessory sucker present on each bothridium; bothridia attached at anterior end** ....
.... *Marsupiobothrium* **Yamaguti, 1952.**

Diagnosis: Scolex with four sac-like, pyriform bothridia, each with anterior opening provided with sphincter-like muscles and an accessory sucker present at anterior end. Myzorhynchus absent. Neck present. Free proglottids greatly elongated. Genital pore preequatorial. Cirrus pouch and cirrus well developed. Testes numerous. Vagina anterior to cirrus pouch. Ovary with two long slender wings. Vitellaria in lateral fields, some follicles postovarian. Uterus median, extending to level of cirrus pouch. Parasites of selachians. Japan, North America.

Type species: M. *alopias* Yamaguti, 1952.

4b. **Bothridia without accessory suckers, not attached at anterior end** 5

5a. **Bothridia attached along entire length** ....
....*Aocobothrium* **Mola, 1907. (Fig. 146)**

Diagnosis: Scolex with four sac-like bothridia attached along their entire length, each with an enlarged rim around the anterior opening. Myzorhynchus absent. Neck present. Proglottids rounded to oval. Genital pores irregularly alternating. Cirrus pouch at an oblique angle. Testes numerous. Vagina anterior to cirrus pouch. Ovary posterior, bilobed. Vitellaria in lateral bands joined at anterior and posterior ends. Uterus reaching equator of proglottid. Parasite of freshwater teleost (?). Europe.

Type species: A. *carrucci* Mola, 1907.

Fig. 146. *Aocobo-thrium carrucci* Mola, 1907. After Southwell (1925). a. Scolex. b. Proglottid.

5b. Bothridia attached at posterior end 6

6a. Vitellaria continuous behind ovary: Myzorhynchus absent ....
....*Cyatocotyle* **Mola, 1908.**

Diagnosis: Scolex with four tubular bothridia attached at their posterior end, each with apical opening. Myzorhynchus absent. Neck present. Exteral segmentation indistinct. Entire strobila with minute spines. Genital pores irregularly alternating. Genital atrium with strong sphincter. Cirrus pouch small. Testes preovarian, numerous. Vagina dorsal and posterior to cirrus pouch. Ovary bilobed, posterior. Vitellaria lateral, joined at anterior and posterior ends of proglottid. Uterus nearly reaching anterior end of proglottid. Parasite of elamosbranchs. Indian Ocean.

Type species: C. *marchesettii* Mola, 1908.

6b. Vitellaria not continuous behind ovary. Myzorhynchus present
....*Pseudanthobothrium* **Baer, 1956.**

Diagnosis: Scolex with four cup-shaped bothridia attached at their posterior ends. Myzorhynchus present. Genital pores irregularly alternating, postequatorial. Cirrus pouch small. Cirrus spined. Testes few, large, anterior to level of cirrus pouch. Vagina ventral to cirrus pouch. Ovary posterior, bilobed in surfacial view, X-shaped in cross section. Vitellaria in lateral fields. Parasites of rays. Europe.

Type species: P. *hanseni* Baer, 1956.

7a. **Scolex without myzorhynchus but with apical sucker. Accessory sucker next to anterior margin of each bothridium** ....
....*Pelichnibothrium* **Monticelli, 1889.**

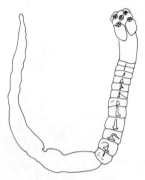

Diagnosis: Scolex with apical sucker. Myzorhynchus absent. Bothridia sessile, each with a single sucker on the anterior margin. Neck absent. Mature and gravid proglottids oval. Testes medullary, in lateral fields medial to osmoregulatory canals. Genital pores irregularly alternating. Cirrus pouch oblique, thin-walled. Vagina posterior to cirrus pouch. Ovary bilobed, compact. Vitellaria in broad lateral fields. Seminal receptacle present. Uterus median. Parasite of elasmobranchs. Madeira, Japan.

Fig. 147. *Pelichnibothrium speciosum* Monticelli, 1889. After Yamaguti (1934).

Type species: *P. speciosum* Monticelli, 1889.

7b. **Scolex without apical sucker** 8
8a. **Transverse ridges forming several loculi on adherant surfaces of bothridia** 9
8b. **Bothridia not as above** 11
9a. **Bothridial ridges incomplete, loculi not completely enclosed**
...........................*Phormobothrium* **Alexander, 1963.** (Fig. 148)

Diagnosis: Scolex possessing slender, retractile myzorhynchus containing subapical muscular organ. Bothridia pedunculate, basket-shaped, delicate, highly mobile; outer posterior rim and base of bothridium with at least four incomplete longitudinal ridges, anterior rim with two incomplete longitudinal apical ridges forming unenclosed loculus. Cephalic peduncle absent. Genital pores in posterior half of proglottid margin. Testes anterior to cirrus pouch. Vitellaria in lateral bands. Parasite of Rajidae. Cosmopolitan.

Fig. 148. *Phormobothrium affine* (Olsson, 1867) Alexander, 1963.

Type species: *P. affine* (Olsson, 1867) Alexander, 1963.

9b. **Bothridial ridges complete** 10

10a. Loculi arranged symmetrically in rows ....
......................*Echeneibothrium* **Beneden, 1850.** (**Fig. 149**)

Diagnosis: Bothridia pedunculate or sessile, with their adhesive surface divided into loculi by transverse, and sometimes also longitudinal ridges. Myzorhynchus present or not. Neck present. External segmentation poorly marked. Genital pores irregularly alternating. Cirrus spined or not. Testes anterior to cirrus pouch. Vagina anterior or ventral to cirrus pouch. Ovary posterior, variable. Vitellaria lateral. Uterus reaching near anterior end of proglottid. Parasite of elasmobranchs. Cosmopolitan.

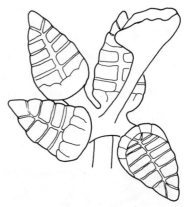

Fig. 149. *Echeneibothrium variable* Beneden, 1849. After Williams (1966).

Type species: *E. variabile* Beneden, 1849.
Key to species: Wardle and McCleod, (1952); Williams (1966).

10b. Loculi 5 in number, arranged radially ....
......................*Pentaloculum* **Alexander, 1963.** (**Fig. 150**)

Diagnosis: Bothridia sessile, each divided by permanent, muscular septa into five radially arranged loculi, more or less equal in size. No cephalic peduncle or myzorhynchus. Strobila small. Proglottids slightly craspedote. Genital pores irregularly alternating on posterior third of proglottid margin. Cirrus, cirrus pouch, vagina and uterus not described. Testes fill proglottid anterior to cirrus pouch. Ovary occupying most of space behind cirrus pouch. Vitellaria in narrow, paired bands of small

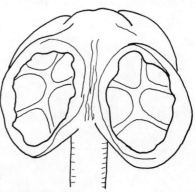

Fig. 150. *Pentaloculum symmetricum* Alexander, 1963.

follicles lateral to testes. Parasite of elasmobranchs. New Zealand.
Type species: *P. macrocephalum* Alexander, 1963.

11a. Each bothridium with two opposed terminal flaps ....
.... *Carpobothrium* **Shipley and Hornell, 1906. (Fig. 151)**

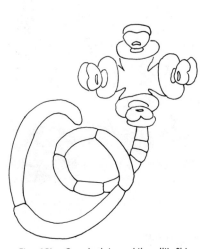

Diagnosis: Scolex with four pedunculate bothridia, each with two opposed flaps bearing minute loculi on their margins. Myzorhynchus absent. Neck short. Mature proglottids much longer than broad. Genital pores irregularly alternating, near middle of lateral margin. Cirrus pouch reaching median line. Cirrus armed. Testes numerous, in whole intervitelline field anterior to ovary. Vagina anterior to cirrus pouch. Ovary bilobed, variable, posterior. Vitellaria in narrow lateral bands. Uterus reaching almost anterior margin of proglottid. Parasite of elasmobranchs. Ceylon.

Fig. 151. *Carpobothrium chiloscyllii* Shipley and Hornell. 1906.

Type species: *C. chiloscyllii* Shipley and Hornell, 1906.

11b. Bothridia without terminal flaps 12
12a. No accessory suckers 13
12b. Accessory suckers present 16
13a. Myzorhynchus absent, bothridia greatly folded on the borders .... *Sphaerobothrium* **Euzet, 1959. (Fig. 152)**

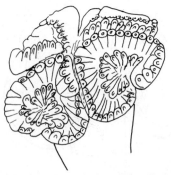

Diagnosis: Scolex with four large bilobed bothridia, each with wide basal margin and narrow anterior margin. When relaxed, each bothridium has a greatly undulated margin; when contracted they are globular and resemble *Scyphophyllidium*. No suckers or myzorhynchus. Cephalic peduncle and neck present. Proglottids triangular. Testes numerous, anterior to ovary. Cirrus spined. Vagina anterior to cirrus pouch. Ovary posterior, bilobed, each half subdivided into lobules. Vi-

Fig. 152. *Sphaerobothrium lubeti* Euzet, 1959.

tellaria in lateral bands. Uterus median with lateral branches. Parasite of selachians. France.

Type species: *S. lubeti* Euzet, 1959.
13b. Myzorhynchus present or absent, bothridia not as above 14

14a. Myzorhynchus with a subapical, musculo-glandular organ ....
.................................*Clydonobothrium* **Euzet, 1959. (Fig. 153)**

Diagnosis: Bothridia thin, pedunculate, highly crumpled, with borders somewhat thickened. Myzorhynchus slender, retractile, with subapical musculo-glandular organ. Cephalic peduncle absent. Proglottids slightly or strongly craspedote. Strobila almost oval in cross section. Apolytic. Genital atrium well-developed. Cirrus stout, heavily armed with minute, stout spines. Cirrus pouch

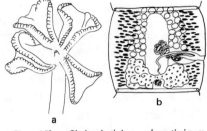

Fig. 153. *Clydonobothrium elegantissimum* (Lönnberg, 1889) Euzet, 1959. a. Scolex. b. Proglottid.

well developed. Testes usually arranged two or three abreast. Genital pore irregularly alternating in posterior third of proglottid margin. Vagina thick-walled, anterior to cirrus pouch. Ovary bilobed, near posterior end of proglottid. Vitellaria in two dense lateral fields extending entire length of proglottid. Parasite of Rajidae. Probably cosmopolitan.

Type species: *C. elegantissimum* (Lönnberg, 1889) Euzet, 1959.

14b. Myzorhynchus not as above **15**

15a. Ovary 2-lobed in cross section. Myzorhynchus present or absent ....*Anthobothrium* **Beneden, 1850. (Fig. 154)**

Diagnosis: Bothridia usually simple, sometimes with loculi. Accessory suckers absent. Myzorhynchus present or absent. Neck present. Genital pores irregularly alternating. Cirrus armed. Testes numerous in single field. Vagina anterior to cirrus pouch. Seminal receptacle usually present. Ovary bilobed, variable. Vitellaria lateral, V-shaped in cross section. Uterus variable between species, reaching level of cirrus pouch or near anterior end of proglottid. Parasite of elasmobranchs. Cosmopolitan.

Type species: *A. cornucopia* Beneden, 1850.

Key to species: Wardle and McCleod, 1952.

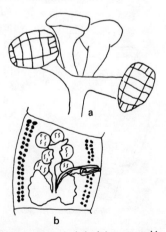

Fig. 154. *Anthobothrium sexorchidum* Williams, 1964. a. Scolex. b. Proglottid.

15b. Ovary 4-lobed in cross section. Myzorhynchus absent ....
....*Rhodobothrium* **Linton, 1889.**

Diagnosis: Scolex with four bothridia, each simple, lacking accessory suckers. Myzorhynchus absent. Neck absent. Genital pores irregularly alternating. Gonoducts pass between osmoregulatory canals. Cirrus armed. Testes in two lateral fields. Vagina anterior to cirrus pouch. Ovary appears bilobed in flat view but is four-lobed in cross section. Vitellaria lateral. Uterus winding in median field. Parasite of elasmobranchs. North America, Europe, Ceylon.

Type species: *R. pulvinatum* Linton, 1889.

16a. Bothridium with shelf-like anterior thickening 17

16b. Bothridium without shelf-like anterior thickening 19

17a. Vitellaria in ventral medulla from ventral osmoregulatory canal to submedian field ....*Gastrolecithus* **Yamaguti, 1952.**

Diagnosis: Bothridia flat or concave, each with anterior accessory sucker and anterolateral appendage which is split at the tip. Myzorhynchus absent. Neck long. All proglottids broader than long. Genital pores irregularly alternating. Cirrus pouch exceeding osmoregulatory canals. Testes numerous, in two lateral fields anterior and lateral to ovary. Vagina ventral to cirrus pouch, armed in its expanded distal portion. Ovary bilobed, posterior. Vitellaria extending in ventral medulla from ventral osmoregulatory canal to submedian field. Uterus transverse, anterior to ovary. Parasite of basking shark. North America, Europe, Japan.

Type species: *G. planus* (Linton, 1922) Yamaguti, 1952.

17b. Vitellaria in two lateral fields 18

18a. Ovary 4-lobed in cross section ....
...............................*Dinobothrium* **Beneden, 1889. (Fig. 155)**

Diagnosis: Scolex nearly cuboidal, very large (up to 10 mm long), unarmed, lacking myzorhynchus. Bothridia sessile, not folded on margins, each fused at anterior margin to a muscular transverse lobe that is bluntly bifid. Accessory or pseudo-suckers may be present on these lobes. Neck absent. Genital pores irregularly alternating. Cirrus armed. Testes numerous, between ovary and anterior end of proglottid in intervitelline field. Vagina anterior to cirrus pouch. Ovary four-lobed, posterior. Vitellaria lateral. Uterus median, with lateral branches. Parasite of elasmobranchs. Europe, Asia, North America.

Fig. 155. *Dinobothrium planum* Linton, 1922.

Type species: *D. septaria* Beneden, 1889.

18b. Ovary fan-shaped in cross section ....*Reesium* **Euzet, 1955.**

Diagnosis: Scolex with four sessile, spinose bothridia, each with margins entire and fused anteriorly with a horn-like projection bearing an accessory sucker and bifid at the tip. Myzorhynchus absent. Neck spinose. Genital pores regularly alternating. Cirrus pouch exceeds median line. Testes large, 28-45, filling intervitelline field anterior to ovary. Vagina posterior to cirrus pouch. Ovary fan-shaped in cross section. Uterus in form of two sacs, anterior and posterior. Vitellaria lateral. Parasite of elasmobranchs. Europe, Japan, Hebrides.

Type species: *R. paciferum* (Sproston, 1948) Euzet, 1955.

19a. Margins of bothridia greatly crumpled and/or loculated ......
...........................*Phyllobothrium* **Beneden, 1849. (Fig. 156)**

Diagnosis: Scolex with myzorhynchus or not. Bothridia sessile or pedunculated, with margins usually folded, curled, often with loculi. One or two accessory suckers on each bothridium. Neck present or absent. Cirrus pouch thin-walled; cirrus often armed. Genital pores irregularly alternating, rarely unilateral. Testes numerous, in entire intervitelline field anterior to ovary. Vagina usually anterior to cirrus pouch. Seminal receptacle usually present. Ovary posterior, four-lobed in cross section. Vitellaria lateral, V-shaped in cross section. Uterus median, reaching level of cirrus pouch. Elasmobranchs. Pacific, Atlantic and Indian Oceans.

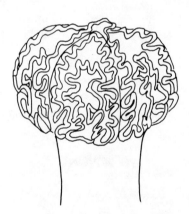

Fig. 156. *Phyllobothrium lactuca* Beneden, 1850. After Southwell (1925).

Type species: *P. lactuca* Beneden, 1850.

Monograph: Williams (1968)

Key to species: Wardle and McCleod, 1952.

19b. Margins of bothridia smooth or lightly sinuous 20

20a. Myzorhynchus present. Single accessory sucker per bothridium ....*Monorygma* Diesing, 1863. (Fig. 157)

Diagnosis: Myzorhynchus present. Bothridia sessile, each hollowed out posteriorly, with thin, smooth margins, and a single anterior accessory sucker. Neck present. Genital pores irregularly alternating. Cirrus pouch thin-walled, cirrus spined. Testes numerous, filling field between osmoregulatory canals anterior to ovary. Vagina opening into genital atrium anterior or ventral to cirrus. Inconspicuous seminal receptacle present. Ovary four-lobed in cross section. Vitellaria lateral. Uterus median, extending to level of cirrus pouch. Eggs spindle-shaped. Parasite of elasmobranchs. North Atlantic, North Pacific, Mediterranian.

Fig. 157. *Monorygma perfectum* (Beneden, 1853) Diesing, 1863.

Type species: *M. perfectum* (Beneden, 1853) Diesing, 1863.

20b. Myzorhynchus absent. Two accessory suckers per bothridium .... *Orygmatobothrium* Diesing, 1863. (Fig. 158)

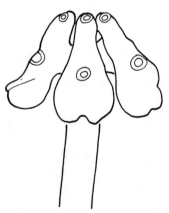

Diagnosis: Myzorhynchus absent. Each bothridium with an accessory sucker at the anterior end and another near the center. Bothridial margins entire or crumpled. Neck present. Genital pores irregularly alternating. Cirrus pouch thin walled, somewhat oblique. Cirrus armed or not. Testes numerous, in broad field anterior to ovary. Vagina opening into atrium in front of cirrus. Seminal receptacle present. Ovary four-lobed in cross section, posterior. Vitellaria in broad lateral bands, V-shaped in cross section. Uterus median, extending to level of cirrus pouch. Parasite of elas-

Fig. 158. *Orygmatobothrium versatile* Diesing, 1863. After Zschokke (1888).

mobranchs. Europe, Africa, Japan, North America.

Type species: *O. versatile* Diesing, 1863.

Key to the Genera in Oncobothriidae

1a. Ruffle-like collar on neck below scolex ....
.................................*Thysanocephalum* **Linton, 1889. (Fig. 159)**

Diagnosis: Scolex small, with four sessile bothridia, each divided by a transverse septum into two loculi. Two stout
spines are found on the ends of the septum of each bothridium. Neck present,
with fleshy, ruffle-like collar with frilled
margins. Cuticle posterior to collar appears scaly. Genital pores irregularly
alternating. Cirrus pouch large. Cirrus
short and stout, armed apically. Testes
very numerous, filling intervitelline field
anterior and lateral to ovary. Vagina anterior to cirrus pouch. Ovary bilobed, at
posterior end of proglottid. Vitellaria in
narrow lateral fields. Uterus median,
over-reaching level of cirrus pouch. Parasite of elasmobranchs. North America,
France.

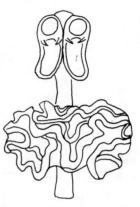

Fig. 159. *Thysanocephalum crispum* (Linton, 1889) Linton, 1891.

Type species: *T. crispum* (Linton,
1889) Linton, 1891.

1b. No such collar 2

2a. Muscular, horn-like appendages on bothridia in place of hooks
..........................*Ceratobothrium* **Monticelli, 1892. (Fig. 160)**

Diagnosis: Four sessile, undivided bothridia,
each directly below large accessory sucker
bearing two projecting horn-like appendages
consisting mainly of circular muscle fibers.
Neck present. Genital pores irregularly alternating. Cirrus pouch thin-walled, long, oblique.
Testes numerous, in two lateral intervitelline
fields. Vagina anterior to cirrus pouch. Ovary
posterior, bilobed in flat view, four-lobed in
cross section. Vitellaria in narrow fields lateral
to osmoregulatory canals. Uterus median,
nearly reaching anterior end of proglottid.
Parasites of elasmobranchs. Italy, U.S.A.,
Japan.

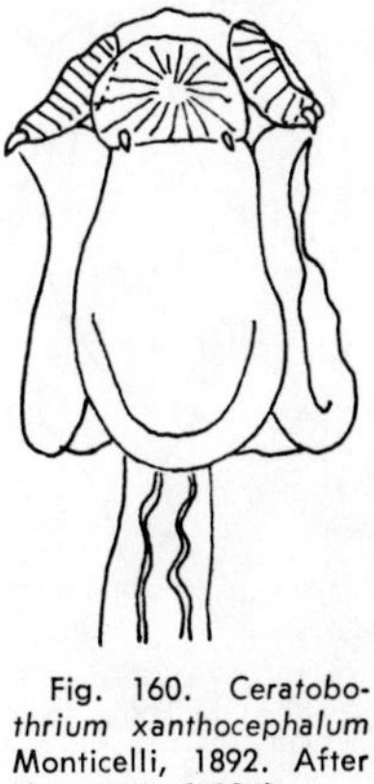

Fig. 160. *Ceratobothrium xanthocephalum* Monticelli, 1892. After Yamaguti (1934).

Type species: *C. xanthocephalum* Monticelli,
1892.

2b. Bothridia with hooks 3

3a. **Bothridia divided by transverse partitions** 4
3b. **Bothridia undivided** **10**
4a. **Each bothridium with two loculi** **5**
4b. **Each bothridium with three loculi** **6**
5a. **Hooks slender, forked, with two antler-like prongs** ....
.................................*Uncibilocularis* Southwell, 1927. (Fig. 161)

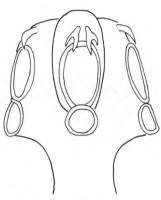

Diagnosis: Four sessile bothridia, each divided into two rounded loculi by a transverse septum. Each bothridium has two dorsal bifid hooks, antler-like in appearance. No accessory suckers. Neck present. Genital pores irregularly alternating. Cirrus pouch small. Cirrus armed at tip. Testes few (15-40) in two broad fields medial to osmoregulatory canals. Vagina opens anterior to cirrus, expanded proximally. Ovary posterior, bilobed. Vitellaria in wide lateral bands. Uterus rosette-like, filling proglottid. Minute ventral uterine pore present. Parasites of elasmobranchs. Ceylon.

Fib. 161. *Uncibilocularis trygonis* (Shipley and Hornell, 1906) Southwell, 1925.

Type species: *U. trygonis* (Shipley and Hornell, 1906) Southwell, 1925.

5b. **Hooks simple, not forked. Bothridia paired, at ends of stalks**
....*Yorkeria* Southwell, 1927. (Fig. 162)

Diagnosis: Scolex with bothridia arranged into two pairs, each pair on the end of a common stalk. Each bothridium divided into a distal small and a proximal large compartment. Two U-shaped hooks on each bothridium, unequal in size, one each end of the septum. Entire scolex spinose. Neck (?). Genital pores irregularly alternating. Cirrus pouch well developed. Cirrus armed. Testes confined anterior to cirrus pouch. Vagina anterior to cirrus pouch, expanded throughout its length. Ovary four-lobed in cross section, about one-fourth from posterior end. Vitellaria lateral. Uterus reaching level of cirrus pouch. Parasites of elasmobranchs. Ceylon, Australia.

Fig. 162. *Yorkeria parva* Southwell, 1927. After Williams (1964).

Type species: *Y. parva* Southwell, 1927.

6a. Each bothridium with two pairs of simple hooks ....
..................................*Calliobothrium* **Beneden, 1850.** (**Fig. 163**)

Diagnosis: Bothridia divided into three loculi by two transverse septa. Two pairs of simple hooks present on muscular pad at anterior end of each bothridium. One to three accessory suckers present on each pad. Neck absent. Genital pores irregularly alternating. Cirrus pouch small, thin walled. Cirrus armed or not. Testes in intervitelline field anterior to ovary. Vagina opening anterior to cirrus. Seminal receptacle present. Ovary large, bilobed, posterior, occupying entire intervitelline field. Vitellaria lateral. Uterus extending nearly to anterior end of proglottid. Numerous ventral uterine pores forming by rupture of body wall in gravid proglottids. Parasites of elasmobranchs. Europe, Japan, India, North America.

Fig. 163. *Calliobothrium verticillatum* (Rudolphi, 1819) Beneden, 1850. After Southwell (1925).

Type species: *C. verticillatum* (Rudolphi, 1819) Beneden, 1850.

6b. Each bothridium with one pair of hooks, simple or forked 7
7a. All hooks simple, may be joined by bar at base 8
7b. All hooks forked 9
8a. Hooks anterior to front loculi ....
.....................................*Oncobothrium* **Blainville, 1828.** (**Fig. 164**)

Diagnosis: Bothridia divided into three loculi by two transverse septa and armed with two thorn-shaped hooks. Each pair of hooks may be joined at their bases by a horseshoe-like plate, or they may be separate. Each hook commonly with tubercle- or hair-like process. Neck present. Genital pores irregularly alternating. Cirrus pouch thin-walled. Cirrus armed or not. Vagina anterior to cirrus pouch, commonly greatly dilated near its distal end. Testes in intervitelline field anterior to ovary. Ovary posterior, transversely elongated or U-shaped, with wings sometimes extending anterior to cirrus pouch. Vitellaria lateral. Uterus extending anterior to level of cirrus pouch. Parasites of elasmobranchs. Atlantic, Pacific, Mediterranean.

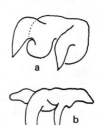

Fig. 164. a. *Oncobothrium pseudouncinatum* (Rudolphi, 1819) Beneden, 1850. Hook. b. *O. convolutum* (Yoshida, 1917) Southwell, 1925. Hook.

Type species: *O. pseudouncinatum* (Rudolphi, 1819) Beauchamp, 1905.

8b. Hooks latero-posterior to front loculi ....
....................................*Spiniloculus* Southwell, 1925. (Fig. 165)

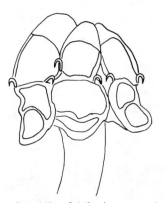

Fig. 165.   *Spiniloculus   mavensis*
Southwell, 1925.

Diagnosis: Scolex globular, each bothridium divided into three loculi by two transverse septa. Postero-lateral corners of anterior loculi each with a single simple hook. Accessory suckers absent. Neck apparently present. Mature proglottids much longer than wide. Genital pores irregularly alternating. Cirrus pouch large. Cirrus armed. Testes numerous, in intervitelline field anterior to ovary. Vagina dilated, anterior to cirrus pouch. Ovary posterior, bilobed. Vitellaria lateral. Uterus median, extending to level of cirrus pouch. Parasites of elasmobranchs. Australia.

Type species: S. *mavensis* Southwell, 1925.

9a. One hook of each pair three-pronged, the other two-pronged
......................................*Platybothrium* Linton, 1890. (Fig. 166)

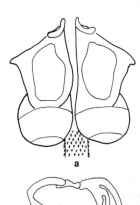

a

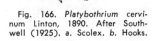

b

Fig. 166.   *Platybothrium cervinum* Linton, 1890. After Southwell (1925). a. Scolex. b. Hooks.

Diagnosis: Bothridia with three loculi, the anterior sometimes being difficult to see. A lateral lobe is sometimes present on the middle loculus, which also has a pair of hooks, one of which is bifid and the other trifid. Hooks may or may not be joined at bases by sclerotized plate. Neck present, spiny. Anterior proglottids spiny. Genital pores irregularly alternating. Testes extending between ovary and anterior end of proglottid, in intervitelline field. Cirrus pouch thin-walled. Vagina anterior to cirrus pouch. Ovary posterior, bilobed. Vitellaria in narrow lateral fields. Uterus median, nearly reaching anterior end of proglottid. Parasites of elasmobranchs. North America, Japan, Europe, India.

Type species: P. *cervinum* Linton, 1890.

9b. Both hooks of each pair two-pronged ....
....................................*Acanthobothrium* **Beneden, 1849.** (Fig. 167)

Diagnosis: Bothridia trilocular, each with two bifurcate hooks at its anterior end. Small spongy pad or sucker sometimes in front of bothridium. Neck present. Genital pores irregularly alternating. Cirrus pouch well developed. Cirrus usually armed. Testes in entire intervitelline field anterior to ovary. Vagina anterior to cirrus pouch. Seminal receptacle sometimes present. Ovary posterior, variable in shape. Vitellaria lateral. Uterus median, reaching anterior end of proglottid. Parasites of elasmobranchs. Cosmopolitan.

Type species: *A. coronatum* (Rudolphi, 1819) Beneden, 1849.

Key to species: Southwell, 1930; Baer, 1948; Wardle and McCleod, 1952.

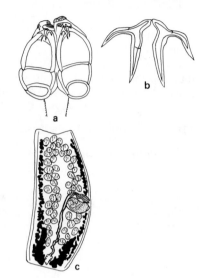

Fig. 167. *Acanthobothrium floridensis* Goldstein, 1964. a. Scolex. b. Hooks. c. Proglottid.

10a. Bothridia with accessory suckers in front of hooks ....
...................................*Phoreiobothrium* **Linton, 1889.** (Fig. 168)

Diagnosis: Bothridia sessile, shallow, undivided, each with two bifid or trifid hooks on anterior margin. Simple accessory sucker present anterior to each pair of hooks. Spiny neck present. Genital pores apparently irregularly alternating. Cirrus unarmed. Testes in entire intervitelline field anterior to ovary. Vagina anterior to cirrus pouch. Ovary posterior, bilobed. Vitellaria lateral. Uterus nearly reaching anterior end of proglottid. Parasites of elasmobranchs. Atlantic North America.

Type species: *P. lasium* Linton, 1889.

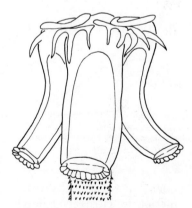

Fig. 168. *Phoreiobothrium lasium* Linton, 1889. After Southwell (1925).

10b. Bothridia lacking accessory suckers **11**

11a. Bothridia embedded in scolex with posterior tip protruding
....*Pinguicollum* **Riser, 1955.**
Diagnosis: Bothridia embedded in scolex except for posterior end which protrudes. Each bothridium with a pair of two-pronged hooks, united at their bases. Accessory suckers absent. Neck long, prominent. Proglottids short, wide. Genital pores irregularly alternating. Cirrus pouch crossing osmoregulatory canals. Testes numerous (110-120). Female genitalia not described. Parasites of elasmobranchs. Pacific North America.
Type species: *P. pinguicollum* (Sleggs, 1927) Riser, 1955.

11b. Bothridia not embedded in scolex 12

12a. Bothridia cylindrical, hollow ....
....*Cylindrophorus* **Diesing, 1863.** (Fig. 169)

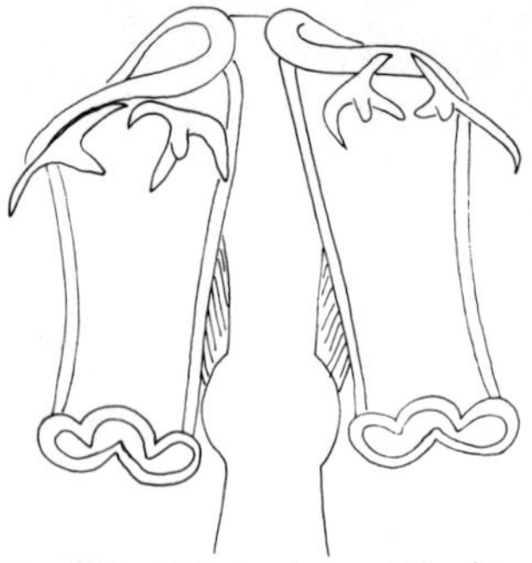

Diagnosis: Bothridia tubular, hollow, each with a bifid and a trifid hook at the anterior margin. No accessory suckers present. Neck present, spiny. Internal anatomy poorly known. Testes numerous, in intervitelline field anterior to ovary. Vagina anterior to cirrus pouch. Ovary posterior, occupying about one-fourth length of proglottid. Vitellaria lateral. Parasites of elasmobranchs. Locality (?).
Type species: *C. typicus* Diesing, 1863.

Fig. 169. *Cylindrophorus triloculatus* Linton, 1901. After Southwell (1925).

12b. Bothridia flattened, not hollow ....
....*Pedibothrium* **Linton, 1909.** (Fig. 170)
Diagnosis: Bothridia flattened, no loculi or accessory suckers, margins smooth. Each bothridium with a pair of single- or double-pronged hooks. Neck distinct. Genital pores irregularly alternating. Cirrus pouch wide. Cirrus armed with very small spines. Testes intervitelline, usually confined anterior to level of cirrus pouch but occasionally reaching antiporal wing of ovary. Vagina anterior to cirrus pouch. Ovary posterior, bilobed. Vitellaria in broad lateral fields, extending behind ovary. Uterus reaching level of cirrus pouch. Parasites of elasmobranchs. North America, India, Ceylon.

Fig. 170. *Pedibothrium globicephalum* Linton, 1909. After Southwell (1925). Hook.

Type species: *P. globicephalum* Linton, 1909.

Key to the Families in Diphyllidea

1a. Scolex with apical dorsal and ventral groups of hooks. Cephalic peduncle with longitudinal rows of hooks ....
.....................................*Echinobothriidae* Perrier, 1897. (P. 115)
Diagnosis: Scolex with well-developed rostellum armed with powerful spines. Peduncle of scolex armed with longitudinal rows of large straight spines. External metamerism distinct, proglottids acraspedote. Genital pores medioventral. Parasites of elasmobranchs.
Type genus: *Echinobothrium* Beneden, 1849.

1b. Scolex and cephalic peduncle lacking hooks ....
.....................................*Ditrachybothridiidae* Fam. N. (P. 116)
Diagnosis: Scolex with short, unarmed peduncle. Apex of scolex blunt, with weakly developed apical organ. External metamerism poorly marked. Vagina opens behind cirrus pouch. Testes in anterior two-thirds of proglottid. Ovary bilobed, posterior. Vitellaria diffuse. Uterine pore absent. Parasites of elasmobranchs.
Type genus: *Ditrachybothridium* Rees, 1959.

DIAGNOSIS OF THE ONLY GENUS IN ECHINOBOTHRIIDAE
Echinobothrium Beneden, 1849 (Fig. 171)

Diagnosis: Scolex with powerful rostellum armed on dorsal and ventral surfaces with a row of large hooks. Hooks largest in middle of row, decreasing in size toward the ends. Two bothridia present, covered with very small, hairlike spines. Cephalic peduncle armed with longitudinal rows of straight hooks, each with root in shape of transverse bar. Neck very short. Strobila small. Posterior proglottids longer than wide. Testes few, medullary, in two longitudinal, preovarian rows. Cirrus median, post-testicular. Cirrus armed. Genital pores median, equatorial or postequatorial, male anterior to female. Ovary bilobed, median, posterior. Vitellaria follicular, in two lateral bands. Uterus median. Uterine pore absent. Eggs may have short filament. Parasites of Batoidea.
Type species: *E. typus* Beneden, 1849.

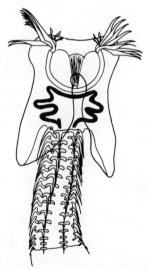

Fig. 171. *Echinobothrium brachysoma* Pintner, 1889. After Rees (1961).

DIAGNOSIS OF THE ONLY GENUS IN DITRACHYBOTHRIDIIDAE
Ditrachybothridium Rees, 1959 (Fig. 172)

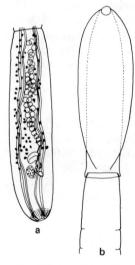

Fig. 172. *Ditrachybothridium macrocephalum* Rees, 1959. a. Proglottid. b. Scolex.

Diagnosis: Scolex consisting of head and short cephalic peduncle. Two oval, flattened or spoon-shaped bothridia, armed along borders and outer convex face with rows of small spines. Neck unarmed, terminated with a velum. Apex of scolex blunt, with feebly developed apical organ. Proglottids acraspedote. Strobila cylindrical, external metamerism barely marked. Last segments 4-5 times longer than broad. Genital pores in posterior quarter of proglottid, female behind male. No uterine pore. Cirrus pouch large, half width of segment. Testes numerous (52-62) in row 1-2 deep in center of anterior two-thirds of proglottid. Ovary posterior, bilobed. Vitellaria inconspicuous, diffuse, anterior to ovary. Elasmobranchs. Scotland.

Type species: *D. macrocephalum* Rees, 1959.

DIAGNOSIS OF THE ONLY FAMILY IN LITOBOTHRIDEA
Litobothridae Dailey, 1969 (P. 116)

Diagnosis: Strobila small, metamerism distinct. Scolex a single sucker followed by modified anterior segments. Genital pores lateral, irregularly alternating. Testes numerous, medullary, preovarian. Cirrus pouch well developed. Ovary posterior. Vitellaria follicular, encircling entire proglottid. Osmoregulatory canals medullary. Parasites of elasmobranchs.

Type genus: *Litobothrium* Dailey, 1969.

DIAGNOSIS OF THE ONLY GENUS IN LITOBOTHRIDAE
Litobothrium Dailey, 1969 (Fig. 173)

Diagnosis: Scolex with single apical sucker followed by modified anterior segments which are cruciform in cross-section. Neck absent. Strobila swollen in width behind scolex, decreasing in width before mature segments. Testes numerous, medullary. Cirrus pouch reaches midline. Vas deferens coiled. Ovary median, posterior. Vitellaria encircling proglottid, extending posterior to ovary. Parasites of sharks.

Type species: L. alopias Dailey, 1969.

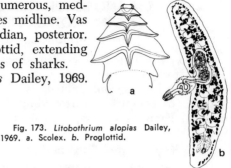

Fig. 173. *Litobothrium alopias* Dailey, 1969. a. Scolex. b. Proglottid.

DIAGNOSIS OF THE ONLY FAMILY IN NIPPOTAENIIDEA
Nippotaeniidae Yamaguti, 1939 (P.117)

Diagnosis: Scolex rounded, with single, large apical sucker and no other attachment devices. Neck very short, poorly marked. Proglottids acraspedote, apolytic. Entire cuticle covered with very minute spines. Single set of reproductive organs per proglottid. Vitellaria bilobed, between ovary and testes. Osmoregulatory canals numerous, anastomosing. Parasites of freshwater teleosts. Asia.

Type genus: Nippotaenia Yamaguti, 1939.

DIAGNOSIS OF THE ONLY GENUS IN NIPPOTAENIIDAE
Nippotaenia Yamaguti, 1939 (Fig. 174)

Diagnosis: Neck showing genital primordia. Strobila round or oval in cross section. Posterior progottids longer than wide. Testes in preovarian medulla. Cirrus pouch thin-walled. Cirrus unarmed. Genital atrium marginal, preequatorial, irregularly alternating. Ovary bilobed, in middle third of proglottid. Vitellaria bilobed, directly in front of ovary. Vagina posterior to cirrus pouch. Uterus with close trans-verse coils, extending nearly en-

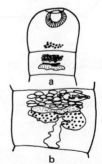

Fig. 174. *Nippotaenia chaenogobii* Yamaguti, 1939.

tire length of proglottid or confined to posterior half. Uterine pore absent. Eggs with three shells. Longitudinal osmoregulatory canals numerous, mostly cortical. Parasites of freshwater teleosts. Japan, Russia.

Type species: N. chaenogobii Yamaguti, 1939.

DIAGNOSIS OF THE ONLY FAMILY
IN PROTEOCEPHALIDEA
Proteocephalidae LaRue, 1911

Scolex with four suckers, sometimes with a fifth apical sucker. Armed rostellum present or absent. Genital pores lateral. Ovary posterior. Uterus longitudinal, with lateral branches. Vitellaria lateral (or completely surrounding internal oragns in Prosobothriinae). Parasites of fish, amphibians and reptiles.

Key to the Subfamilies of Proteocephalidae
(Figures modified from Woodland (1933))

1a. Vitellaria medullary 2

1b. Vitellaria cortical 4

2a. Vitellaria surrounding all internal organs, dorsal and ventral as well as lateral (Fig. 175) ....
..................................Prosobothriinae Yamaguti, 1959. (P. 120)

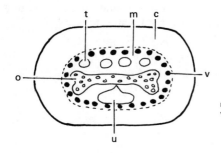

Fig. 175. Prosobothriinae. c-cortex. m-medulla. o-ovary. t-testis. u-uterus. v-vitelline gland.

2b. Vitellaria only lateral 3

3a. Testes medullary (Fig. 176) ....
..................................Proteocephalinae Mola, 1929. (P. 121)

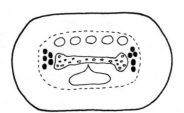

Fig. 176. Proteocephalinae.

3b. Testes in dorsal cortex (Fig. 177) ....
..............................Marsipocephalinae Woodland, 1933. (P. 126)

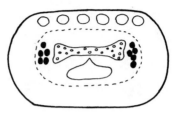

Fig. 177. Marsipocephalinae.

4a. Testes medullary 5
4b. Testes cortical 6
5a. Uterus medullary (Fig. 178) ....
...........................Zygobothriinae Woodland, 1933. (P. 127)

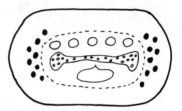

Fig. 178. Zygobothriinae.

5b. Uterus cortical (Fig. 179) ....
......................................Endorchiinae Woodland, 1934. (P. 128)

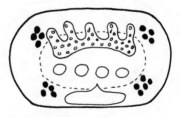

Fig. 179. Endorchiinae.

6a. Uterus and ovary cortical (Fig. 180) ....
....Monticelliinae Mola, 1929. (P. 129)

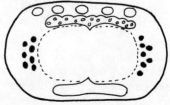

Fig. 180. Monticelliinae.

6b. Uterus and/or ovary medullary 7

7a. Uterus and ovary medullary (Fig. 181) ....
....Ephedrocephalinae Mola, 1929. (P. 130)

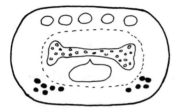

Fig. 181. Ephedrocephalinae.

7b. Ovary medullary, uterus cortical (Fig. 182) ....
...............................Peltidocotylinae Woodland, 1934. (P. 130)

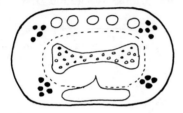

Fig. 182. Peltidocotylinae.

7c. Ovary cortical, uterus medullary (Fig. 183) ....
..............................Rudolphiellinae Woodland, 1935. (P. 131)

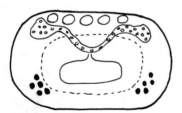

Fig. 183. Rudolphiellinae.

DIAGNOSIS OF THE ONLY GENUS
IN PROSOBOTHRIINAE
Prosobothrium Cohn, 1902

Diagnosis: Scolex normal, with suckers directed anteriad. Neck present. Genital pores irregularly alternating. Cirrus pouch well developed, containing coiled ejaculatory duct. Cirrus spined. Testes medullary, in broad field anterior to ovary. Vagina anterior or lateral to cirrus pouch. Small seminal receptacle present. Ovary medullary, bilobed, at posterior end of proglottid. Vitellaria medullary, completely surrounding gonads in cross section. Uterus median, medullary, greatly swollen when gravid. Parasites of sharks. Japan, North America, Europe.

Type species: *P. armigerum* Cohn, 1902.

Key to the Genera in Proteocephalinae

1a. Scolex armed with hooks 2

1b. Scolex unarmed 5

2a. Rostellum with several alternating rows of small hooks 3

2b. Rostellum with not more than two rows of hooks 4

3a. No testes in anterior median field. Internal seminal vesicle present .... *Electrotaenia* Nybelin, 1942. (Fig. 184)

Diagnosis: Scolex with rostellum armed with several circles of small hooks. Neck present. Acraspedote. Genital atrium deep, muscular. Genital pores irregularly alternating? Cirrus pouch elongated. Inner seminal vesicle present. Testes in two broad lateral fields, median to vitellaria. Vitellaria lateral to osmoregulatory canals. Ovary bilobed, median, at posterior end of proglottid. Uterus median, with lateral branches. Parasites of siluroid fish. Africa.

Type species: *E. malopteruri* (Fritsch, 1886) Nybelin, 1942.

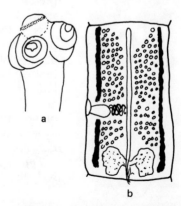

Fig. 184. *Electrotaenia malopteruri* (Fritsch, 1886) Nybelin, 1942. a. Scolex. b. Proglottid.

3b. Testes present in anterior median field. No internal seminal vesicle .... *Silurotaenia* **Nybelin, 1942. (Fig. 185)**

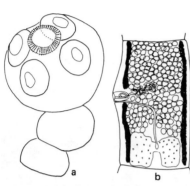

Diagnosis: Scolex with rostellum armed with several alternating circles of small hooks. Neck present? Acraspedote. Genital pores irregularly alternating. Genital atrium shallow, not muscular. Cirrus pouch small, rounded. Seminal vesicles absent. Testes fill entire field anterior to ovary. Ovary with two large lateral lobes, at posterior margin of proglottid. Vitellaria lateral to osmoregulatory canals. Uterus median, with lateral branches. Parasites of siluroid fishes. Europe.

Fig. 185. *Silurotaenia siluri* (Batsch, 1786) Nybelin, 1942. a. Scolex. b. Proglottid.

Type species: S. *siluri* (Batsch, 1786) Nybelin, 1942.

4a. Vitellaria short, in lateral preovarian fields. One circle of hooks ....*Vermaia* **Nybelin, 1942. (Fig. 186)**

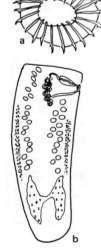

Diagnosis: Scolex with rostellum armed with single circle of hooks. Minute spines on margins of suckers, neck and proglottids. Neck present. Poterior proglottids much longer than wide. Cirrus pouch small, thin-walled. Ducts pass between osmoregulatory canals. Genital pores regularly alternating, in posterior half of proglottid. Seminal vesicles absent. Testes in two lateral fields anterior to ovary. Vitellaria in short, lateral fields between level of genital pore and ovary. Uterus with lateral branches. Eggs embryonated, some developing a neck and bladder (?) while still in uterus. Parasites of siluroid fishes. India.

Type species: V. *pseudotropii* (Verma, 1928) Nybelin, 1942.

Fig. 186. *Vermaia pseudotropii* (Verma, 1928) Nybelin, 1942. a. Rostellar hooks. b. Proglottid.

**4b. Vitellaria extending entire lateral fields. One or two circles of
hooks** .... *Gangesia* **Woodland, 1924. (Fig. 187)**

Diagnosis: Scolex with rostellum armed with one or two circles of hooks. Neck present. Mature proglottids about square. Genital pores irregularly alternating. Cirrus pouch large, cirrus unarmed. Seminal vesicles absent. Testes in continuous field between vitelline fields. Ovary between posterior ends of vitelline fields. Vitellaria lateral, extending entire length of proglottid. Uterus median, with lateral branches. Parasites of siluroid fishes. India, Europe, Russia, Japan.

Type species: *G. bengalensis* (Southwell, 1913) Woodland, 1924.

Key to species: Singh (1948) Frese (1965).

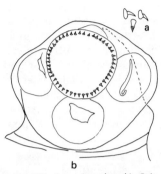

Fig. 187. *Gangesia polyonchis* Roitman and Frese, 1964. a. *Typical* hooks. b. Scolex.

5a. Scolex with fleshy folds covering suckers 6
5b. Suckers completely exposed 8

6a. Only base of suckers covered by folds ....
....*Choanoscolex* **LaRue, 1911. (Fig. 188)**

Diagnosis: Scolex with swollen base and cone-shaped apex. Base of suckers covered with fold of tissue. Neck present. Terminal proglottids longer than wide. Genital pore in anterior fourth of proglottid margin. Cirrus pouch large, muscular. Cirrus with large lumen. Seminal vesicles absent. Testes in one field between vitellaria. Ovary bilobed, at posterior end of proglottid. Vitellaria in lateral fields, entire length of proglottid. Uterus with lateral branches. Egg with polar swellings. Parasites of siluroid fishes. Paraguay.

Type species: *C. abscisus* (Riggenbach, 1895) LaRue, 1911.

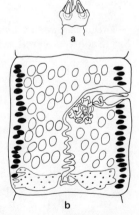

Fig. 188. *Choanoscolex abscisus* (Riggenbach, 1895) LaRue, 1911. a. Scolex. b. Proglottid.

6b. Entire suckers covered by folds 7

7a. Opening of each sucker with powerful sphincter ....
.... *Megathylacus* **Woodland, 1934.**
Diagnosis: Scolex large, with four large lobes. Suckers consist
of large, thin-walled sacs, each with powerful sphincter at orifice,
completely covered by folds. Neck present. Genital pore near
middle of proglottid margin. Seminal vesicles absent. Cirrus pouch
less than one third proglottid width. Testes in two lateral fields (?).
Vagina apparently anterior to cirrus pouch. Ovary transversely
elongated, at posterior end of proglottid. Vitellaria lateral to osmoregulatory canals. Uterus with lateral outpocketings. Parasites of
siluroid fish. Brazil.
    Type species: *M. jandia* Woodland, 1934.
7b. Suckers without powerful sphincters ....
.... *Corallobothrium* **Fritsch, 1886. (Fig. 189)**

                    Diagnosis: Scolex flat on apical end,
                    with four suckers on flat surface, cov-
                    ered with folds. Neck short, broad. Geni-
                    tal pores irregularly alternating, in an-
                    terior half of proglottid margin. Cirrus
                    pouch well developed. Seminal vesicles
                    absent. Testes in single field between
                    osmoregulatory canals. Ovary posterior,
                    variable in shape. Vitellaria lateral, med-
                    ullary. Uterus with lateral branches.
                    Parasites of siluroid fishes. Africa,
                    U.S.A.

Fig. 189. *Corallobothrium fim-
briatum* Essex, 1928.

                    Type species: *C. solidum* Fritsch,
                    1886.
Table of species characters: Wardle and McLeod (1952).
8a. Scolex covered with small spines ....
.... *Acanthotaenia* **Linstow, 1903. (Fig. 190)**

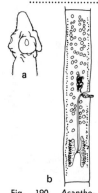

                Diagnosis: Apex of scolex cone-shaped or
                truncated. Suckers normal. Scolex and anterior
                part of strobila covered with spines. Neck
                present. External segmentation sometimes in-
                distinct. Genital pores irregularly alternating.
                Cirrus pouch well developed. Vagina opening
                anterior or posterior to cirrus. Ovary bilobed,
                near posterior end of proglottid. Vitellaria lat-
                eral, cortical. Parasites of lizards and snakes.
                Ceylon, Celebes, New Guinea, India, Australia,
                Africa, Komodo, South America.

Fig. 190. *Acantho-
taenia shipleyi* Linstow,
1903. a. Scolex. b.
Proglottid.

                Type speceis: *A shipleyi* Linstow, 1903.
                Key to species: Wardle and McLeod (1952).

8b. Scolex not covered with spines 9

9a. Suckers each with distinct ventral notch ....
........................*Crepidobothrium* **Monticelli, 1900. (Fig. 191)**

Diagnosis: Scolex large, with four large suckers, each with a ventral notch in the rim. Neck present. Genital pores irregularly alternating. Testes in two large lateral fields. Vagina anterior or posterior to cirrus pouch. Ovary bilobed, near posterior margin of proglottid. Vitellaria marginal. Uterus median, with lateral branches. Parasites of snakes. South America, Mexico, Burma.

Type species: *C. gerrardii* (Baird, 1860) Monticelli, 1900.

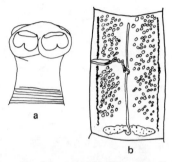

Fig. 191. *Crepidobothrium gerrardii* (Baird, 1860) Monticelli, 1900. a. Scolex. b. Proglottid.

9b. Suckers with margins entire 10

10a. Testes in two separate lateral fields ....
....*Ophiotaenia* **LaRue, 1911. (Fig. 192)**

Diagnosis: Scolex unarmed, with typical suckers. Neck present. Genital pores irregularly alternating. Cirrus pouch well developed. Testes in two separate, lateral fields. Vagina anterior, posterior or dorsal to cirrus pouch. Ovary bilobed. H-, or M-shaped. Vitellaria lateral. Uterus median, with lateral branches. Parasites of fishes, amphibians and reptiles. Cosmopolitan.

Type species: *O. perspicua* LaRue, 1911.

Key to species: Wardle and McLeod (1952), Frese (1965).

Fig. 192. *Ophiotaenia dubinini* Frese and Shapiro, 1965. a. Scolex. b. Proglottid.

10b. Testes in single continuous field ....
....*Proteocephalus* Mola, 1929. (Fig. 193)

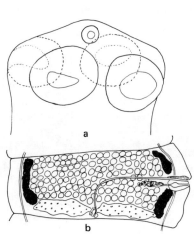

a

b

Fig. 193. *Proteocephalus macrocephalus* (Creplin, 1815) Nufer, 1905. a. Scolex. b. Proglottid.

Diagnosis: Scolex unarmed, with four normal suckers. A fifth apical sucker or apical organ present in some species. Neck present. Genital pores irregularly alternating. Cirrus pouch well developed. Testes in single broad field anterior to ovary. Vagina anterior, posterior or dorsal to cirrus pouch. Ovary bilobed, transverse, at posterior end of proglottid. Vitellaria lateral. Uterus median, with lateral branches. Parasites of freshwater fishes, amphibians and reptiles.

Type species: P. *filicollis* (Rudolphi, 1902) Weinland, 1858.

Key to species: Frese (1965.)

DIAGNOSIS OF THE ONLY GENUS IN MARSIPOCEPHALINAE
Marsipocephalus Wedl, 1861 (Fig. 194)

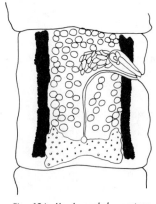

Fig. 194. *Marsipocephalus rectangulus* Wedl, 1861.

Diagnosis: Scolex swollen, unarmed, with four simple suckers and no apical organ. Posterior proglottids with median ventral groove. Genital pores irregularly alternating, preequatorial. Cirrus pouch large. Testes in one broad dorsal cortical layer anterior to ovary. Vagina posterior to cirrus pouch. Ovary bilobed, medullary, posterior. Vitellaria in lateral medulla. Uterus in median medulla, with lateral outgrowths. Parasites of siluroid fishes. Africa.

Type species: M. *rectangulus* Wedl, 1861.

Key to the Genera in Zygobothriinae

1a. Suckers sunken, entire sucker region surrounded by fleshy collar ....*Amphoteromorphus* **Diesing, 1850. (Fig. 195)**

Diagnosis: Scolex with suckers sunken, entire sucker region surrounded by fleshy collar. Neck absent. Genital pores irregularly alternating. Cirrus pouch well developed. Cirrus unarmed. Testes medullary, dorsal to uterus, in broad field anterior to ovary. Vagina anterior to cirrus pouch. Ovary medullary, bilobed, at posterior end of proglottid. Vitellaria lateral, cortical.

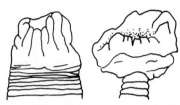

Fig. 195. *Amphoteromorphus peniculus* Diesing, 1850. Two forms of scolex.

Uterus medullary, with lateral branches. Parasites of siluroid fishes. South America.

Type species: *A. peniculus* Diesing, 1850.

1b. Suckers not surrounded by fleshy collar 2

2a. Genital pores unilateral ....
....*Zygobothrium* **Diesing, 1850. (Fig. 196)**

Diagnosis: Scolex with four massive, barrel-shaped suckers, each with prominent irregular hole in one side. Neck absent. Strobila with median groove on each flat surface. Genital pores unilateral. Cirrus pouch well developed. Cirrus unarmed. Testes medullary, dorsal, in broad preovarian field. Vagina posterior to cirrus pouch. Ovary transverse, medullary, at posterior end of proglottid. Vitellaria in lateral cortex. Uterus medullary, with lateral branches. Parasites of siluroid fishes. South America.

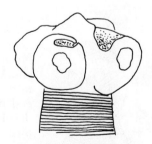

Fig. 196. *Zygobothrium megacephalum* Diesing, 1850.

Genotype: *Z. megacephalum* Diesing, 1850.

2b. Genital pores irregularly alternating ....
...................................*Nomimoscolex* Woodland, 1934. (Fig. 197)

Fig. 197. *Nomimoscolex do-rad* (Woodland, 1934) Frese, 1965.

Diagnosis: Scolex normal but variable, with or without apical organ. Neck present. Genital pores irregularly alternating. Cirrus pouch large, well developed. Cirrus unarmed. Testes medullary, in broad preovarian field. Vagina anterior or posterior to cirrus pouch. Ovary medullary, bilobed, at posterior end of proglottid. Vitellaria in lateral cortex. Uterus ventral, medullary, with lateral branches and median ventral pore. Parasites of siluroid fishes. South America.

Type species: *N. piraeeba* Woodland, 1934.

Key to species: Frese (1965).

Key to the Genera in Endorchiinae

1a. Suckers with minute spines ....
.... *Endorchis* Woodland, 1934. (Fig. 198)

Fig. 198. *Endorchis piraeeba* Woodland, 1934.

Diagnosis: Scolex small, with glandular apical organ. Suckers with triangular or trilocular opening and spinulate margin. Short neck present. Mature proglottids longer than wide. Genital pores irregularly alternating, near anterior end of proglottid. Cirrus pouch small, weakly developed. Cirrus large, unarmed. Testes medullary, in broad field anterior to ovary. Vagina anterior to cirrus pouch. Ovary bilobed, mostly medullary, at posterior end of proglottid. Vitellaria lateral in cortex. Parasites of siluroid fishes. South America.

Type species: *E. piraeeba* Woodland, 1934.

1b. Suckers not spined .....*Myzophorus* **Woodland, 1934. (Fig. 199)**

Diagnosis: Scolex unarmed, with apical organ or not. Suckers lacking minute spines on their margins. Neck short or absent. Genital pores irregularly alternating, in anterior half of proglottid margin. Cirrus pouch well developed. Cirrus unarmed. Testes in broad ventral field anterior to ovary. Vagina apparently anterior to cirrus pouch. Ovary bilobed, posterior, with dorsal branches. Vitellaria lateral, often crescentic in cross section. Uterus median, medullary, with lateral outpocketings. Oncosphere lacking hooks. Parasites of siluroid fish. South America.

Type species: *M. admonticellia* Woodland, 1934.

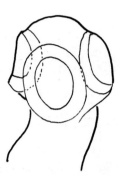

Fig. 199. *Myzophorus admonticellia* Woodland, 1934.

DIAGNOSIS OF THE ONLY GENUS IN MONTICELLIINAE
Monticellia LaRue, 1911 (Fig. 200)

Diagnosis: Scolex swollen, unarmed, with simple suckers. Fold of tissue sometimes present around base of scolex. No apical organ. Neck present or absent. Genital pores irregularly alternating, preequatorial. Cirrus pouch with thin walls. Cirrus unarmed. Testes in broad band in dorsal cortex, anterior to ovary. Vagina anterior or posterior to cirrus pouch. Ovary bilobed, mostly cortical, partly medullary. Vitellaria in lateral cortex. Uterus in ventral cortex. Parasites of siluroid fishes. South America.

Type species: *M. coryphicephala* (*Monticelli*, 1891) LaRue, 1911.

Fig. 200. *Monticellia rugosa* Woodland, 1935.

DIAGNOSIS OF THE ONLY GENUS
IN EPHEDROCEPHALINAE
Ephedrocephalus Diesing, 1850 (Fig. 201)

Fig. 201. *Ephedro-cephalus microcephalus* Diesing, 1850.

Diagnosis: Scolex unarmed, with suckers small, sunken; entire sucker region surrounded by fleshy collar. Neck present. (?) Uterine pores present, opening in median ventral groove in strobila. Genital pores irregularly alternating, in anterior half of proglottid margin. Cirrus pouch small. Testes in broad cortical field, dorsal, anterior to ovary. Vagina anterior (or posterior?) to cirrus pouch, with powerful sphincter near distal end. Ovary transverse, entirely medullary. Vitellaria ventral, cortical. Uterus in ventral medulla, with ventral median pore. Eggs longer than wide. Parasites of siluroid fishes. South America.

Type species: *E. microcephalus* Diesing, 1850.

DIAGNOSIS OF THE ONLY GENUS
IN PELTIDOCOTYLINAE
Peltidocotyle Diesing, 1850 (Fig. 202)

Fig. 202. *Peltidocotyle rugosa* Diesing, 1850.

Diagnosis: Scolex dorsoventrally flattened posteriorly, rugose. Each sucker divided into two loculae by distinct transverse muscular septum. Neck absent. Strobila wide behind scolex, tapering toward posterior end. All proglottids broader than long. Genital pores irregularly alternating, at anterior edge of proglottid. Cirrus pouch and cirrus muscular, well developed. Testes in dorsal cortex. Ovary transverse, medullary, at posterior end of proglottid. Vitellaria cortical, lateral. Uterus in ventral cortex, with lateral branches. Parasites of siluroid fishes. Brazil.

Type species: *P. rugosa* Diesing, 1850.

DIAGNOSIS OF THE ONLY GENUS
IN RUDOLPHIELLINAE
Rudolphiella Fuhrmann, 1916

Diagnosis: Scolex wrinkled, furrowed, with central prominence bearing suckers. Neck absent(?) Genital pores preequatorial, irregularly alternating. Cirrus pouch with thin walls. Cirrus unarmed. Testes cortical, dorsal, in entire field anterior to, and sometimes lateral to, ovary. Vagina anterior or posterior to cirrus pouch. Ovary mostly cortical. Vitellaria entirely cortical, in lateral fields. Uterus entirely medullary, median, with lateral branches. Eggs with polar elongations. Parasites of siluroid fishes. South America.

Type species: *R. lobosa* (Riggenbach, 1895) Fuhrmann, 1916.

KEY TO THE FAMILIES IN CYCLOPHYLLIDEA

1a. Two strobilas per scolex ....
............................Triplotaeniidae Yamaguti, 1959. (P. 135)
Diagnosis: Scolex with four unarmed suckers. Rostellum lacking. Two strobilas on each scolex. External metamerism lacking, each strobila twisted and fringed. Testes single, unilateral. Cirrus pouch multiple. Genital pores unilateral. Parasites of marsupials.

Type genus: *Triplotaenia* Boas, 1902.

1b. One strobila per scolex 2
2a. Genital openings median ....
..................................Mesocestoididae Perrier, 1897. (P. 135)
Diagnosis: Scolex with simple, unarmed suckers; lacking rostellum. Single set of reproductive organs per proglottid. Genital pore median, ventral. Uterine pore absent. Uterus present or replaced by paruterine organ. Parasites of birds and mammals.

Type genus: *Mesocestoides* Vaillant, 1863.

2b. Genital openings lateral 3
3a. Vitellaria usually anterior to ovary (see also *Arostellina*, Anoplocephalidae). Suckers usually with muscular outgrowths. ....Tetrabothriidae Linton, 1891. (P. 136)
Diagnosis: Rostellum lacking. Suckers unarmed, variable from simple to possessing muscular appendages; rarely diminutive or lacking. Neck present or absent. Proglottids craspedote or acraspedote, usually wider than long. Genital atrium unilateral. Cirrus pouch small. Testes numerous. Ovary transversely elongated, with many lobes. Vitellaria anterior, ventral or posterior to ovary. Uterus a transverse tube. Parasites of birds and mammals.

Type species: *Tetrabothrius* Rudolphi, 1819.

3b. Vitellaria not anterior to ovary. Suckers without muscular outgrowths 4

4a. Strobila cylindrical. Segmentation weak, only in posterior region. One or two testes. Genital pores irregularly alternating. Rostellum absent ....Nematotaeniidae Lühe, 1910. (P. 139) *Diagnosis*: Scolex lacking rostellum and with four simple, unarmed suckers. Strobila cylindrical. External metamerism evident only near posterior end. Genital pores irregularly alternating. Testes numbering one or two. Ovary compact. Two or more paruterine organs per proglottid. Parasites of Amphibians and reptiles. *Type genus*: *Nematotaenia* Lühe, 1899.

4b. **Metamerism well marked throughout most of body** **5**

5a. **Dioecious forms, either entire worm or regionally** ....*Dioecocestidae* **Southwell, 1930.** (P. 141) *Diagnosis*: Dioecious forms, sexes completely separated or strobilas regionally unisexual. Rostellum present or absent; if present it may be armed or not. Vagina present or absent; if present it may lack external opening. Parasites of birds. *Type genus*: *Dioecocestus* Fuhrmann, 1900.

5b. **Entire strobila monoecious** **6**

6a. **Proterogynous forms, testes developed in posterior proglottids only** ....**Progynotaeniidae Fuhrmann, 1936.** (P. 144) *Diagnosis*: Scolex with armed rostellum; may be divided by constriction into anterior portion bearing the rostellum and posterior portion bearing the suckers. Strobila small, with weakly developed musculature. Proglottids proterogynous; hermaphroditic, or with male and female segments regularly alternating. Vagina absent. Parasites of birds. *Type genus*: *Progynotaenia* Fuhrmann, 1909.

6b. **Proterandrous forms, testes developing before ovary** **7**

7a. **Rostellum, if present, not retractable. Eggshell with radial striations** .... *Taeniidae* **Ludwig, 1886.** (P. 148) *Diagnosis*: Rostellum not retractable (absent in *Taeniarhynchus, Insinuarotaenia* and *Anoplotaenia*). With one or two circles of hooks. Strobila usually medium to very large, rarely very small. Gravid proglottids longer than wide. Single set of genitalia per segment. Genital pores irregularly alternating. Testes numerous. Ovary posterior. Gravid uterus median, with lateral branches. Middle eggshell thick, with radial striations. Larval forms bladder worms. Parasites of birds and mammals. *Type genus*: *Taenia* Linnaeus, 1758.

7b. **Rostellum retractable or absent. Eggshell lacking radial striations** **8**

8a. **Male genitalia double, female organs single (see also** *Amabilia*, **Amabiliidae)** .**Diploposthidae Poche, 1926. (P. 152)**
Diagnosis: Scolex with armed or unarmed rostellum and simple, unarmed suckers. Proglottids wider than long. Each segment with double set of male genitalia and single set of female genitalia. Vaginal pores present or absent. Parasites of birds.
Type genus: *Diploposthe* Jacobi, 1896.

8b. **Male genitalia single, or if doubled female organs also doubled** 9

9a. **Vaginal pores absent, may be replaced by accessory canal** ..10

9b. **Vaginal pores present** 11

10a. **Vaginal pore replaced by dorso-ventral accessory canal arising from seminal receptacle and opening on one or both flat surfaces** ....**Amabiliidae Ransom, 1909. (P. 153)**
Diagnosis: Scolex with armed rostellum. Strobila small. Proglottids with lateral lappets bearing male genital pores, alternating regularly or irregularly. Single set of male and female genitalia per segment, or in *Amabilia* double male and single female sets. Vaginal pore dorsal and/or ventral surfaces. Parasites of birds.
Type genus: *Amabilia Diamare*, 1893.

10b. **Vagina swollen as seminal receptacle, not replaced by accessory canal** ....**Acoleidae Fuhrmann, 1907. (P. 155)**
Diagnosis: Scolex with armed rostellum and simple suckers. Proglottids wider than long. Male genital pore regularly alternating. Testes numerous. Vagina represented by a large, transverse seminal receptacle lacking external opening. Uterus saclike. Parasites of birds.
Type genus: *Acoleus* Fuhrmann, 1899.

11a. **Rostellum with many very small T- or hammer-shaped hooks. Suckers often spinose** ....
...................................**Davaineidae Fuhrmann, 1907. (P. 155)**
Diagnosis: Rostellum retractable, with one to several circles of very small, very numerous T- or hammer-shaped hooks. Suckers commonly armed with very small spines which are easily lost from dead specimens. Reproductive systems usually single but may be double per proglottid. Genital pores lateral. Uterus saclike or replaced by egg capsules or paruterine organ. Parasites of birds and mammals.
Type genus: *Davainea* Blanchard, 1891.

11b. **Rostellar hooks otherwise, or rostellum absent. Suckers rarely spinose** 12

12a. **Testes 12 or fewer, usually one to four. Rostellum usually present; if absent, testes number three or fewer** ....
................**Hymenolepididae Railliet and Henry, 1909. (P. 163)**
Diagnosis: Rostellum present or absent; usually armed when present. Suckers armed or not, rarely in two nearly fused pairs or so small as to be nearly absent. Pseudoscolex sometimes present behind true scolex. Single, rarely double, set of reproductive organs per proglottid. Testes 12 or fewer, usually one to four. Genital pores unilateral. Uterus usually saccular, may be reticular or replaced by egg capsules. Parasites of birds and mammals.
Type genus: **Hymenolepis** Weinland, 1858.

12b. **Testes usually more than 12. Rostellum present or absent; if absent, testes numerous** **13**

13a. **Uterus a median stem with paired lateral branches, as in Taeniidae** ....**Catenotaeniidae Spassky, 1950. (P. 178)**
Diagnosis: Scolex lacking rostellum. Apical sucker present in young specimens, but disappears as worm matures. Genital pores irregularly alternating. Testes usually postovarian, rarely in two fields lateral to ovary. Ovary lobated, anterior. Vitellaria postovarian, lobated, poral. Uterus with median stem and lateral branches, recalling *Taenia*. Parasites of rodents.
Type genus: **Catenotaenia** Janicki, 1904.

13b. **Uterus otherwise** **14**

14a. **Armed rostellum usually present. If absent, gravid proglottids usually longer than broad. Eggs never with pyriform apparatus** ....**Dilepididae Railliet and Henry, 1909. (P. 179)**
Diagnosis: Armed rostellum usually present, occasionally absent or rudimentary and unarmed. Suckers unarmed (except *Cotylorhipis*). Reproductive organs single or double. Genital pores lateral. Gravid proglottids usually longer than broad. Testes commonly numerous, occasionally few. Gravid uterus usually saclike, occasionally reticular or replaced by egg capsules or with paruterine organ. Parasites of reptiles, birds and mammals.
Type genus: **Dilepis** Weinland, 1858.

14b. **Rostellum always lacking. Gravid proglottids usually broader than long. Eggs commonly with pyriform apparatus** ....
........................**Anoplocephalidae Cholodkovsky, 1902. (P. 217)**
Diagnosis: Scolex lacking rostellum. Suckers unarmed. Neck short or absent. Proglottids numerous, craspedote or acraspedote, usually wider than long. Reproductive systems single or double in each segment. Genital pores marginal. Testes numerous. Uterus saccular, tubular or reticular, or replaced by egg capsules, or with one to several paruterine organs. Eggs commonly with pyriform apparatus. Parasites of reptiles, birds and mammals.
Type genus: **Anoplocephala** Blanchard, 1848.

DIAGNOSIS OF THE ONLY GENUS OF TRIPLOTAENIIDAE
Triplotaenia Boas, 1902 (Fig. 203)

Diagnosis: Suckers arranged in dorsal and ventral pairs; tissue posterior to each pair drawn out into pointed process. Strobilas arising on each side of scolex posterior to level of suckers. Anterior portion of each strobila very slender, becoming wider posteriorly, with one margin thickened and the other thin and fringed. Internal and external metamerism reduced. Genital pores unilateral. Testes few, unilateral. Cirrus pouches four or five per testis. Cirrus unarmed. Ovary and vitellaria compact, medial to testis. Seminal receptacle absent. Uterus poral, a transversely elongated sac. Eggs with pyriform apparatus. Parasites of marsupials. Australia.

Type species: *T. mirabilis* Boas, 1902.

Fig. 203. *Triplotaenia mirabilis* Boas, 1902. After Janicki (1906). a. Scolex with bases of strobilas. b. Region of one strobila.

Key to the Genera of Mesocestoididae

1a. **Paruterine organ present** ....
................................*Mesocestoides* **Vaillant, 1863.** (Fig. 204)

Diagnosis: Scolex with four simple suckers. Rostellum absent. Neck present. Proglottids craspedote, apolytic. Cirrus pouch oval, preequatorial. Genital atrium midventral, posterior to equator of cirrus pouch. Seminal vesicle absent. Testes numerous, preovarian. Ovary bilobed, posterior. Vitellaria bilobed, behind ovary. Vaginal pore anterior or lateral to cirrus. Uterus first developing as a median, sinuous tube: eggs moving into paruterine organ early. Parasites of birds and mammals. Cosmopolitan.

Type species: *M. ambiguus* Vaillant, 1863.

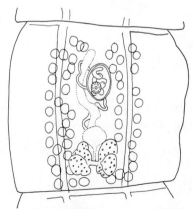

Fig. 204. *Mesocestoides lineatus* (Goeze, 1782) Railliet, 1893. After Dollfus (1965).

1b. Paruterine organ absent .... *Mesogyna* **Voge, 1952.**

Diagnosis: Scolex with four simple, unarmed, elongate suckers. Rostellum absent. Neck present. Proglottids craspedote, wider than long. Genital pore midventral. Cirrus pouch pyriform, preequatorial. Seminal vesicles absent. Testes in two lateral fields overreaching osmoregulatory canals and extending posterior to level of ovary. Ovary bilobed, near posterior end. Vitellaria bilobed, behind ovary. Vaginal pore not observed. Uterus fills with eggs, not replaced by paruterine organ. Parasites of liver of foxes. California.

Type species: *M. hepatica* Voge, 1952.

Key to the Genera in Tetrabothriidae

1a. **Scolex without suckers, cone-shaped with collar-like base** ....
.... *Priapocephalus* **Nybelin, 1922. (Fig. 205).**

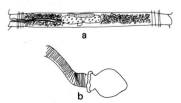

Fig. 205. *Priapocephalus grandis* Nybelin, 1922. After Fuhrmann (1932). *a.* Proglottid. *b.* Scolex.

Diagnosis: Scolex conical, basal portion collar-like. Suckers absent. Neck present (?). Proglottids much wider than long, slightly craspedote. Genital atrium not muscular. Cirrus pouch small, pyriform. Cirrus armed. Testes numerous (300-400), in two lateral fields. Ovary slightly poral, multilobated. Vitelline gland with many branches, anterioventral to ovary. Vagina lined with hairlike spines, opening ventral to cirrus. Seminal receptacle absent. Uterus saclike, with dorsal diverticula. Parasites of whales. Antarctica, France, Sweden.

Type species: *P. grandis* Nybelin, 1922.

1b. **Scolex with suckers** 2

2a. **Suckers small, triangular, sunken into base of swollen scolex**
.... *Strobilocephalus* **Baer, 1932. (Fig. 206)**

Diagnosis: Scolex globular, with four small, triangular suckers sunken into its base. Neck present. Proglottids much wider than long. Genital ducts passing between osmoregulatory canals. Cirrus pouch small, muscular. Cirrus armed, opening on papilla within atrium dorsal to vaginal pore. Testes few (24) surrounding female organs, separated by uterus. Genital pores unilateral. Ovary transversely bilobed, extending entire length of proglottid. Vitelline gland anterioventral to ovary. Vagina thick-walled, lined with hair-like spines. Seminal receptacle absent. Uterus a transverse sac extending between dorsal and ventral osmoregulatory canals and possessing a rudimentary middorsal pore. Parasites of Cetacea (dolphins). Atlantic and Pacific.

Fig. 206. *Strobilocephalus triangularis* (Diesing, 1850) Baer, 1932.

Type species: *S. triangularis* (Diesing, 1850) Baer, 1932.

2b. Scolex not as above 3

3a. Suckers lacking muscular appendages ....
....*Anophryocephalus* Baylis, 1922. (Fig. 207)

Diagnosis: Scolex simple, with four simple suckers lacking appendages but with slit-like apertures. Neck long. Proglottids wider than long, slightly craspedote. Genital pores unilateral, dextral. Cirrus pouch elongate. Genital atrium with muscular wall ventral to vaginal pore. Testes large, few (30), in dorsal medulla surrounding female organs. Ovary massive, bilobed, extending entire width between osmoregulatory canals. Vitelline gland compact, preovarian. Vagina narrow distally, wide proximally. Uterus in shape of transverse crescent. Parasites of seals. North Atlantic, Russia.

Fig. 207. *Anophryocephalus anophrys* Baylis, 1922.

Type species: *A. anophrys* Baylis, 1922.

3b. Suckers possessing muscular appendages 4

4a. Suckers triangular, with small outgrowth at each corner ......
.... *Trigonocotyle* Baer, 1932. (Fig. 208)

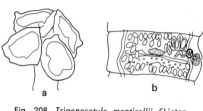

Diagnosis: Scolex with four large, triangular suckers, each with a small, fleshy appendage at each corner. Neck present. Genital pore unilateral. Genital atrium very muscular. Cirrus pouch pyriform, elongate, muscular. Testes few, large, surrounding female glands. Ovary bilobed, postequatorial. Vitellaria compact, preovarian. Vagina thick-walled. Seminal receptacle absent. Uterus a transverse, intervascular sac. Parasites of toothed whales. Atlantic, Pacific, Mediterranean.

Fig. 208. *Trigonocotyle monticellii* (Linton, 1923) Baer, 1932. a. Scolex. b. Proglottid.

Type species: *T. monticellii* (Linton, 1923) Baer, 1932.

4b. Suckers rounded, each with outgrowth on anterior margin 5

5a. Genital atrium not muscular ...... *Chaetophallus* Nybelin, 1916.

Diagnosis: Scolex rectangular. Suckers rounded, each with single muscular appendage extending laterally from the anterior margin. Neck absent. Proglottids broader than long, craspedote. Genital pores unilateral. Cirrus pouch elongate. Genital atrium muscular, sucker-like. Testes entirely postovarian. Ovary multilobate, anterior. Vitellaria median, postovarian. Vagina ventral to cirrus pouch. Seminal receptacle present. Gravid uterus filling proglottid. Parasites of Podicipediformes, Pelecaniformes. Japan, Mexico, Russia.

Type species: *C. robustus* Nybelin, 1916.

6b. Testes partly lateral or preovarian. Vitellaria preovarian 7

7a. Cirrus and vagina opening separately ....
.... *Tetrabothrius* Rudolphi, 1819. (Fig. 209)

Diagnosis: Scolex rectangular, with four large suckers, each of which has a muscular appendage on its anterior margin. Neck absent. Proglottids wider than long. Genital pores unilateral. Genital atrium muscular. Cirrus pouch rounded, muscular. Testes surrounding female gonads. Ovary multilobated, about equatorial. Vitellaria compact, preovarian.

Fig. 209. *Tetrabothrius macrocephalus* (Rudolphi, 1810) Rudolphi, 1819. After Fuhrmann (1932).

Vagina thick-walled. Seminal receptacle present in some species. Uterus saccular or lobated, often with dosral pore. Parasites of

Podicipediformes, Charadriiformes, Falconiformes, Anseriformes, Ciconiiformes, Pelecaniformes, Procellariiformes, Spheniscriformes. Also in whales, seals, dolphins, fox. Cosmopolitan.
Type species: *T. macrocephalus* (Rudolphi, 1810) Rudolphi, 1819.

7b. Cirrus and vagina opening through common duct ....
....*Neotetrabothrius* **Nybelin, 1929.**
Diagnosis: Scolex rectangular, with four large suckers. Each sucker has a muscular appendage on its anterior margin. Neck absent. Proglottids craspedote, dorso-ventrally flattened. Genital pores unilateral. Genital atrium deep, muscular. Cirrus pouch round. Cirrus armed. Cirrus and vagina opening into common duct which opens at tip of a papilla into the atrium. Genital ducts ventral to osmoregulatory canals. Testes surrounding female gonads. Ovary bilobed, median. Vitelline gland compact, preovarian. Uterus in form of lobated sac. Dorsal pores sometimes present. Parasites of penguins. Tierra del Fuego, Juan Fernandez Island.
Type species: *N. pellucidus* Nybelin, 1929.

Key to the Genera in Nematotaeniidae

1a. One testis per proglottid. Two paruterine organs united basally, each with three to six eggs ....
....*Cylindrotaenia* **Jewell, 1916. (Fig. 210)**

Diagnosis: Scolex lacking rostellum. Suckers simple. Neck long. Strobila cylindroid, thinnest near ends. Proglottids acraspedote. External metamerism present only near posterior end. Genital pores irregularly alternating. Cirrus pouch short. Testis single, aporal. Ovary and vitellaria compact, medullary. Vagina posterior to cirrus pouch. Two paruterine organs in each proglottid, dorsal and ventral, each with three to six eggs. Parasites of toads and frogs. Africa, North and South America.
Type species: *C. americana* Jewell, 1916.

Fig. 210. Cylindrotaenia quadrijugosa Lawler, 1939. a. Scolex. b. Gravid proglottid.

1b. Two testes per proglottid. Two or more paruterine organs 2

2a. Two paruterine organs, united basally, per proglottid. Cuticle spinous ....*Baerietta* Hsü, 1935. (Fig. 211)

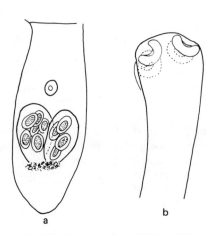

a

b

Fig. 211. *Baerietta diana* (Helfer, 1948) Douglas, 1958. a. Gravid Proglottid. b. Scolex.

Diagnosis: Scolex lacking rostellum. Suckers simple. Neck long, lacking constriction behind scolex. Strobila covered with fine spines. External metamerism present only on gravid proglottids. Genital pores irregularly alternating. Cirrus pouch cortical and medullary anteriorly, entirely cortical posteriorly. Testes two, in dorsal medulla. Ovary and vitelline gland compact, in ventral medulla posterior to testes. Two paruterine organs, dorsal and ventral, united basally, 20 to 25 eggs in each. Parasites of toads and frogs. Asia, Japan, Africa, North America.

Type species: *B. baeri* Hsü, 1935.

2b. More than two paruterine organs 3

3a. Paruterine organs numerous, with bases fused ....……….
.....................................*Distoichometra* Dickey, 1921. (Fig. 212)

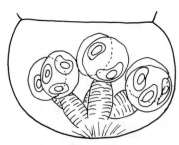

Fig. 212. *Distoichometra kozloffi* Douglas, 1957. Gravid proglottid.

Diagnosis: Rostellum lacking, suckers simple. Neck present. Genital pores irregularly alternating. Strobila cylindroid. Cirrus pouch cortical. Testes two, in dorsal medulla. Ovary and vitelline gland compact, in ventral medulla. Vagina posterior to cirrus pouch. Paruterine organs numerous, with bases fused, each with three to six egg capsules. Parasites of toads. North America.

Type species: *D. bufonis* Dickey, 1921.

3b. Paruterine organs numerous, bases not fused, scattered
throughout parenchyma or arranged in two parallel rows ......
....*Nematotaenia* Lühe, 1899. (Fig. 213)

Diagnosis: Scolex simple, lacking rostellum. Neck present. Strobila cylindrical;
external metamerism present only near
posterior end. Genital pores irregularly
alternating. Cirrus pouch intruding into
medulla. Testes two, in dorsal medulla.
Ovary compact, in ventral medulla. Vitelline gland medullary, dorsal to ovary.
Vagina ventral to cirrus pouch. Paruterine
organs numerous, with bases not fused;
first arranged in two lateral rows, then
scattered throughout parenchyma. Parasites of toads, frogs, lizards, salamanders.
Europe, Asia, North America (?).
Type species: *N. dispar* (Goeze, 1782)
Lühe, 1899.

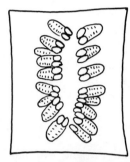

Fig. 213. *Nematotaenia dispar* (Goeze, 1782) Lühe, 1899.
After Hsü (1935). Gravid
proglottid.

Key to the Genera of Dioecocestidae

1a. Completely dioecious, male with double set of reproductive
organs ....…..2

1b. Completely or regionally dioecious, male with single set of
reproductive organs 3

2a. Scolex with armed rostellum ....…............
....*Dioecocestus* Fuhrmann, 1900.

Diagnosis: Rostellum with single circle of hooks. Proglottids
wider than long, craspedote. Male strobilas more slender than
females, with two sets of reproductive organs per proglottid. Cirrus
pouch large, with internal seminal vesicle. Cirrus large, armed.
Testes numerous, in two submedian groups. Ovary lobated, transversely elongated, slightly poral. Vitellaria also lobated, posteriodorsal to ovary. Vagina irregularly alternating, ending blindly
near cuticle. Seminal receptacle near distal end of vagina. Uterus
a strongly lobed sac. Parasites of Ciconiiformes (heron) and Podicipediformes. Europe, Asia, Australia, New Guinea, North and
South America.
Type species: *D. paronai* Fuhrmann, 1900.

2b. Scolex lacking rostellum or hooks ....
..............................*Neodioecocestus* **Siddiqui, 1960. (Fig. 214)**

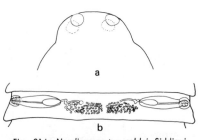

Fig. 214. *Neodioecocestus cablei* Siddiqui, 1960. a. Scolex. b. Male proglottid.

Diagnosis: Dioecious. Scolex lacking rostellum and hooks. Neck very small. Proglottids craspedote, short and wide. Genital pores bilateral. Two sets of male reproductive organs in each proglottid. Female unknown. Genital atrium well-developed. Genital ducts pass between canals. Cirrus pouch well-developed, exceeding poral canals. Cirrus stout, spined. Internal seminal vesicle present, external lacking. Testes numerous, in two submedian fields, present only in anterior proglottids. Parasites of Podicipediformes. India.

Type species: *N. cablei* Siddiqui, 1960.

3a. Scolex lacking rostellum or hooks. Uterus horseshoe-shaped
.... *Shipleya* **Fuhrmann, 1908. (Fig. 215)**

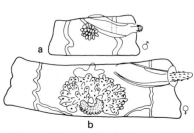

Fig. 215. *Shipleya inermis* Fuhrmann, 1908. a. Male proglottid. b. Female proglottid.

Diagnosis: Scolex large, spheroid, with apical pit and shallow, glandular, longitudinal grooves. Scolex imbedded in wall of gut of host. Neck present. Male strobila more slender than female, usually found anterior to female in host intestine. Male genital pores regularly alternating. Cirrus pouch powerful, passing between osmoregulatory canals, and containing internal seminal vesicle. Cirrus large, heavily armed. Testes median, in small, tightly packed cluster. Male has vestigial uterus and seminal receptacle. Female with cirrus pouches and cirri as in male, but lacking testes. Ovary large, median, ventral, strongly lobated. Vitellaria compact, dumbbell-shaped, posteriodorsal to ovary. Vagina absent. Large seminal receptacle present anterior to ovary. Uterus at first horseshoe-shaped with anterior stem, later filling most of proglottid. Parasites of Charadriiformes. North and South America, Russia.

Type species: *S. inermis* Fuhrmann, 1908.

3b. Rostellum present, armed or not. Uterus ring-shaped 4

4a. **Rostellum armed. Strobila completely or regionally dioecious** ....*Gyrocoelia* **Fuhrmann, 1899. (Fig. 216)**

Diagnosis: Rostellum armed. Strobilas regionally or individually dioecious. Single set of reproductive organs per proglottid. Male genital pores irregularly alternating. Cirrus pouch large, passing between osmoregulatory canals. Cirrus armed. Testes few, postovarian. Ovary large, median, lobated. Vitelline gland postovarian. Vagina absent. Seminal receptacle present. Uterus ring-shaped, with lateral branches, often opening near posterior border of segment. Parasites of Charadriiformes. Europe, Africa, Australia, Philippines, Ceylon, Puerto Rico, Asia, North Central and South America.

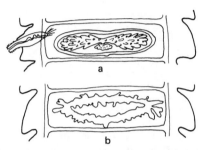

Fig. 216. *Gyrocoelia perversa* Fuhrmann, 1899. a. Mature proglottid. b. Gravid proglottid.

Type species: *G. perversa* Fuhrmann, 1899.

4b. **Rostellum unarmed** 5

5a. **Completely dioecious. Testes numerous (65-75). Vagina present** ....*Infula* **Burt, 1939.**

Diagnosis: Unarmed rostellum. Strobilas completely dioecious. Proglottids craspedote. Single set of reproductive organs per proglottid. Genital pores usually regularly alternating. Cirrus pouch very large, passing between osmoregulatory canals, and containing seminal vesicle. Cirrus armed. External seminal vesicle absent. Ovary large, biwinged, lobated. Vitellaria lobated, median, postovarian. Vagina opens to exterior, cirrus-like distally. Small seminal receptacle present. Uterus ring-like with marginal branches, opening on dorsal and ventral surfaces in median line at posterior margin of segment. Parasites of Charadriiformes. Ceylon, India, Australia, Africa, Mexico.

Type species: *I. burhini* Burt, 1939.

5b. Regionally dioecious. Testes few (about 8). Vagina absent ....
.............................*Pseudoshipleya* Yamaguti, 1959. (Fig. 217)

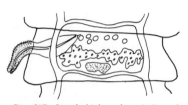

Fig. 217. *Pseudoshipleya farrani* (Inamdar, 1942) Yamaguti, 1959.

Diagnosis: Scolex with unarmed rostellum. Neck present. Strobilas regionally dioecious. Proglottids craspedote. Single set of reproductive organs per proglottid. Male genital pores alternating irregularly. Cirrus pouch large, ventral to osmoregulatory canals. Cirrus large, armed. Testes about eight in number, anterior. Ovary posttesticular, bialate, lobated. Vitellaria posterior to ovary. Vagina absent. Seminal receptacle not observed. Uterus first ring-shaped, later filling most of proglottid. Parasites of Charadriiformes. India.

Type species: *P. farrani* (Inamdar, 1942) Yamaguti, 1959.

Key to the Genera of Progynotaeniidae

1a. Male and female proglottides alternating regularly. Scolex may be divided into anterior proscolex with rostellum and posterior metascolex with suckers 2
1b. Mature proglottids hermaphroditic 3
2a. Scolex divided into proscolex with armed rostellum and metascolex with armed suckers. Strobila with 14-17 proglottids ......
.... *Gynandrotaenia* Fuhrmann, 1936.
Diagnosis: Scolex with inflated, flattened, spinous proscolex with retractable rostellum, and a normal metascolex with four armed suckers. Rostellum with a circle of six long-handled hooks. Neck absent. Strobila with large female proglottids alternating regularly with smaller male proglottids. Proterogynous, male systems maturing in tenth or eleventh segments from scolex, female in fifth. Male pores irregularly alternating. Vagina absent. Genital atrium deep, protrusible into large cone. Cirrus pouch containing numerous prostatic cells. Cirrus armed. Testes 35-45 in number, extending laterally over osmoregulatory canals. External seminal vesicle present. Ovary filling most of medulla. Vitelline gland posterior to ovary. Seminal receptacle large. Uterus a median stem, becoming saclike with lateral pouches when gravid. Eggs with recurved polar processes on middle membrane. Parasites of flamingo. Europe.

Type species: *G. stammeri* Fuhrmann, 1936.
2b. Scolex not divided, rostellum absent, suckers not armed. Strobila with up to 80 proglottids ....
....*Thomasitaenia* Ukoli, 1965. (Fig. 218)

Diagnosis: Scolex simple, lacking rostellum or hooks, with four unarmed suckers. Neck absent. Strobila with up to 80 individually dioecious proglottids, male and female regularly alternating. Gonads proterogynous. Vagina absent. Male genital pores irregularly alternating. Cirrus pouch well developed. Cirrus large, armed. Testes about 90 in number, overreaching osmoregulatory canals. External seminal vesicle

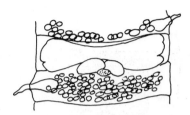

Fig. 218. *Thomasitaenia nunguae* Ukoli, 1965. Middle proglottid female, with gravid uterus.

present. Ovary filling most of medulla. Vitelline gland median, postovarian. Seminal receptacle present, posterior to uterus. Uterus appearing horseshoe-shaped; when gravid it is a transverse sac, not lobed. Parasites of Charadriiformes (black-legged stilt). Ghana.

Type species: *T. nunguae* Ukoli, 1965.

3a. **Cirrus pouch regularly alternating. One circle of rostellar hooks** **4**

3b. **Cirrus pouch regularly or irregularly alternating. One or two circles of rostellar hooks or hooks unknown.** **5**

4a. **Testes poral only** ....*Leptotaenia* **Cohn, 1901. (Fig. 219)**

Diagnosis: Rostellum long, slender, with single circle of hooks. Suckers unarmed. Neck lacking. Proglottids few (12-15), wider than long. Proterogynous. Vagina absent. Male pores alternating regularly. Cirrus pouch oblique, containing an oval seminal vesicle (?). Cirrus long, armed. Testes poral, 12-15 in number, present only in gravid segments. Ovary bilobed, filling most of medulla, present only in first three proglottids. Vitelline gland median, ventral to ovary, extending most of length of segment. Vagina absent. Seminal receptacle longitudinally elongated. Uterus a lobed, transverse sac. Parasites of flamingos. Africa, Cuba.

Type species: *L. ischnorhyncha* (Lühe, 1898) Cohn, 1901.

Fig. 219. *Leptotaenia ischnorhyncha* (Lühe, 1898) Cohn, 1901. After Fuhrmann (1932).

4b. Testes in two groups, poral and aporal. One circular or zig-zag row of rostellar hooks ....
.... *Progynotaenia* Fuhrmann, 1909. (Fig. 220)

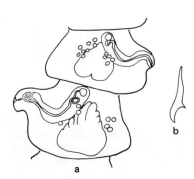

Diagnosis: Rostellum well developed, sometimes with bilobed apex, with single circle or zig-zag row of long-handled hooks. Neck absent. Strobila small, short. Proglottids craspedote. Vagina absent. Male genital pore lateral, regularly alternating. Cirrus pouch long, oblique. Internal seminal vesicle present. Cirrus armed. Testes developed only in posterior proglottids, in two groups, one on each side of uterus. Ovary bilobed or chevron-shaped, developed only in anterior proglottids. Vitelline gland near poste-

Fig. 220. *Progynotaenia americana* Webster, 1951. After Eckmann (1966, unpublished). a. Portion of strobila. b. Rostellar hook.

rior margin of segment. Seminal receptacle between ovary and vitelline gland, or absent. Uterus saclike or lobated. Parasites of Charadriiformes. Europe, Africa, India, North America.

Type species: *P. jägerskiöldi* Fuhrmann, 1909.

5a. Cirrus pouch dorsal to osmoregulatory canals. Rostellar hooks not observed. Cirrus pouch irregularly alternating ....
................................*Andrepigynotaenia* Davies and Rees, 1947.

Diagnosis: Hooks not observed. Rostellum present. Neck absent. Strobila long (over 30 segments), craspedote. Genitalia developing slowly. Vagina absent. Cirrus pouch alternating irregularly. Cirrus pouch dorsal to osmoregulatory canals. Cirrus armed at base. Internal seminal vesicle present. Testes only in segments 31 to 35, 50 to 70 in number in two groups, one group on each side of uterus. Poral group less numerous than aporal group, and confined posterior to cirrus pouch. Ovary lobated, anterior. Vitelline gland median, reniform, anteriodorsal to ovary. Seminal receptacle large, anterior to ovary. Uterus saclike, protruding into preceding segment. Parasites of Charadriiformes. England.

Type species: *A. haematopodis* Davies and Rees, 1947.

5b. Cirrus pouch between osmoregulatory canals 6

6a. Two circles of rostellar hooks. Cirrus pouch regularly or irregularly alternating ....
................................*Proterogynotaenia* **Fuhrmann, 1911.** (Fig. 221)

Diagnosis: Rostellum well developed, with two circles of hooks. Neck absent. Strobila small, proglottids craspedote. Vagina absent. Cirrus pouch regularly or irregularly alternating. Cirrus pouch passing between osmoregulatory canals, elongate. Cirrus armed. Testes developed only in posperior proglottids, in two fields, on each side of

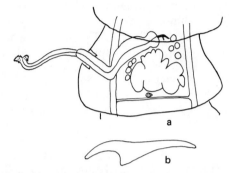

Fig. 221. *Proterogynotaenia neoarctica* Webster, 1951. a. Proglottid. b. Rostellar hook.

uterus. Ovary developed only in anterior segments, anterior, lobated. Vitelline gland postovarian. Seminal receptacle between ovary and vitelline gland. Uterus saclike or lobated. Parasites of Charadriiformes. Aru Islands, Japan, Africa, Russia, North America.
Type species: *P. rouxi* Fuhrmann, 1911.

6b. One circle of rostellar hooks. Cirrus pouch irregularly alternating ....*Paraprogynotaenia* **Rysavy, 1966.** (Fig. 222)

Diagnosis: Rostellum armed with single circle of hooks. Short neck present. Proglottids craspedote, wider than long except last segments. Genital pores irregularly alternating. Cirrus pouch passing between osmoregulatory canals. Testes only in posterior proglottids, in two lateral groups. Internal seminal vesicle present. Cirrus armed. Ovary antiporal. Vitelline gland postovarian. Vagina absent. Seminal receptacle present. Uterus median, elongated. Parasites of Charadriiformes. Cuba.
Type species: *P. jimenezi* Rysavy, 1966.

Fig. 222. *Paraprogynotaenia jimenezi* Rysavy. 1966. a. Rostellar hooks. b. Portion of strobila.

Key to the Genera of Taeniidae

1a. Scolex unarmed 2
1b. Scolex armed 4
2a. Blunt, unarmed apical organ present. Cervical swelling present behind scolex .... *Insinuarotaenia* Spassky, 1948. (Fig. 223)

Diagnosis: Scolex with complex muscular apical organ with inner meridional muscle bundles and outer longitudinal and radial muscle fibers. Hooks absent. Four simple suckers present. Constriction separates neck from scolex. Neck expanded proximal to scolex, narrowed distally. Proglottids craspedote. Gravid segments longer than wide. Genital pores irregularly alternating, in anterior third of margin. Testes 200 to 250, surrounding ovary. Ovary posterior, oval, median, separated from posterior margin by one or two rows of testes. Vitelline gland postovarian, bilobed. Uterus with median stem and lateral branches. Parasites of Mustelidae. Russia.

Type species: *I. schikhobolovi* Spassky, 1948.

Fig. 223. *Insinuarotaenia schikhobolovi* Spassky, 1948.

2b. Apical organ absent. No cervical swelling 3
3a. Testes present behind vitellaria. Cirrus pouch spherical ....
.... *Anoplotaenia* Beddard, 1911. (Fig. 224)

 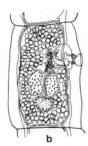

Diagnosis: Scolex large, unarmed, arostellate, with four large, powerful suckers, each with mid-dorsal, circular pit. Genital pores irregularly alternating. Cirrus pouch spherical. Testes numerous, encircling ovary and vitelline gland. Ovary bilobed, median. Vitelline gland compact, postovarian, separated from posterior margin of proglottid by numerous testes. Genital atri-

Fig. 224. *Anoplotaenia dasyuri* Beddard, 1911. After Sandars (1957). a Scolex. b. Proglottid.

um with very powerful musculature, pierced laterally by vagina. Uterus with median stem and numerous lateral branches. Parasites of marsupials (Tasmanian devil). Australia.

Type species: *A. dasyuri* Beddard, 1911.

3b. No testes behind vitellaria. Cirrus pouch pear-shaped ....
.............................*Taeniarhynchus* **Weinland, 1858. (Fig. 225)**

Diagnosis: Rostellum absent, four simple suckers present. Strobila large (4-12 meters). Genital pores irregularly alternating. Cirrus pouch pear-shaped. Testes very numerous in single field, none posterior to vitelline gland. Ovary biwinged, posterior. Vitelline gland postovarian. Vagina opening posterior to cirrus. Uterus a median stem with numerous lateral branches. Larva a cysticercus. Parasites of man. Cosmopolitan.

Type species: T. saginatus (Goeze, 1782) Weinland, 1858.

Key to species: Abuladze (1964).

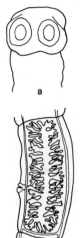

Fig. 225. *Taeniarhynchus saginatus* (Goeze, 1782) Weinland, 1858. After Stiles (1906). a. Scolex. b. Gravid proglottid.

4a. One circle of rostellar hooks ....
....*Monordotaenia* **Little, 1967.**

Diagnosis: Rostellum with a single circle of hooks. Proglottids craspedote. Genital pores irregularly alternating. Cirrus pouch elliptical. Testes numerous, in single field anterior and lateral to ovary. Ovary bialate, posterior. Vitelline gland postovarian, transversely elongated. Seminal receptacle present. Uterus with median stem and lateral branches. Parasites of Mustelidae (Badger). North America.

Type species: M. taxidiensis (Skinker, 1935) Little, 1967.

4b. Two circles of rostellar hooks 5

5a. Strobila with fewer than six proglottids ....
....*Echinococcus* Rudolphi, 1801. (Fig. 226)

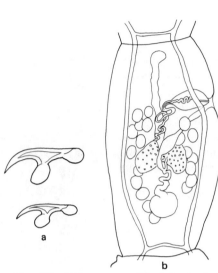

Diagnosis: Strobila very small, with fewer than six proglottids. Rostellum with a double circle of hooks. Neck absent. Genital pores irregularly alternating. Testes few, anterior and lateral to female organs. Ovary bilobed, posterior. Vitelline gland compact, postovarian. Vagina with terminal sphincter. Seminal receptacle present. Uterus with median stem and short, undivided lateral branches. Gravid uterus only in last proglottid. Larva a hydatid. Parasites of Canidae and Felidae. Cosmopolitan.

Fig. 226. *Echinococcus multilocularis* Leuckart, 1863. After Rausch and Schiller (1954). a. Rostellar hooks. b. Proglottid.

Type species: E. granulosis (Batsch, 1786) Rudolphi, 1801.

5b. Strobila with more than six proglottids 6
6a. Genital pores unilateral ....
.................................*Dasyurotaenia* Beddard, 1912. (Fig. 227)

Diagnosis: Scolex poorly known, apparently with rostellum bearing two circles of hooks. Proglottids very short, wide and muscular. Genital pores unilateral. Testes numerous, mainly lateral, confluent behind vitelline gland. Ovary and vitelline gland transversely elongated, posterior. Large seminal receptacle present. Uterus with median stem and lateral branches. Eggs thin-shelled, middle shell not striated. (Affinities with Taeniidae doubtful). Parasites of marsupials (Tasmanian devil). Australia.

Fig. 227. *Dasyurotaenia robusta* Beddard, 1912. After Sandars (1957). a. Scolex. hs-hook scars. b. Gravid proglottid.

Type species: D. robusta Beddard, 1912.

6b. Genital pores irregularly alternating 7

7a. Testes situated in two lateral fields, medial to osmoregulatory canals ....*Cladotaenia* **Cohn, 1901.** (Fig. 228)

Diagnosis: Rostellum small, with two circles of hooks. Proglottids craspedote. Genital pores irregularly alternating. Cirrus pouch not reaching osmoregulatory canals. Testes numerous, in two submedian fields, occasionally meeting behind vitelline gland. Ovary two-winged, posterior. Vitelline gland postovarian. Internal seminal vesicle present or not. Small, proximal seminal receptacle present. Uterus with median stem and lateral branches,

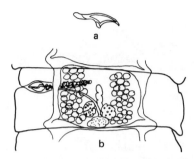

Fig. 228. *Cladotaenia globifera* (Batsch, 1786) Cohn, 1901. a. Rostellar hook. b. Proglottid.

usually not intruding into anterior quarter of proglottid, but doing so in a few species. Parasites of Falconiformes, (also in Armenian hedgehog). Europe, Asia, Africa, Taiwan, North America.

Type species: C. *cylindracea* (Bloch, 1782) Cohn, 1901.

Key to species: Freeman (1959).

7b. Testes in one field medial to osmoregulatory canals ....
.....................................…..... *Taenia* **Linnaeus, 1758.** (Fig. 229)

Diagnosis: Rostellum armed with two circles of hooks. Strobila large, with many proglottides. Genital pores irregularly alternating. Cirrus pouch pyriform. Testes numerous, in single field anterior and lateral to female organs. Ovary bialate, posterior. Vitelline gland compact, postovarian. Vagina opening behind cirrus. Uterus with median stem and lateral branches. Larva a cysticercus, coenurus or strobilocercus. Parasites of mammals. Cosmopolitan.

Type species: T. *solium* Linnaeus, 1758.

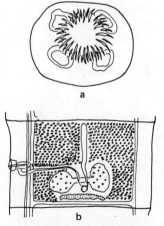

Fig. 229. a. *Taenia pisiformis* (Bloch, 1780) Gmelin, 1790. After Hall (1919). Apical view of scolex. b. *T. hydategena* Pallas, 1766. After Abuladze (1964). Proglottid.

Key to the Genera of Diploposthidae

1a. **Rostellum unarmed** ....*Himantocestus* **Ukoki, 1965.** (Fig. 230)

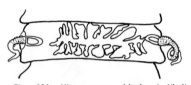

Fig. 230. *Himantocestus blanksoni* Ukoli, 1965. Gravid proglottid.

Diagnosis: Scolex with unarmed rostellum. Neck absent. Proglottids wider than long. Two cirrus pores per proglottid. Vaginal pores lacking. Female organs single per proglottid. Cirrus pouches not exceeding osmoregulatory canals except in immature proglottids. Cirrus large, armed. Testes number about 60, preequatorial in a single, intervascular field. Ovary bilobed, median, posterior. Vitelline gland compact, median, preovarian. Uterus first a simple, transverse sac; when gravid it has anterior and posterior pouches. Parasites of Charadriiformes (stilt). Ghana.

Type species: *H. blanksoni* Ukoli, 1965.

1b. **Rostellum armed** 2

2a. **Testes in a single, median field** ....*Diploposthe* **Jacobi, 1896.**

Diagnosis: Rostellum with single circle of 10 hooks. Proglottids wider than long. Double set of male reproductive organs per proglottid. Female organs single, except for vaginae which are double. Genital pores marginal. Cirrus pouch small. Cirrus large, armed. Testes 3-17, in single postovarian field. External seminal vesicle present. Ovary bilobed, median. Vitellaria compact, postovarian. Each vagina opens into atrium ventral to cirrus pouch. Uterus a transverse tube. Parasites of Anseriformes. Europe, Asia, Africa, Australia, North America.

Type species: *D. laevis* (Bloch, 1782) Jacobi, 1896.

2b. **Testes in two fields, separated by ovary** 3

3a. **Testes few (2-6). Vagina doubled, vaginal pores present** ....
....*Jardugia* **Southwell and Hilmy, 1929.**

Diagnosis: Rostellum with single circle of hooks. Proglottids wider than long. Single set of female and double set of male reproductive organs per segment (some segments may contain only a single set of male organs). Genital pores lateral. Genital ducts dorsal to osmoregulatory canals. Cirrus pouch elongate. Cirrus armed. Internal and external seminal receptacles present. Testes few (2-6), preovarian, in two submedian groups. Ovary median, lobated. Vitelline gland lobated, posteromedian to ovary. Two vaginae present, each with proximal seminal receptacle and opening in atrium ventral to cirrus. Uterus a transverse tube. Parasites of herons. Nigeria.

Type species: *J. paradoxa* Southwell and Hilmy, 1929.

3b. Testes numerous. Vagina replaced by elongated seminal vesicle. Vaginal aperture atrophied ....
.... *Diplophallus* **Fuhrmann, 1900. (Fig. 231)**

Diagnosis: Rostellum with a single circle of hooks. Proglottids wider than long. Each segment with a double set of male and single set of female reproductive organs. Male genital pores bilateral. Cirrus pouch well developed. Internal and external seminal vesicles present. Cirrus armed. Testes 16-100 in number, in two submedian fields. Ovary transversely elongated. Vitelline gland compact, posterodorsal to ovary. Vaginae absent, represented by transversely elongated seminal receptacle. Parasites of Charadriiformes and chinchilla. Europe, Russia, Peru, Chile, U.S.A.

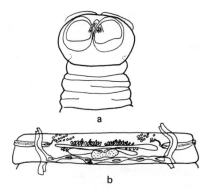

Fig. 231. *Diplophallus taglei* Olsen, 1966. a. Scolex. b. Proglottid.

Type species: *D. polymorphus* (Rudolphi, 1819) Fuhrmann, 1900.

Key to the Genera in Amabiliidae

1a. Male organs doubled in each proglottid, female organs single. Ovary and vitelline gland dendritic ..*Amabilia* **Diamare, 1893.**
Diagnosis: Rostellum armed. Proglottids craspedote, wider than long. Male reproductive organs doubled in each segment, female organs single. Male genital pores marginal, with large base when cirrus is extruded. Testes in two submedian fields. Cirrus pouch not reaching osmoregulatory canals. Internal seminal vesicle present. Cirrus armed. Ovary and vitellaria dendritic, median. Seminal receptacle present, with dorso-ventral openings to flat surfaces. Uterus a network of tube-like branches. Eggs fusiform with polar filaments. Parasites of flamingos. Europe, Africa, Ceylon.
Type species: *A. lamilligera* (Owen, 1832) Diamare, 1893.

1b. Male organs single per proglottid **2**

2a. Accessory canals opening for seminal receptacle to both flat surfaces. Testes numerous ....
.................................*Schistotaenia* **Cohn, 1900.** (**Fig. 232**)

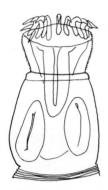

Diagnosis: Scolex partly spinose. Rostellum strongly developed, with a single circle of strong hooks. Suckers sometimes armed. Proglottids wider than long, with marginal extensions. Single set of reproductive organs per segment. Male genital pores marginal, irregularly alternating. Testes dorsal, posterior, in single field. Cirrus pouch weak. Cirrus usually armed. External seminal vesicle present. Ovary lobated but not dendritic, wide. Vitelline gland median, postovarian. Vagina passing between osmoregulatory canals, ending blindly near cuticle. Seminal receptacle median, with dorsal and ventral accessory canals opening on both flat surfaces. Uterus a transverse sac. Eggs spheroid. Osmoregulatory canals in three pairs. Parasites of grebes. Europe, Africa, Asia, North America.

Fig. 232. *Schistotaenia macrorhyncha* (Rudolphi, 1810) Cohn, 1900.

Type species: *S. macrorhyncha* (Rudolphi, 1810) Cohn, 1900.
Key to species: Chandler (1948).

2b. Accessory canal opening from seminal receptacle on one surface or not at all. Testes few ....
.................................*Tatria* **Kowaleski, 1904.** (**Fig. 233**)

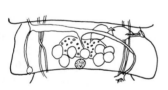

Diagnosis: Scolex, rostellum and suckers covered with fine spines. Rostellum long, armed with 10-14 large hooks in a single circle. Proglottids with large lateral lobes. Single set of reproductive organs per proglottid. Male pores regularly alternating. Cirrus pouch passing between osmoregulatory canals. Cirrus armed. Testes

Fig. 233. *Tatria duodecacantha* Fuhrmann, 1913. After Schultz (1940).

few. Internal and external seminal vesicles present. Ovary compact, sometimes bilobed. Vitellaria median, postovarian. Seminal receptacle with one accessory duct that ends blindly or joins same duct in next proglottid, and another duct on opposite side that sometimes opens to outside. Uterus? Parasites of grebes. Europe, Asia, Africa, Japan, North and South America.

Type species: *T. biremis* Kowaleski, 1904.
Key to species: Olsen (1939), Schultz (1940).

DIAGNOSIS OF THE ONLY GENUS IN ACOLEIDAE
Acoleus Fuhrmann, 1899 (Fig. 234)

Diagnosis: Scolex with armed rostellum and simple suckers. Male genital pores regularly alternating. Cirrus pouch large. Cirrus armed. Testes numerous, in a single transverse field. Ovary equatorial, lobated, transversely elongated. Vitellaria compact, median, postovarian. Vagina represented by an enlarged, transverse seminal receptacle lacking external opening. Uterus first appearing as a transverse tube, becoming saclike when gravid. Eggs with polar thickenings of middle shell. Parasites of Charadriiformes and Rallidae.

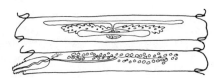

Fig. 234. *Acoleus vaginatus* (Rudolphi, 1819) Fuhrmann, 1899.

Type species: A. *vaginatus* (Rudolphi, 1819) Furhmann, 1899.

Key to the Subfamilies of Davaineidae

1a. Paruterine organ present ....
.............................Idiogeninae Fuhrmann, 1907. (P. 155)
1b. Paruterine organ absent 2
2a. Uterus sac-like, persistent ....
.............................Ophryocotylinae Fuhrmann, 1907. (P. 158)
2b. Uterus replaced by egg capsules ....
.............................Davaineinae Braun, 1900. (P. 159)

Key to the Genera of Idiogeninae

1a. Rostellum absent ....*Ascometra* Cholodkovsky, 1912. (Fig. 235)
Diagnosis: Rostellum absent. Suckers each with pair of muscular lappets, unarmed. Neck absent. Proglottids craspedote. Genital pores unilateral. Genital ducts dorsal to osmoregulatory canals. Cirrus pouch crosses osmoregulatory canals. Testes dorsal, numerous, nearly surrounding ovary. Ovary median. Vitelline gland postovarian. Vagina posterior to cirrus pouch. Seminal receptacle present. Uterus saclike, with anterior paruterine organ. Parasites of Gruiformes (bustards). Africa, Asia.

Fig. 235. *Ascometra vestita* Cholodkovsky, 1912.

Type species: A. *vestita* Cholodkovsky, 1912.
1b. Rostellum present 2

2a. Rostellum with 10 to 12 circles of hooks ....
...........................*Sphyroncotaenia* **Ransom, 1911.** (Fig. 236)

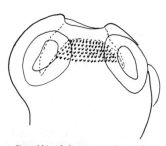

Diagnosis: Rostellum with 10 to 12 circles of small, hammer-shaped hooks. Neck very short. Genital pores unilateral. Cirrus pouch not reaching osmoregulatory canals. Testes numerous, medullary. Cirrus armed. Ovary transversaely elongated. Vitelline gland dorsal, poral to testes. Vaginal pore posteroventral to cirrus pore. Seminal receptacle proximal. Uterus voluminous, with anterior paruterine organ. Parasites of Gruiformes (bustards). Africa.

Fig. 236. *Sphyroncotaenia uncinata* Ransom, 1911.

Type species: S. *uncinata* Ransom, 1911.

2b. Rostellum with two circles of hooks, or scolex replaced with pseudoscolex 3

3a. Uterus horseshoe-shaped ....*Idiogenes* **Krabbe, 1868.** (Fig. 237)

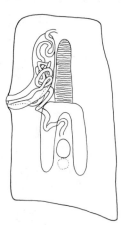

Diagnosis: Scolex commonly absent, replaced by pseudoscolex. When present it has two circles of small, hammer-shaped hooks. Suckers armed. Neck absent. Proglottids craspedote. Genital pores unilateral. Cirrus pouch large. Cirrus armed. Testes in single, posterior field. Ovary dumbbell shaped. Vitelline gland compact, postovarian. Vagina posterior to cirrus pouch, convoluted. Seminal receptacle proximal. Uterus horseshoe-shaped, posterior to longitudinal paruterine organ. Parasites of Gruiformes, Falconiformes, Passeriformes. Africa, Europe, Asia, North and South America.

Type species: I. *otidis* Krabbe, 1868. *Table of species:* Dollfus (1957).

Fig. 237. *Idiogenes otidis* Krabbe, 1868. After Dollfus (1957).

3b. Uterus sac-like 4

4a. Testes mainly behind ovary. Suckers unarmed ....
....*Otiditaenia* **Beddard, 1912. (Fig. 238)**

Diagnosis: Rostellum with two circles of small, hammer-shaped hooks. Suckers with two marginal lappets, unarmed. Proglottids wider than long, craspedote. Genital pores irregularly alternating. Cirrus pouch small. Testes numerous, mainly posterior to ovary. Ovary and vitelline gland poral. Uterus a transverse sac, with anterior paruterine organ. Parasites of Gruiformes. Europe, Africa.

Type species: O. conoides (Bloch, 1782) Beddard, 1912.

Fig. 238. *Otiditaenia conoides* (Bloch, 1782) Beddard, 1912. After Dollfus (1957).

4b. Testes scattered, surrounding ovary. Suckers armed ....
....*Chapmania* **Monticelli, 1893. (Fig. 239)**

Diagnosis: Rostellum with two simple or wavy circles of small, hammer-shaped hooks. Suckers armed. Neck present or absent. Proglottids craspedote. Genital pores irregularly alternating. Genital atrium deep. Cirrus pouch reaches osmoregulatory canals. Cirrus armed. Testes scattered. Genital ducts between osmoregulatory canals. Ovary median. Vitelline gland postovarian. Vagina posterior to cirrus pouch. Seminal receptacle proximal. Uterus sac-like, with anterior paruterine organ. Parasites of Gruiformes, Rheiformes, Bucerotiformes. Europe, Africa.

Type species: C. tauricollis (Chapman, 1876) Monticelli, 1893.

Fig. 239. *Chapmania macrocephala* Fuhrmann, 1943.

Key to the Genera of Ophryocotylinae

1a. Genital pores unilateral ....
...........................*Ophryocotyloides* Fuhrmann, 1920. (Fig. 240)

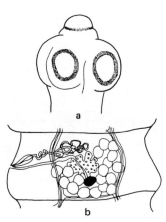

Diagnosis: Rostellar hooks in two simple circles. Suckers armed. Mature proglottids wider than long. Genital pores unilateral. Cirrus pouch variable. Testes mainly lateral to ovary. Ovary median or submedian. Vitelline gland postovarian. Vagina posterior to cirrus pouch. Seminal receptacle small or absent. Uterus sac-like. Parasites of Passeriformes, Bucerotiformes. Africa, India, Brazil.

Type species: *O. uniuterina* (Fuhrmann, 1908) Fuhrmann, 1920.

Key to species: Singh (1962).

Fig. 240. *Ophryocotyloides makundi* Singh, 1962. a. Scolex. b. Proglottid.

1b. Genital pores irregularly alternating 2

2a. Suckers unarmed ....*Fernandezia* López-Neyra, 1936. (Fig. 241)

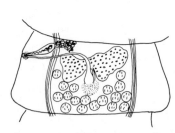

Diagnosis: Scolex relatively large. Rostellum armed with two circles of numerous (300-1000), small, hammer-shaped hooks. Suckers unarmed. Neck absent. Proglottids wider than long, craspedote. Genital pores irregularly alternating. Cirrus pouch reaches or crosses osmoregulatory canals. Seminal vesicles absent. Testes posterior to ovary. Vitelline gland postovarian. Ovary bilobed, anterior. Vagina postero-ventral to cirrus pouch. Seminal receptacle proximal. Uterus an irregular sac. Parasites of Passeriformes. Europe, Africa, Grenada, Russia.

Fig. 241. *Fernandezia indicus* Singh, 1964.

Type species: *F. goizuetai* López-Neyra, 1936.

2b. Suckers armed on anterior margin ....
....*Ophryocotyle* **Friis, 1870. (Fig. 242)**

Diagnosis: Rostellum large, with two undulating circles of small, hammer-shaped hooks. Suckers armed. Genital pores irregularly alternating. Cirrus pouch crosses osmoregulatory canals. Testes in single field posterior to ovary. Genital ducts dorsal to osmoregulatory canals. Ovary median, anterior. Vitelline gland postovarian. Vagina posterior or ventral to cirrus pouch. Seminal receptacle present. Uterus an irregular sac. Parasites of Charadriiformes, Anseriformes, Ciconiiformes, Bucerotiformes. Europe, Malagasy, Africa, North and South America.

Type species: *O. proteus* Friis, 1870.

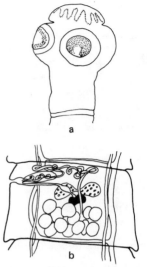

Fig. 242. *Ophryocotyle prud-hoei* Burt, 1962. a. Scolex. b. Proglottid.

Key to the Genera of Davaineinae

1a. Two sets of reproductive organs in each proglottid ....
.... *Cotugnia* **Diamare, 1893. (Fig. 243)**

Diagnosis: Rostellum armed with very small, hammer-shaped hooks. Suckers un-armed. Proglottids each with two sets of reproductive organs. Genital ducts dorsal to osmoregulatory canals. Genital pores bilateral. Testes in one or two median fields. Ovaries

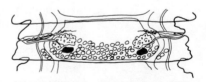

Fig. 243. *Cotugnia meggitti* Yamaguti, 1935.

paired. Vitelline glands postovarian. Vagina posterior to cirrus pouch. One egg in each egg capsule. Parasites of Anseriformes, Casuariiformes, Columbiformes, Galliformes, Passeriformes, Psittaciformes. Cosmopolitan.

Type species: *C. digonopora* (Pasquale, 1890) Diamare, 1893.

1b. One set of reproductive organs per proglottid 2

2a. Rostellum rudimentary, unarmed ....
....Baerfainia Yamaguti, 1959. (Fig. 244)

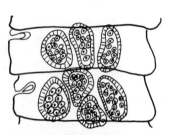

Fig. 244. *Baerfainia anoplocephaloides* (Baer and Fain, 1955) Yamaguti, 1959. Gravid proglottids.

Diagnosis: Rudimentary, unarmed rostellum present. Suckers armed. Proglottids wider than long. Dorsal osmoregulatory canals absent. Genital pores unilateral. Cirrus pouch extravascular. Internal seminal vesicle present, external absent. Testes few (3-4), one poral, others antiporal. Ovary median. Vitelline gland postovarian. Vagina posterior to cirrus pouch, armed at distal end. Three or four egg capsules per segment, each with 10-16 eggs. Parasites of Pholidota. Africa.

Type species: *B. anoplocephaloides* (Baer and Fain, 1955) Yamaguti, 1959.

2b. Rostellum well developed, armed 3

3a. Strobila very small, of few proglottids. Suckers small. Neck lacking. Testes few. One egg per capsule ....
....Davainea Blanchard, 1891. (Fig. 245)

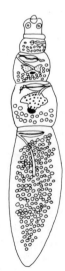

Fig. 245. *Davainea proglottina* (Davaine, 1860) Blanchard, 1891. After Artyukh (1966). Entire Worm.

Diagnosis: Scolex globular. Rostellum armed with one or two circles of very small, hammer-shaped hooks. Suckers small. Neck absent. Strobila very small, of few proglottids. Genital pores irregularly alternating or unilateral. Cirrus pouch crosses osmoregulatory canals. Testes few, mainly posterior to ovary. Ovary median or poral. Vitelline gland postovarian. Vagina posterior to cirrus pouch, may have spinous, distal diverticulum. Seminal receptacle present. Egg capsules each with single egg. Parasites of Galliformes, Charadriiformes, Piciformes. Cosmopolitan.

Type species: *D. proglottina* (Davaine, 1860) Blanchard, 1891.

Key to species: Artyukh (1966).

3b. Strobila medium to large, of many proglottids. Suckers usually large. One or many eggs per capsule 4

4a. **Six to 20 osmoregulatory canals. Testes numerous (90-150). Genital pores irregularly alternating. One egg per capsule ....** ....*Davaineoides* **Fuhrmann, 1920. (Fig. 246)**

Diagnosis: Strobila of numerous proglottids. Genital pores irregularly alternating. Cirrus pouch crosses osmoregulatory canals or not. Testes numerous (90-150) mainly surrounding ovary. Ovary bilobed, median. Vitelline gland postovarian. Vagina posterior or dorsal to cirrus pouch. Seminal receptacle present. Egg capsules each with single egg. Six to 20 osmoregulatory canals present. Parasites of Galliformes. Brazil.

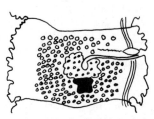

Fig. 246. *Davaineoides virgintivasus* (Skrjabin, 1914) Fuhrmann, 1926.

Type species: *D. virgintivasus* (Skrjabin, 1914) Fuhrmann, 1926.

4b. **Two to four osmoregulatory canals. Genital pores unilateral or alternating. One or many eggs per capsule** 5

5a. **Two circles of large rostellar hooks, followed by several rows of small spines. Suckers unarmed** ....*Houttuynia* **Fuhrmann, 1920. (Fig. 247)**

Diagnosis: Rostellum large, with two circles of hooks followed by several circles of very small spines. Suckers unarmed. Proglottids wider than long, craspedote. Genital pores unilateral. Cirrus pouch well developed. Testes in two lateral fields, antiporal field with more testes than poral field. Ovary bilobed, slightly poral. Vitelline gland postovarian. Vagina posterior to cirrus pouch. Seminal receptacle present. Each egg capsule with

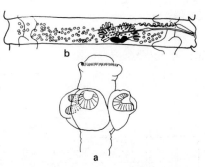

Fig. 247. *Houttuynia struthionis* (Houtuyn, 1772) Fuhrmann. 1920. a. Scolex. b. Proglottid.

several eggs. Parasites of Rheiformes, Struthioniformes. South America, Africa.

Type species: *H. struthionis* (Houttuyn, 1772) Fuhrmann, 1920.

5b. **No spines behind rostellar hooks. Suckers armed** 6

6a. Three rows of rostellar hooks. Genital pores unilateral. Ovary distinctly poral; vitelline gland medial to ovary ....
....*Porogynia* **Railliet and Henry, 1909.**
Diagnosis: Rostellum with three circles of hooks. Suckers armed. Proglottids much wider than long. Genital pores unilateral. Dorsal osmoregulatory canals absent. Testes in single, antiporal field. Ovary and vitelline gland poral; vitelline gland antiporal to ovary. Parasites of Galliformes and Hyracoidea. Africa, Europe.
Type species: *P. paronai* (Moniez, 1892) Railliet and Henry, 1909.

6b. **Two rows of rostellar hooks. Genital pores unilateral or alternating. Ovary median or nearly so; vitelline gland postovarian** 7

7a. Two testes per proglottid ....
.... *Diorchiraillietina* **Yamaguti, 1959.**

Diagnosis: Rostellum with two circles of small, hammer-shaped hooks. Genital pores unilateral. Cirrus pouch reaches osmoregulatory canals, genital ducts pass between them. Testes two, antiporal to ovary. Ovary bilobed, median. Vitelline gland postovarian. Each egg capsule with single egg. Parasites of Pholidota. Ceylon, Java.
Type species: *D. contorta* (Zschokke, 1895) Yamaguti, 1959.

7b. **More than two testes per proglottid** 8

8a. **Rostellar hooks arranged in simple circles** ....
....*Raillietina* **Fuhrmann, 1920. (Fig. 248)**

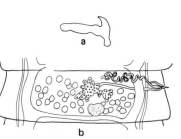

Diagnosis: Rostellum with two circles of small, hammer-shaped hooks. Suckers armed. Strobila with many proglottids. Genital pores unilateral or irregularly alternating. Cirrus pouch small. Testes numerous. Ovary variable, median or poral. Vitelline gland postovarian. Vagina posterior to cirrus pouch. Seminal receptacle present. Egg capsules with one or several eggs. Parasites of Falconiformes, Anseriformes, Ciconiiformes, Casuariformes, Cuculiformes, Galliformes, Passeriformes, Psittaciformes, Bucerotiformes, Coliiformes, Columbiformes, Piciformes, Pterocliformes, Tinamiformes, Capitoniformes, Caprimulgiformes. Also, Rodentia, Carnivora, Primates, Pholidota, Chiroptera, Lagomorpha. Cosmopolitan.

Fig. 248. *Raillietina bakeri* Chandler, 1942. a. Rostellar hook. b. Proglottid.

Type species: *R. tetragona* (Molin, 1858) Fuhrmann, 1920.

Key to the Subgenera of Raillietina

1a. One egg per capsule 2
1b. Several eggs per capsule 3
2a. Genital pores unilateral ...... R. (Paroniella) Fuhrmann, 1920.
2b. Genital pores irregularly alternating ....
.... R. (Skrjabinia) Fuhrmann, 1920.
3a. Genital pores unilateral .... R. (Raillietina) Fuhrmann, 1920.
3b. Genital pores irregularly alternating ....
.... R. (Fuhrmannetta) Stiles and Orlemann, 1926.

8b. Rostellar hooks arranged in elaborate cross, as viewed apically
.... Calostaurus Sandars, 1957. (Fig. 249)

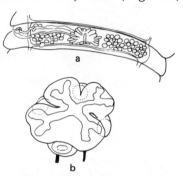

Diagnosis: Strobila fairly small. Rounded scolex with huge four-lobed rostellum armed with two circles of small hooks arranged in an elaborate cross, as viewed apically. Suckers armed with several rows of small hooks. Neck absent. Proglottides craspedote. Genital pores unilateral. Genital atrium small. Genital ducts pass between osmoregulatory canals. Cirrus pouch very small. Cirrus spined. Internal and external seminal vesicles absent. Testes numerous, in two groups lateral to ovary, medial to osmoregulatory canals. Vagina spined distally. Ovary median, composed of several tubular lobules. Vitellaria postovarian. Egg capsules each with a single egg. Parasites of marsupials. Africa.(?)

Fig. 249. *Calostaurus macropus* (Ortlepp, 1922) Sandars, 1957. a. Proglottid. b. Scolex.

Type species: *C. macropus* (Ortlepp, 1922) Sandars, 1957.

Key to the Subfamilies of Hymenolepididae

1a. Pseudoscolex present. Uterus reticulate ....
....Fimbriariinae Wolfhügel, 1899. (P. 164)
1b. Pseudoscolex absent. Uterus not reticulate 2
2a. Uterus breaking up into egg capsules ....
..........Pseudhymenolepidinae Joyeux and Baer, 1935. (P. 166)
2b. Uterus a transverse or longitudinal sac, persistant 3
3a. Gravid uterus continuous between proglottids. Each pair of suckers almost completely fused ....
..............................Ditestolepidinae Yamaguti, 1959. (P. 167)
3b. Uterus separate in each proglottid. All suckers separate ......
.............................Hymenolepidinae Perrier, 1897. (P. 167)

Key to the Genera of Fimbriariinae

1a. No external segmentation; internal segmentation obscure. Six osmoregulatory canals ....*Fimbriaria* Fröhlich, 1802. (Fig. 250)

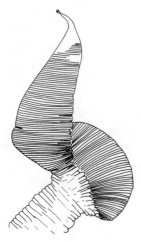

Diagnosis: Rostellum with single circle of 10 hooks. Scolex very small. Pseudoscolex well developed, lacking genital primordia. External metamerism absent, internal metamerism obscure. Genital pores unilateral. Cirrus pouches crowded. Testes ovoid. Ovary transversely elongated, reticular, nonmetameric. Uterus reticulate, nonmetameric. Osmoregulatory canals six in number. Parasites of Anseriformes. Cosmopolitan.

Type species: *F. fasciolaris* (Pallas, 1781) Frölich, 1802.

Fig. 250. *Fimbriaria fasciolaris* (Pallas, 1781) Frölich, 1802. After Reid (1962).

1b. External segmentation present or not, internal segmentation conspicuous. Eight to 11 osmoregulatory canals 2

2a. No external segmentation; internal segmentation conspicuous. Nine or 11 osmoregulatory canals ....
...............................*Fimbriarioides* Fuhrmann, 1932. (Fig. 251)

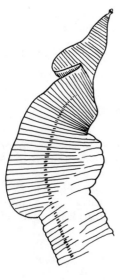

Diagnosis: Rostellum with 10 hooks in single circle. Pseudoscolex poorly developed, containing genital primordia. External metamerism absent, internal metamerism evident. Genital pores unilateral. Cirrus pouch fusiform. Testes lobated or ovoid. Internal and external seminal vesicles present. Cirrus armed. Ovary reticulate. Vitelline gland median, lobate. Vagina opening ventral to cirrus in large atrium. Uterus reticulate, continuous between segments. Osmoregulatory canals, nine or 11 in number. Parasites of Anseriformes and Charadriiformes. Europe, North America.

Type species: *F. intermedia* (Fuhrmann, 1913) Fuhrmann, 1932.

Fig. 251. *Fimbriarioides intermedia* (Fuhrmann, 1913) Fuhrmann, 1932.

2b. External and internal segmentation conspicuous. Eight osmo-
regulatory canals 3

3a. Testes lobate. Internal seminal vesicle present ....
...................................*Fimbriariella* Wolffhügel, 1936. (Fig. 252)

Diagnosis: Rostellum with 10 hooks in single
circle. Neck absent. Pseudoscolex poorly developed, containing genital primordia. External
and internal metamerism well developed. Proglottids wider than long. Genital pores unilateral. Cirrus pouch fusiform. Cirrus armed at
tip. Testes three, lobate. Internal and external
seminal vesicles present. Ovary reticulate.
Vitelline gland median, lobate. Vaginal pore
ventral to cirrus pore. Seminal receptacle present. Uterus first a bilobed sac, becoming reticulate. Osmoregulatory canals eight in number. Parasites of Anseriformes. North America.
Type species: *F. falciformis* (Linton, 1927)
Wolffhügel, 1936.

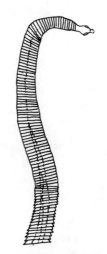

Fig. 252. Fimbriari-
ella falciformes (Lin-
ton, 1927) Wolffhügel,
1936. After Webster
(1943).

3b. Testes rounded. Internal seminal vesicle absent ....
.... *Profimbriaria* Wolffhügel, 1936.

Diagnosis: Scolex and pseudoscolex unknown. External and internal metamerism evident. Proglottids wider than long, with lateral
fringes. Genital pores unilateral. Cirrus pouch not reaching poral
osmoregulatory canal. Cirrus armed. Testes rounded. Internal seminal vesicle absent. Ovary tubular, extending into region of eight
osmoregulatory canals. Vitelline gland large, bilobed, dorsal to
ovary. Vagina ventral to cirrus pouch, spined at distal end. Seminal
receptacle present. Uterus unknown. Parasites of Charadriiformes.
Russia.
Type species: *P. multicanalis* (Baczynska, 1914) Wolffhügel,
1936.

Key to the Genera of Pseudhymenolepidinae

1a. Genital pores irregularly alternating ....
.... *Allohymenolepis* Yamaguti, 1956. (Fig. 253)

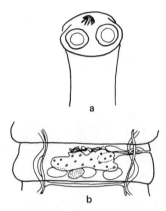

Fig. 253. *Allohymenolepis mitudori* Yamaguti, 1956. *a.* Scolex. *b.* Proglottid.

Diagnosis: Rostellum with single circle of 10 hooks. Neck present. Proglottids wider than long, craspedote. Genital pores irregularly alternating. Osmoregulatory canals ventral to genital ducts. Cirrus pouch small. Testes three, posterior to ovary. Internal and external seminal vesicles present. Ovary transversely elongate. Vitelline gland postovarian. Vagina posterior to cirrus pouch. Seminal receptacle large. Uterus first a transverse tube, then sac-like, breaking into egg capsules each with one to three eggs. Parasites of Passeriformes (Meliphagidae). Celebes, Macassar.

Type species: *A. mitudori* Yamaguti, 1956.

1b. Genital pores unilateral 2

2a. Single circle of 14 rostellar hooks. Three testes present behind ovary .... *Pseudhymenolepis* Joyeux and Baer, 1935.
Diagnosis: Rostellum with single circle of 14 hooks. Neck present. External metamerism indistinct. Proglottids apolytic. Genital pores unilateral. Cirrus pouch claviform. Internal seminal vesicle present. Testes three, in triangle with apex directed posteriad, behind ovary. External seminal vesicle present. Ovary horseshoe-shaped with convexity directed anteriad, with compact vitelline gland within the arms. Vaginal pore ventroposterior to cirrus pouch. Seminal receptacle large. Uterus quickly breaking into numerous egg capsules, each containing a single egg. Parasites of shrews. Europe.
Type species: *P. redonica* Joyeux and Baer, 1935.

2b. Single circle of numerous T-shaped hooks. Three testes, one poral and two antiporal ....
.... *Paradicranotaenia* López-Neyra, 1943.
Diagnosis: Rostellum short, broad, with numerous T-shaped hooks, each with guard longer than blade. Neck absent. Proglottids shorter than wide, craspedote. Genital pores unilateral. Osmoregulatory canals ventral to genital ducts. Cirrus pouch long. Testes

three, one poral, two antiporal. External and internal seminal vesicles present. Ovary bilobed, slightly poral. Vitelline gland compact, postovarian. Vagina posterior to cirrus pouch. Seminal receptacle large, between lobes of ovary. Uterus sac-like, breaking into egg capsules, each with single egg. Parasites of Columbiformes, Galliformes. Europe.

Type species: *P. anormalis* López-Neyra, 1943.

DIAGNOSIS OF THE ONLY GENUS
IN DITESTOLEPIDINAE
Ditestolepis Soltys, 1952

Diagnosis: Rostellum rudimentary, unarmed. Suckers almost completely fused in pairs. Neck present. Proglottids craspedote. Genital pores unilateral. Testes two, one on each side of ovary. Ovary and vitelline gland compact, median. Gravid uterus sac-like, continuous in posterior gravid segments. Parasites of shrews. Estonia, Poland.

Type species: *D. diaphana* (Cholodkowski, 1906) Soltys, 1952.

Key to the Genera of Hymenolepidinae

1a. Two sets of reproductive organs in each proglottid ....
....*Diplogynia* **Baer, 1925.** (Fig. 254)

Diagnosis: Rostellum with a single circle of hooks. Neck present. Proglottids wider than long. Male and female reproductive systems double. Genital pores bilateral. Cirrus pouch not reaching poral osmoregulatory canals. Cirrus armed. Testes few (usually three in each group), pre- or postovarian. External and internal seminal vesicles present. Osmoregulatory canals ventral to genital ducts. Ovary and vitelline gland compact, poral. Vitelline gland postovarian. Vagina ventral to cirrus. Seminal receptacle present. Uterus a transverse sac. Parasites of Anseriformes, Ciconiiformes (green heron). Australia, Java, North America.

Type species: *D. oligorchis* (Maplestone, 1922) Baer, 1925.

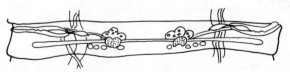

Fig. 254. *Diplogynia oligorchis* (Maplestone, 1922) Baer, 1925.

1b. One set of reproductive organs per proglottid 2

2a. Suckers absent from scolex ....
...................................*Acotylolepis* **Yamaguti, 1959. (Fig. 255)**

Diagnosis: Scolex elongate. Suckers lacking. Rostellum with a single circle of minute, U-shaped hooks. Neck absent. Proglottids wider than long, acraspedote. Genital pores unilateral. Cirrus pouch reaching median line of segment. Testes three, one poral, two aporal. Ovary and vitelline glands compact, median. Vagina? Uterus saclike, forming a single capsule. Parasites of Rodentia. Poland.

Type species: *A. anacetabula* (Soltys, 1954) Yamaguti, 1959.

Fig. 255. *Acotylolep-is anacetabula* (Soltys, 1954) Yamaguti, 1959.

2b. Suckers present on scolex (may be vestigial) 3

3a. One testis per proglottid 4

3b. More than one testis per proglottid 7

4a. Rostellum rudimentary, unarmed ....
...................................*Protogynella* **Jones, 1943. (Fig. 256)**

Diagnosis: Scolex with four simple suckers and unarmed, rudimentary rostellum. Neck present. Strobila small (0.75 mm long). Proglottids wider than long, about 30 in number. Genital pores unilateral. Cirrus pouch slender. Testes single, lobate or compact. Large external seminal vesicle present. Osmoregulatory canals ventral to genital ducts. Ovary median. Vitelline gland antiporal. Vaginal pore ventral to cirrus pore. Seminal receptacle large, poral to ovary. Gravid uterus saccular. Parasites of shrews. North America.

Type species: *P. blarinae* Jones, 1943.

Fig. 256. *Protogynella blarinae* Jones, 1943. Entire worm.

4b. Rostellum well-developed, armed 5

5a. Suckers armed. Vitellaria antiporal to ovary. Cirrus pouch very long ....*Skrjabinoparaxis* **Krotov, 1949. (Fig. 257)**

Diagnosis: Entire sucker cavity and margin lined with minute hooks. Rostellum with a single circle of 10 hooks. Neck short. Genital pores unilateral. Cirrus pouch slender, nearly reaching antiporal osmoregulatory canals. Testes single, median. External seminal vesicle present. Ovary compact, median. Vitelline gland compact, antiporal to ovary. Gravid uterus saclike, with few eggs. Parasites of Anseriformes. Russia.

Type species: S. *tatianae* Krotov, 1949.

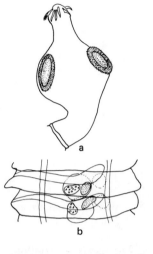

Fig. 257. *Skrjabinoparaxis tatianae* Krotov, 1949. a. Scolex. b. Proglottids.

5b. Suckers unarmed. Vitellaria posterior to ovary 6

6a. External seminal vesicle absent. Genital pores opening separately ....*Allohaploparaxis* **Yamaguti, 1959.**

Diagnosis: Rostellum long, slender, with single circle of hooks bearing handles longer than blades. Suckers unarmed, with posterior margins somewhat reflected, giving scolex arrowhead-like appearance. Neck present. Proglottids wider than long, craspedote. Genital pores lateral, male anterior to and separate from female. Cirrus unarmed. Internal seminal vesicle present, external seminal vesicle absent. Testes single, antiporal. Ovary bilobed. Vitelline gland compact, postovarian. Vagina looped, dilated distally. Seminal receptacle median. Uterus a transverse row of six or more globular pouches eventually filling entire proglottid. Egg shell with bipolar thickenings. Parasites of Anseriformes. Locality not known.

Type species: A. *sagitta* (Rosseter, 1906) Yamaguti, 1959.

6b. External seminal vesicle present. Genital pores opening together in common atrium ....

....*Aploparaxis* **Clerc, 1903. (Fig. 258)**

Diagnosis: Rostellum prominent, with single circle of hooks with large guards. Suckers prominent or vestigeal. Neck present. Proglottids wider than long. Genital pores unilateral, marginal or submarginal. Cirrus pouch well developed. Internal and external seminal vesicles present. Testes single. Osmoregulatory canals ventral to genital ducts. Ovary compact or irregularly lobed. Vitelline gland postovarian. Vaginal pore in atrium dorsal or ventral to cirrus pore. Seminal receptacle median. Uterus saccular. Parasites of Charadriiformes, Anseriformes, Passeriformes, Galliformes. Cosmopolitan.

Type species: *A. filum* (Goeze, 1782) Clerc, 1903.

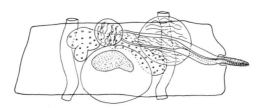

Fig. 258. *Aploparaxis orientalis* Spassky and Bobova, 1961.

7a. **Two testes per proglottid** 8
7b. **More than two testes per proglottid** 11
8a. **Rostellum with apical sucker and single row of many (about 100) minute hooks** ....
........................*Pseudodiorchis* **Skrjabin and Mathevossian, 1948.**
Diagnosis: Rostellum with large apical sucker and about 100 minute hooks in single circle. Genital pores unilateral, equatorial. Cirrus pouch reaching to median field. Cirrus armed. Testes two, dorsal and poral to ovary. External and internal seminal vesicles absent (?). Ovary bilobed. Vitelline gland anteroventral to ovary. Ovary bilobed. Vitelline gland anteroventral to ovary. Vagina tightly coiled 10 to 16 times. Uterus unknown. Parasites of shrews. North America, Poland.
Type species: *P. reynoldsi* (Jones, 1944) Skrjabin and Mathevossian, 1948.
8b. **Rostellum lacking apical sucker** 9
9a. **Genital pore absent, male and female ducts joined** ....
....*Aporodiorchis* **Yamaguti, 1959.**
Diagnosis: Rostellum with eight hooks in single circle. Proglottids wider than long. Genital pores absent; male and female ducts joining together near lateral margin, on same side throughout strobila. Armed cirrus and internal seminal vesicle present in cirrus pouch. Testes two in number. Ovary lobated, median. Vitellaria horseshoe-shaped, dorsal to ovary. Vagina spinous internally. Seminal receptacle present. Uterus unknown. Parasites of flamingo. Ceylon.
Type species: *A. occlusus* (Linstow, 1906) Yamaguti, 1959.
9b. **Genital pore present** 10
10a. **Suckers armed. Ducts of reproductive organs passing between osmoregulatory canals** ....
.............................*Schillerius* **Yamaguti, 1959. (Fig. 259)**

Diagnosis: Rostellum with single circle of 10 hooks. Suckers armed with small spines. Proglottids wider than long. Genital ducts coursing between osmoregulatory canals. Genital pores unilateral, dextral. Cirrus pouch nearly reaching aporal osmoregulatory canals. Internal and external seminal vesicles present. Cirrus armed at base. Testes two, one on each side of ovary. Ovary median, irregular to trilobate. Vitelline gland compact, post-

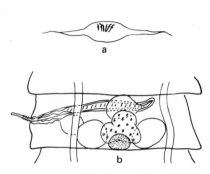

Fig. 259. *Schillerius longiovum* (Schiller, 1953) Yamaguti, 1959. *a.* Egg. *b.* Proglottid.

ovarian. Vagina ventral and posterior to cirus pouch. Seminal receptacle present. Uterus first a simple transverse tube, becoming saclike when gravid. Eggs fusiform, with polar filaments. Parasites of Anseriformes. Alaska, Russia.

Type species: S. *longiovum* (Schiller, 1953) Yamaguti, 1959.

10b. Suckers unarmed. Genital ducts passing dorsal to osmoregulatory canals ....*Diorchis* **Clerc, 1903. (Fig. 260)**

Diagnosis: Suckers unarmed. Rostellum with 10 hooks in single circle. Neck present. Proglottids wider than long. Genital pores unilateral. Genital ducts dorsal to osmoregulatory canals. Cirrus pouch long or short, cirrus armed or not. Testes two. Internal and external seminal vesicles present. Ovary median or submedian. Vitelline gland compact, posterior or ventral to ovary. Vagina posterior or ventral to cirrus pouch. Seminal receptacle present. Uterus trans-

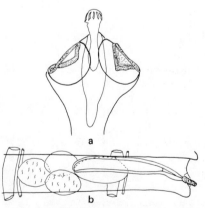

Fig. 260. *Diorchis elisae* (Skrjabin, 1914) Spassky and Frese, 1961. *a.* Scolex. *b.* Proglottid.

versely elongated, with saccular outgrowths. Parasites of Anseriformes, Gruiformes, Columbiformes, Charadriiformes. Cosmopolitan.

Type species: D. *acuminatus* (Clerc, 1902) Clerc, 1903.

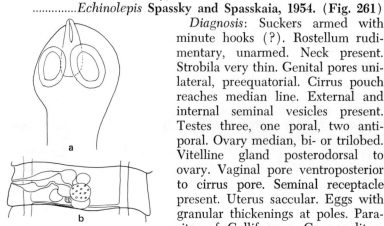

Diagnosis: Suckers armed with minute hooks (?). Rostellum rudimentary, unarmed. Neck present. Strobila very thin. Genital pores unilateral, preequatorial. Cirrus pouch reaches median line. External and internal seminal vesicles present. Testes three, one poral, two antiporal. Ovary median, bi- or trilobed. Vitelline gland posterodorsal to ovary. Vaginal pore ventroposterior to cirrus pore. Seminal receptacle present. Uterus saccular. Eggs with granular thickenings at poles. Parasites of Galliformes. Cosmopolitan.

Fig. 261. *Echinolepis carioca* (Magalhães, 1898) Spassky and Spasskaia, 1954. After Reid (1962). a. Scolex. b. Proglottid.

Type species: E. *carioca* (Magalhães, 1898) Spassky and Spasskaia, 1954.

13b. Rostellum present, armed ....
.................................*Echinocotyle* Blanchard, 1891. (Fig. 262)

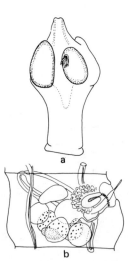

Diagnosis: Suckers armed with minute hooks. Rostellum with 8-10 large hooks with reduced guards, in single circle. Neck present. Genital pores unilateral. Cirrus pouch short or long. Cirrus armed. Testes three. External and internal seminal vesicles present. One or two accessory sacs often present in genital atrium. Ovary median or submedian. Vitelline gland compact, postovarian. Vaginal pore posterior or ventral to cirrus pore. Seminal receptacle present. Uterus saclike. Parasites of Anseriformes, Charadriiformes, Passeriformes; also, Rodentia, Europe, Asia, Taiwan, Africa, North America.

Fig. 262. *Echinocotyle longirostris* (Rudolphi, 1819) Deblock, 1964. a. Scolex. b. Proglottid.

Type species: E. *rosseteri* Blanchard, 1891.

14a. Rostellum absent or rudimentary, unarmed ....
.... *Hymenolepis* **Weinland, 1858.** (Fig. 263)
Diagnosis: Rostellum absent, rudimentary and unarmed, or well developed and armed. Suckers unarmed. Neck present or absent. Proglottids usually wider than long, but considerable variation present between species in several morphological aspects. Genital pores unilateral. Genital ducts dorsal to osmoregulatory canals. Cirrus pouch usually well developed, containing internal seminal vesicle. Cirrus usually armed, may contain a hollow stylet. Commonly an accessory sac is associated with genital atrium. Testes three, variously arranged. External seminal vesicle present. Ovary usually compact, commonly bilobed. Vitelline gland compact, postovarian. Vagina posterior or ventral to cirrus, armed or unarmed. Seminal receptacle usually present. Uterus saccular, often somewhat lobated. Parasites of birds and mammals. Cosmopolitan.

Type species: H. diminuta (Rudolphi, 1819) Weinland, 1858.
Key to Species: Hughes (1941); Deblock (1964).

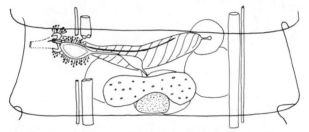

Fig. 263. *Hymenolepis deblocki* Schmidt and Neiland, 1968.

14b. Armed rostellum present, rudimentary or well developed ..15
15a. External segmentation lacking, internal segmentation conspicuous. ......*Parafimbriaria* **Voge and Read, 1954.** (Fig. 264)
Diagnosis: Rostellum with single circle of hooks. Neck present. External metamerism absent, internal metamerism evident. Genital pores unilateral. Cirrus pouch elongate. Cirrus armed. Testes three, in antiporal, transverse row. External and internal seminal vesicles present. Ovary lobated, poral to testes. Vitelline gland ventral to ovary. Seminal receptacle present. Uterus in form of irregular sac. Parasites of Podicepediformes. North America.

Type species: P. websteri Voge and Read, 1954.

Fig. 264. *Parafimbriaria websteri* Voge and Read, 1954.

15b. External segmentation evident 16

16a. Five pairs of osmoregulatory canals ....
....*Hymenofimbria* **Skrjabin, 1914.**
Diagnosis: Rostellum with single circle of 10 books. Proglottids craspedote, much wider than long. Cirrus pouch elongate. Genital pores unilateral. Genital atrium with accessory sac. Testes three, two antiporal, one poral. External and internal seminal vesicles present. Ovary compact, median. Vitelline gland median, postovarian. Uterus saclike. Ten osmoregulatory canals present. Parasites of Anseriformes (merganser). Russia.
Type species: *H. merganseri* Skrjabin, 1914.

16b. Two pairs of osmoregulatory canals 17
17a. Rostellum with many small hooks behind apical circle ....
..............................*Vigisolepis* **Mathevossian, 1945. (Fig. 265)**

Diagnosis: Rostellum well developed, with single, wavy circle of 18-20 hooks, and numerous smaller hooks posterior to it. Genital pores unilateral. Cirrus pouch reaches median line, with sphincter at base. Testes three, in triangle, one poral, two antiporal. Internal and external seminal vesicles present. Ovary and vitelline gland median. Uterus saclike. Parasites of shrews. Russia, Europe.
Type species: *V. spinulosa* (Cholodkowsky, 1906) Mathevossian, 1945.

Fig. 265. *Vigisolepis barboscolex* Spassky, 1949.

17b. Rostellum with only apical circle of hooks 18
18a. All three testes poral to ovary ....

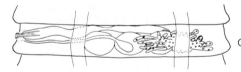

Fig. 266. *Drepanidotaenia barrowensis* (Schiller, 1952) Yamaguti, 1959.

..............................*Drepanidotaenia* **Railliet, 1892. (Fig. 266)**
Diagnosis: Suckers armed or unarmed. Rostellum with 8-10 hooks in single circle. Neck short. Proglottids much wider than long. Genital pores unilateral. Cirrus pouch well developed. Accessory sac present or absent. Testes three, in transverse row or triangle, all poral to ovary. External and internal seminal vesicles present. Ovary lobated, antiporal to testes. Vitelline gland posterior or ventral to ovary. Seminal receptacle present. Uterus a transverse sac with saccular outpocketings. Parasites of Anseriformes, Ciconi-

iformes, Podecipediformes, Charadriiformes, Primates. Cosmopolitan.

Type species: *D. lanceolata* (Bloch, 1782) Railliet, 1892.

18b. Testes not as above **19**
19a. Uterus reticulate ....
..............*Flamingolepis* **Spassky and Spasskaia, 1954.** (**Fig. 267**)

Diagnosis: Rostellum with single circle of eight spiniform hooks. Suckers unarmed. Cirrus pouch not reaching median line. Internal seminal vesicle present. Testes three, lobated, in triangle, one poral and two antiporal. Vas deferens strongly convoluted. Internal seminal vesicle absent. Ovary and vitelline gland median. Uterus reticular. Parasites of Ciconiiformes (flamingo). Europe, Asia, Africa, Cuba.

Type species: *F. liguloides* (Gervais, 1847) Spassky and Spasskaia, 1954.

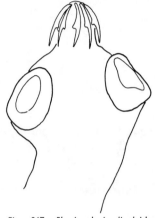

Fig. 267. *Flamingolepis liguloides* (Gervais, 1847) Spassky and Spasskaia, 1954.

19b. Uterus not as above **20**
20a. Gravid uterus divided into two separate sacs ....
................*Passerilepis* **Spassky and Spasskaia, 1954.** (**Fig. 268**)

Diagnosis: Rostellum with single circle of 10 hooks. Suckers unarmed. Genital pores unilateral. Cirrus pouch usually not reaching median line. Testes three, in triangle, one poral, two antiporal. Internal and external seminal vesicles present. Ovary and vitelline gland median. Gravid uterus in two separated, or nearly separated, sacs. Parasites of Passeriformes, Ciconiformes (Herons). Europe, Africa, Celebes, Asia, Hawaii, Ceylon, Taiwan, South America.

Type Species: *P. passeris* (Gmelin, 1790) Spassky and Spasskaia, 1954.

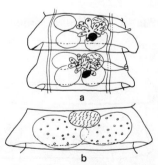

Fig. 268. *Passerilepis passeris* (Gmelin, 1790) Spassky and Spasskaia, 1954. a. Mature proglottids. b. Gravid proglottid.

20b. Gravid uterus saclike, often lobated. Testes variously arranged ....
........*Hymenolepis* **Weinland, 1858.** (**See number 14a, above**).

21a. Four testes per proglottid ....
................................*Oligorchis* Fuhrmann, 1906. (Fig. 269)

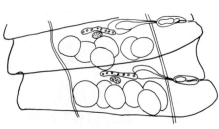

Diagnosis: Rostellum with single circle of 10 or more hooks. Neck present. Proglottids wider than long. Genital pores unilateral, marginal or dorsal. Cirrus pouch small. Testes three to seven, usually four. Osmoregulatory canals ventral to genital ducts. External and internal seminal vesicles present. Ovary and vitelline gland median. Vaginal pore

Fig. 269. *Oligorchis paucitesticulatus* Fuhrmann, 1913. After Deblock and Rose (1964).

ventral to cirrus pore. Seminal receptacle present. Uterus large, sacklike. Parasites of Pelicaniformes, Charadriiformes, Falconiformes; Rodentia, Insectivora. Europe, North and South America, Philippines, Africa, Asia.

Type species: *O. strangulatus* Fuhrman, 1906.

21b. More than four testes per proglottid (see also 21a) 22

22a. Five or six testes per proglottid 23

22b. More than six testes per proglottid 24

23a. Genital pores unilateral. Rostellum unarmed ....
....*Pentorchis* Meggitt, 1927. (Fig. 270)

Diagnosis: Rostellum unarmed (?). Proglottids wider than long. Genital pores unilateral, provided with sphincter. Cirrus pouch reaches osmoregulatory canal. Testes five, in transverse, postequatorial row. External seminal vesicle absent. Ovary large, median. Vitelline gland compact, post-

Fig. 270. *Pentorchis arkteios* Meggitt, 1927. After Fuhrmann (1932).

ovarian. Vagina posterior to cirrus pouch. Seminal receptacle well developed. Uterus saclike. Parasites of Carnivora (*Ursus*). Burma.

Type species: *P. arkteios* Meggitt, 1927.

23b. Genital pores irregularly alternating ....
....*Neoligorchis* **Johri, 1960. (Fig. 271)**

Diagnosis: Scolex lacking rostellum or hooks. Neck present. Proglottids acraspedote, external segmentation faintly marked. Genital pores irregularly alternating. Genital atrium small and poorly developed. Genital ducts pass between osmoregulatory canals. Cirrus pouch crosses canals; poral to ovary. Cirrus unarmed. External seminal vesicle present. Testes five or six, dorsal, anterior and lateral to ovary on aporal side; medial to osmoregulatory canals. Vagina narrow, posterior to cirrus pouch. Seminal receptacle absent. Ovary transversely elongated, not lobed, slightly poral. Vitelline gland ventral and aporal to ovary. Uterus an irregularly lobed sac occupying entire segment. Eggs spindleshaped, outer membrane tapering at both poles. Charadriiformes. India.

Type species: *N. alternatus* Johri, 1960.

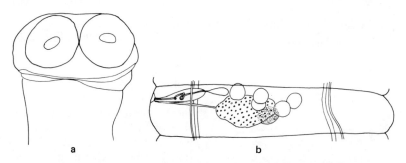

Fig. 271. *Neoligorchis alternatus* Johri, 1960. a. Scolex. b. Proglottid.

24a. **Nine to 12 testes per proglottid, in single, transverse row interrupted by ovary. Rostellum rudimentary, unarmed ....**
....*Chitinolepis* **Baylis, 1926. (Fig. 272)**

Diagnosis: Rostellum rudimentary, unarmed. Proglottids much wider than long. Genital pores unilateral. Cirrus pouch elongate, not reaching median line. Testes 9-12 in single, transverse

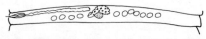

Fig. 272. *Chitinolepis mjoebergi* Baylis, 1926. After Fuhrmann (1932).

row, interrupted by ovary. Internal and external seminal vesicles present. Ovary lobated, median. Vitelline gland compact, postovarian. Seminal receptacle present. Gravid uterus a simple sac as wide as segment. Parasites of Rodentia (*Rattus*). Sarawak, Borneo.

Type species: *C. mjoebergi* Baylis, 1926.

24b. Eight to 12 testes per proglottid, grouped laterally and behind ovary. Rostellum unarmed ..*Pseudoligorchis* Johri, 1934.

Diagnosis: Rostellum small, unarmed. Suckers unarmed. Neck
absent. Proglottids wider than long. Genital pores unilateral. Cirrus
pouch reaching ventral osmoregulatory canal. Testes 8-12, surrounding ovary. External and internal seminal vesicles present.
Genital ducts passing between osmoregulatory canals. Ovary median. Vitelline gland postovarian. Seminal receptacle large. Uterus
an irregular sac. Parasites of Chiroptera. India.

Type species: P. magnireceptaculatus Johri, 1934.

Key to the Genera of Catenotaeniidae

1a. Testes in two lateral, postovarian fields ....
...........................*Skrjabinotaenia* Akhumian, 1946. (Fig. 273)

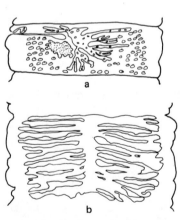

Diagnosis: Scolex unarmed,
lacking rostellum, with four
small suckers near apex. Neck
short. Proglottids craspedote,
shorter than wide. Genital pores
irregularly alternating. Cirrus
pouch small. Cirrus unarmed.
Testes postovarian, in two submedian fields. Seminal vesicles
absent. Ovary highly lobated,
extensive, slightly poral. Vitellaria also lobated, poral to center of ovary. Vagina posterior to
cirrus. Seminal receptacle present. Uterus taenioid, with median stem and numerous lateral
branches. Parasites of rodents.
Africa, Europe.

Fig. 273. *Skrjabinotaenia lobata* (Baer,
1925) Spassky, 1951. a. Mature proglottid.
b. Gravid proglottid.

Type species: S. oranensis (Joyeux and Foley, 1930) Akhumian,
1946.

Key to species: Tenore (1964).

1b. Ovary anterior to single field of testes ....
.... *Catenotaenia* Janicki, 1904. (Fig. 274)
Diagnosis: Scolex unarmed, without rostellum. Neck short. Mature and gravid proglottids longer than wide. Genital pores preequatorial, irregularly alternating. Cirrus unarmed. Seminal vesicles absent. Testes numerous, in single postovarian field. Ovary strongly lobated, extensive, slightly poral. Vitellaria also lobated, poral to ovary. Uterus taenioid, with median stem and lateral branches. Parasites of rodents. Europe, Africa, Japan, Russia, North America, Philippines.
Type species: *C.* *pusilla* (Goeze, 1782) Janicki, 1904.
Key to species: Tenora (1964).

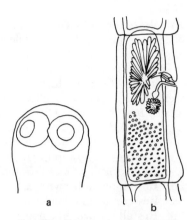

Fig. 274. *Catenotaenia cricetorum* Kershenblat, 1949. a. Scolex. b. Proglottid.

Key to the Subfamilies of Dilepididae

1a. Paruterine organs present ....
........................Paruterininae Fuhrmann, 1907. (P. 179)

1b. Paruterine organs absent 2

2a. Uterus replaced with egg capsules containing one or more eggs ....Dipylidiinae Stiles, 1896. (P. 187)

2b. Uterus reticular, ring-shaped or saccular ....
........................Dilepidinae Fuhrmann, 1907. (P. 195)

Key to the Genera in Paruterininae

1a. Rostellum with four circles of hooks, those in first circle triangular ....*Neyraia* Joyeux and David, 1934.
Diagnosis: Rostellum with four circles of hooks of varying sizes. Neck long. Proglottids wider than long. Genital ducts pass between osmoregulatory canals. Genital pores alternating irregularly. Cirrus pouch nearly reaches median line. Cirrus unarmed. Testes few (7-10), intervascular, surrounding ovary or lateral to it. Ovary bilobed, median, posterior. Vitelline gland postovarian. Vaginal pore posterior to cirrus pore. Seminal receptacle small. Paruterine

organ single, large, with median constriction. Uterine sacs two, near posterior end of segment. Parasites of Upupiformes. Europe, Africa.

Type species: *N. intricata* (Krabbe, 1878) Joyeux and David, 1934.

1b. Rostellum otherwise 2

2a. Rostellum with one circle of hooks ....
.... *Zosteropicola* Johnston, 1912.

Diagnosis: Rostellum with a single circle of hooks. Proglottids craspedote. Genital ducts pass ventral to osmoregulatory canals. Gential pores regularly alternating (?). Cirrus pouch extravascular. Testes few, posterior. Ovary median, bilobed. Vitelline gland post-ovarian. Vaginal pore posterolateral to cirrus pore. Uterus rounded, somewhat poral. Paruterine organ anterior to uterus. Parasites of Passeriformes. (Zosteropidae). Australia.

Type species: *Z. clelandi* Johnston, 1912.

2b. Rostellum otherwise 3

3a. Rostellum and hooks absent 4

3b. Rostellum present, hooks present or absent 10

4a. Mature oncospheres vermiform ....
.... *Anoncotaenia* Cohn, 1900. (Fig. 275)

Diagnosis: Rostellum absent. Scolex unarmed. Proglottids wider than long. Strobila cylindroid. Genital pores irregularly alternating. Genital ducts ventral to osmoregulatory canals. Cirrus pouch short. Testes few, anterior. Ovary and vitelline gland compact. Vagina ventral or posterior to cirrus pouch. Seminal receptacle present. Uterus small, ovoid. Paruterine organ lateral or anterior to uterus. Mature oncospheres vermiform. Parasites of Passeriformes. Europe, Asia, North, Central and South America, Australia, Oceanica, Japan.

Type species: *A. globata* (Linstow, 1879) Cohn, 1900.

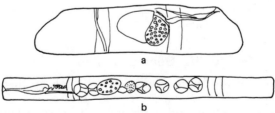

Fig. 275. *Anoncotaenia mexicana* Voge and Davis, 1953. a. Gravid proglottid. b. Mature proglottid.

4b. Mature embryos not vermiform 5

5a. Genital pores open irregularly on either dorsal or ventral surface, lateral, sublateral or medial in mature proglottids ....
.... *Anomaloporus* Voge and Davis, 1953. (Fig. 276)

Diagnosis: Scolex un-armed, lacking rostellum. Neck long. Proglottids acraspedote, wider than long except some gravid ones, which are longer than wide. Genital pores irregular on either side, lateral, sublateral or medial. Atrium weakly developed. Cirrus not described. Inner and outer seminal vesicles absent. Testes number 7 to 14, in one or two groups poral to ovary. Vagina posterior to cirrus pouch. Ovary compact, on aporal side. Vitellaria anterior,

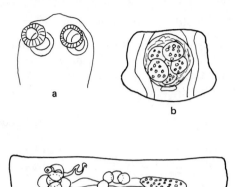

Fig. 276. *Anomaloporus hesperiphonae* Voge and Davis, 1953. a. Scolex. b. Gravid proglottid. c. Mature proglottid.

posterior or lateral to ovary. Paruterine organ anterior to uterus. Eggs further enclosed in fibrous capsules, or not. Parasites of Passeriformes, Apodiformes. Mexico.

Type species: *A. hesperiphonae* Voge and Davis, 1953.

5b. Genital pores lateral 6
6a. Each sucker almost covered by two lobe-like flaps ....
....*Octopetalum* Baylis, 1914. (Fig. 277)

Diagnosis: Rostellum absent, scolex unarmed. Suckers each with a pair of lappets, separated by a median cleft. Proglottids craspedote, longer than wide when gravid. Genital pores irregularly alternating. Genital ducts dorsal to osmoregulatory canal. Dorsal osmoregulatory canal not described. Cirrus pouch crossing osmoregulatory canal or not.

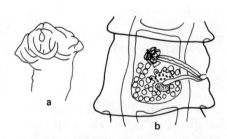

Fig. 277. *Octopetalum longicirrosum* Baer, 1925. After Fuhrmann (1932). a. Scolex. b. Proglottid.

Testes numerous in intervascular medulla. Ovary slightly poral. Vitelline gland posterior or lateral to ovary. Vaginal pore posterior to cirrus. Seminal receptacle present. Uterus saclike, posterior. Paruterine organ anterior to uterus. Parasites of Galliformes. Africa, France.

Type species: *O. gutterae* Baylis, 1914.

6b. Suckers without flaps 7

7a. Testes five to seven in number 8

7b. Testes 20 or more in number 9

8a. Uterus a multiseptate sac. Genital pores alternating irregularly. Vagina posterior to cirrus ....
............................*Multiuterina* Mathevossian, 1948. (Fig. 278)

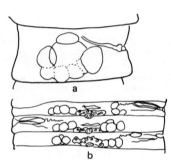

Fig. 278. *Multiuterina skrjabini* Mathevossian, 1948. a. Gravid proglottid. b. Mature proglottids.

Diagnosis: Rostellum absent. Scolex unarmed. Gravid proglottids wider than long, craspedote. Genital pores irregularly alternating, equatorial. Genital ducts passing between osmoregulatory canals. Cirrus pouch well developed. Internal seminal vesicle present. Testes few (6-7), in two lateral groups. Ovary median. Vitelline gland postovarian. Vagina posterior to cirrus pouch. Gravid uterus a multiseptate sac. Paruterine organ rounded, anterior to uterus. Parasites of passeriformes. Russia.

Type species: *M. skrjabini* Mathevossian, 1948.

8b. Uterus not multiseptate. Genital pores unilateral. Vagina anterior to cirrus ....*Lallum* johri, 1960.

Diagnosis: Scolex spheroid, no rostellum, suckers unarmed. Short neck present. Proglottids craspedote. Genital pores unilateral, in small atrium at middle of lateral margin. Genital ducts pass dorsal to osmoregulatory canals. Cirrus pouch reaches or slightly crosses poral osmoregulatory canals. Internal seminal vesicle absent, external seminal vesicle present. Five to seven testes, postovarian, intervascular. Ovary not lobed, in anterior half of proglottid, sometimes extending into posterior part of preceding segment. Vitellaria triangular, dorsal and posterior to ovary. Vagina anterior to cirrus pouch. Large seminal receptacle present. Uterus a transverse sac. Paruterine organ posterior to uterus, extending into following proglottid. Parasites of Anseriformes. India.

Type species: *L. magniparuterina* Johri, 1960.

9a. Gravid uterus a double sac ....
........................*Metroliasthes* **Ransom, 1900. (Fig. 279)**

Diagnosis: Rostellum absent. Scolex unarmed. Proglottids craspedote, may be longer than wide. Genital pores irregularly alternating. Genital ducts pass between osmoregulatory canals. Cirrus pouch crossing osmoregulatory canals or not. Cirrus armed. Testes in two lateral groups. Ovary median. Vitelline gland posterior to ovary. Vagina posterior to cirrus pouch. Gravid uterus in form of two sacs, side by side. Paruterine organ anterior to uterine sacs. Parasites of Galliformes. Cosmopolitan.

Fig. 279. *Metroliasthes lucida* Ransom, 1900. After Fuhrmann (1932). Gravid proglottid.

Type species: *M. lucida* Ransom, 1900.

9b. Gravid uterus a single sac ....
....................*Rhabdometra* **Cholodkowsky, 1906. (Fig. 280)**

Diagnosis: Rostellum absent. Scolex unarmed. Proglottids craspedote, wider than long. Genital pores irregularly alternating. Genital ducts pass between osmoregulatory canals. Cirrus pouch claviform, may cross osmoregulatory canals. Testes in single, posterior

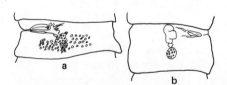

Fig. 280. *Rhabodometra nullicollis* Ransom, 1909. After Fuhrmann (1932). a. Mature proglottid. b. Gravid proglottid.

field. Ovary median. Vitelline gland postovarian. Vagina posterior to cirrus pouch. Seminal receptacle present. Uterus a single, median sac. Paruterine organ anterior to uterus. Parasites of Galliformes. Africa, Russia, North America, Europe.

Type species: *R. tomica* Cholodkowsky, 1906.

10a. Rostellum rudimentary, lacking hooks 11

10b. Rostellum with a double circle of hooks 12

11a. Gravid uterus tree-like or fungiform. Paruterine organ on a short stalk ....*Dendrometra* **Jordano and Diaz-Ungria, 1956.**
Diagnosis: Scolex unarmed, rostellum rudimentary. Neck poorly defined. Proglottids acraspedote. Genital pores irregularly alter-

nating. Genital ducts pass between osmoregulatory canals. Testes scattered randomly throughout proglottid, mainly lateral and posterior to ovary. Cirrus pouch well-developed, in front of vagina. Cirrus not described. Seminal receptacle? Ovary median, irregularly shaped. Vitelline gland compact, postovarian. Uterus first a simple, transversely arched sac, then shaped like an inverted mushroom, with paruterine organ anterior and attached to uterus by slender stalk. Eggs contained in several capsules. Parasites of Pelecaniformes (frigate bird). Venezuela.

Type species: D. ginesi Jordano and Diaz-Ungria, 1956.

11b. Gravid uterus not as above ....*Orthoskrjabinia* Spassky, 1947.

Diagnosis: Rostellum rudimentary, unarmed. Proglottids craspedote, wider than long. Genital pores irregularly alternating. Genital ducts ventral to osmoregulatory canals. Cirrus pouch may cross osmoregulatory canals. Internal seminal vesicle present. Testes few (9-12) in two lateral fields. Ovary compact, median. Vitelline gland postovarian. Uterus first simple, then dividing into several lobes in transverse row. Paruterine organ anterior to uterus. Oncosphere elongate. Parasites of Passeriformes. Europe, Africa, Russia, North America.

Type species: O. bobica (Clerc, 1903) Spassky, 1947.

12a. Uterus breaking down into egg capsules, surrounded by paruterine tissues ....*Deltokeras* Meggett, 1927.

Diagnosis: Rostellum armed with two circles of triangular hooks. Proglottids craspedote. Genital pores unilateral or irregularly alternating. Cirrus pouch may cross osmoregulatory canals. Testes numerous, lateral and posterior to ovary. Ovary median. Vitelline gland postovarian. Vagina posterior to cirrus pouch. Seminal receptacle present. Uterus breaking into egg capsules surrounded by paruterine tissue. Parasites of Passeriformes. Asia, Africa, Europe, South America, Oceanica.

Type species: D. ornitheios Meggett, 1927.

12b. Uterus not breaking into egg capsules 13

**13a. Uterus divided into two symmetrical sacs behind spherical paruterine organ. Hooks triangular ....
..................................*Biuterina* Fuhrmann, 1902. (Fig. 281)**

Diagnosis: Rostellum with two circles of triangular hooks. Proglottids craspedote. Genital pores irregularly alternating. Genital ducts pass between osmoregulatory canals. Cirrus pouch small. Testes numerous, anterior, lateral, sometimes posterior to ovary. Ovary bilobed, posterior, median. Vitelline gland postovarian. Vagina ventral or posterior to cirrus pouch. Uterus first a single sac, then dividing into two connected sacs. Paruterine or-

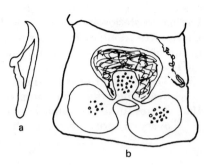

Fig. 281. a. *Biuterina campanulata* (Rudolphi, 1819) Fuhrmann, 1902. After Krabbe (1869). Typical rostellar hook. b. *B. distincta* Fuhrmann, 1908. Gravid proglottid.

gan anterior to uterus. Parasites of Upupiformes, Coraciiformes, Caprimulgiformes, Passeriformes. Africa, Asia, Europe, New Guinea, South and Central America.

Type species: *B. clavulus* (Linstow, 1888) Fuhrmann, 1908.

13b. Uterus not as above 14

14a. Uterus a transversely elongated sac with short branches, behind paruterine organ ....
.... *Culcitella* Fuhrmann, 1906. (Fig. 282)

Diagnosis: Rostellum with two circles of long-handled hooks. Proglottids craspedote. Genital pores unilateral or irregularly alternating. Genital ducts pass between osmoregulatory canals. Testes numerous, posterior and lateral to ovary. Vagina posterior or ventral to cirrus pouch. Seminal

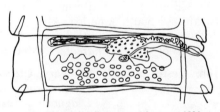

Fig. 282. *Culcitella crassa* Fuhrmann, 1906.

receptacle present. Ovary median or poral. Vitelline gland postovarian. Uterus a transversely elongated sac with short branches. Paruterine organ anterior to uterus. Parasites of Accipitriformes. Africa, Central and South America.

Type species: *C. rapacicola* Fuhrmann, 1906.

14b. Uterus not as above ....…..............................15

15a. Testes dorsal to ovary and vitellaria, five in number ....
....*Notopentorchis* Burt, 1938.

Diagnosis: Rostellum with two circles of triangular hooks. Proglottids craspedote. Genital pores irregularly alternating. Genital ducts ventral to osmoregulatory canals. Cirrus pouch extravascular.

Testes five. Ovary compact, median. Vitelline gland postovarian.
Vagina posterior to cirrus pouch. Seminal receptacle present.
Uterus first double, then a single sac. Paruterine organ anterior
to uterus. Parasites of Apodiformes. Ceylon, India.
   Type species: *N. collocaliae* Burt, 1938.
15b.   **Testes posterior, sometimes also partly lateral or anterior to
    ovary and vitellaria, more than five in number** 16
16a.   **Testes posterior and lateral, sometimes partly anterior to
    ovary. Uterus horseshoe-shaped** ....
    ....*Paruterina* Fuhrmann, 1906. (Fig. 283)

Diagnosis: Rostellum with
two circles of hooks. Proglottids craspedote. Genital
pores irregularly alternating
or unilateral. Genital ducts
pass between osmoregula-
tory canals. Cirrus pouch
may cross osmoregulatory
canals. Testes mainly posterior and lateral to ovary.
Ovary median. Vitelline
gland postovarian. Vagina

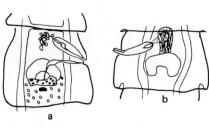

Fig. 283. *Paruterina augustata* Fuhrmann, 1906.
a. Mature proglottid. b. Gravid proglottid.

posterior to cirrus pouch. Seminal receptacle present. Uterus horse-
shoe-shaped or transversely elongate. Paruterine organ anterior to
uterus. Parasites of Accipitriformes, Bucerotiformes, Cuculiformes,
Cypseliformes, Passeriformes, Strigiformes. Europe, Asia, Java,
North and South America, Africa.
   Type species: *P. candelabraia* (Goeze, 1782) Fuhrmann, 1906.
   Table of species characters: Mettrick (1963).

16b.   **Testes posterior to ovary. Uterus spherical or irregular** ....
    ....*Sphaeruterina* Johnston, 1914. (Fig. 284)

Diagnosis: Rostellum with two circles of
hooks. Neck absent. Proglottids craspedote.
Genital pores alternating irregularly. Genital
ducts pass between osmoregulatory canals.
Cirrus pouch extravascular. Cirrus short. Testes
few. Postovarian. Ovary bilobed, slightly poral.
Vitelline gland? Vagina posterior to cirrus
pouch. Seminal receptacle present. Uterus
rounded. Paruterine organ anterior to uterus,
with apical dilation. Parasites of Jaccamari-
formes, Passeriformes. New Caledonia, Europe,
South America.
   Type species: *S. punctata* Johnston, 1914.

Fig. 284. *Sphaeru-
terina punctata* John-
ston, 1914.

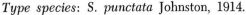

Key to the Genera in Dipylidiinae

1a. Two sets of reproductive organs in each proglottid 2

1b. One set of reproductive organs in each proglottid 5

2a. Rostellum with a single circle of hooks ....
....*Diskrjabiniella* Mathevossian, 1954.

Diagnosis: Rostellum with a single circle of hooks. Two sets of reproductive organs per proglottid. Genital pores bilateral. Testes numerous. Ovary compact. Each egg capsule with a single egg. Parasites of Accipitriiformes (vulture), Columbiformes. Africa.

Type species: *D. avicola* (Fuhrmann, 1906) Mathevossian, 1954.

2b. Rostellum with several circles of hooks 3

3a. Each egg capsule with several eggs ....
.....................................*Dipylidium* Leuckart, 1863. (Fig. 285)

Diagnosis: Rostellum with several circles of rose-thorn shaped hooks. Mature and gravid proglottids longer than wide, acraspedote, constricted at intersegments. Each proglottid with two sets of reproductive organs. Testes numerous, in entire intervascular field. Genital pores postequatorial. Ovary bilobed. Vitelline gland postovarian. Vagina ventral or posterior to cirrus pouch. Uterus first reticular, then breaking into egg capsules each with several eggs. Parasites of Carnivora, rarely in reptiles or man. Cosmopolitan.

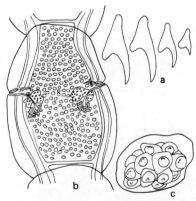

Fig. 285. *Dipylidium otocyonis* Joyeux, Baer and Martin, 1936. a. Rostellar hooks. b. Proglottid. c. Egg capsule.

Type species: *D. caninum* (Linnaeus, 1758) Leuckart, 1863.
Key to species: Wardle and McLeod (1952).

3b. Each egg capsule with a single egg 4

4a. Cirrus anterior to vagina ....
.....................................*Joyeuxiella* Fuhrmann, 1935. (Fig. 286)

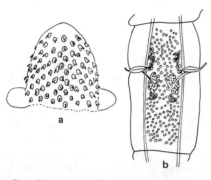

Fig. 286. *Joyeuxiella rossicum* (Skrjabin, 1923) Fuhrmann, 1935. a. Rostellum. b. Proglottid.

Diagnosis: Rostellum with several circles of rosethorn-shaped hooks. Mature proglottids usually wider than long. Two sets of reproductive organs per proglottid. Genital pores bilateral, preequatorial. Cirrus pouch crosses osmoregulatory canals. Testes numerous, filling intervascular space. Ovary lobated. Vitelline gland postovarian. Vagina posterior to cirrus pouch. Uterus breaks into egg capsules, each with a single egg. Parasites of Carnivora. Europe, Africa, Palestine, Asia.

Type species: *J. chyzeri* (Ratz, 1897) Fuhrmann, 1935.

4b. Cirrus posterior to vagina ....
.....................................*Diplopylidium* Beddard, 1913. (Fig. 287)

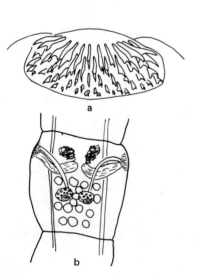

Fig. 287. *Diplopylidium nolleri* (Skrjabin, 1924). a. Rostellum. b. Proglottid.

Diagnosis: Rostellum with several circles of hooks. Each proglottid with double sets of reproductive organs. Genital pores bilateral, preequatorial. Testes mainly posterior to level of ovaries. Cirrus pouch large, nearly reaching median line of segment. Ovary lobated. Vitelline gland postovarian. Vagina opens anterior to cirrus. Egg capsules each with single egg. Parasites of Carnivora. Europe, Africa, Asia, Palestine, Cyprus.

Type species: *D. genettae* Beddard, 1913.

Key to species: Wardle and McLeod (1952).

5a. Rostellum unarmed (hooks may have been lost) 6
5b. Rostellum armed 7

6a. Genital pores alternating regularly or irregularly ....
.... *Pseudochoanotaenia* **Burt, 1938.**
Diagnosis: Rostellum retractable, unarmed (hooks lost?). Suckers large, unarmed. Proglottids craspedote, wider than long except when gravid. Genital pores alternating regularly or irregularly. Cirrus pouch crosses osmoregulatory canals. Seminal vesicles absent. Testes few (10-20), postequatorial. Ovary bilobed, nearly reaching osmoregulatory canals. Vitelline gland postovarian. Vagina posterior to cirrus pouch. Seminal receptacle proximal. Uterus first reticular, later breaking into egg capsules each with single egg. Parasites of Apodiformes (swiftlet) Ceylon.
Type species: *P. collocaliae* Burt, 1938.

6b. Genital pores unilateral ....
.................................*Eugonodaeum* **Beddard, 1913.** (**Fig. 288**)

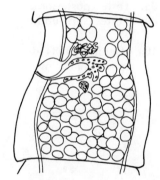

Diagnosis: Rostellum unarmed (hooks may have been lost). Proglottids acraspedote. Genital pores unilateral. Cirrus pouch large. Cirrus armed. Testes mainly posterior. Genital ducts pass between poral osmoregulatory canals. Ovary slightly poral. Vitelline gland postovarian. Vagina posterior to cirrus pouch. Egg capsules each with single egg. Parasites of Charadriiformes, Accipitriformes (eagle). Asia, South America.
Type species: *E. oedicnemi* Beddard, 1913.

Fig. 288. *Eugonodaeum bybralis* Johri, 1951.

7a. Genital pores unilateral 8

7b. Genital pores alternating 12

8a. Ovary poral. Two circles of rostellar hooks ....
....*Malika* **Woodland, 1929.** (**Fig. 289**)

Diagnosis: Rostellum with double circle of hooks. Proglottids craspedote, most wider than long. Genital ducts pass between osmoregulatory canals. Genital pores unilateral. Genital atrium large. Cirrus pouch long. Cirrus unarmed. Testes mainly postovarian. Ovary poral, anterior. Vitelline gland median or postovarian. Vagina posterior to cirrus pouch. Seminal receptacle small.

Uterus first with lateral branches, later breaking into egg capsules, each with several eggs. Parasites of Charadriiformes, Passeriformes (*Pitta*). Celyon, Asia.

Type species: *M. oedicnemus* Woodland, 1929.

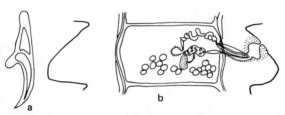

Fig. 289. *Malika kalawewaensis* Burt, 1940. After Fuhrmann (1932). a. Rostellar hook. b. Proglottid.

8b. **Ovary median. One or two rows of rostellar hooks** 9
9a. **Testes posterior, sometimes also lateral to ovary** 10
9b. **Testes surrounding ovary** 11

10a. **Genital ducts dorsal to osmoregulatory canals. Testes only posterior to ovary. Single circle of rostellar hooks** ....
....*Spiniglans* **Yamaguti, 1959. (Fig. 290)**

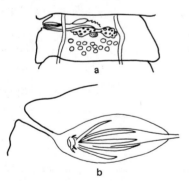

Fig. 290. *Spininglans microsoma* Southwell, 1922) Yamaguti, 1959. a. Proglottid. b. Cirrus pouch.

Diagnosis: Rostellum with single circle of hooks. Suckers large, prominent. Neck absent. Strobila small, of few proglottids. Segments craspedote, wider than long. Genital ducts dorsal to osmoregulatory canals. Genital pores unilateral (?). Cirrus pouch extravascular. Cirrus with short spines at right angles on tip and with very long subapical spines. Testes few (16-20), posterior to ovary. External seminal vesicle present. Ovary bialate, median, preequatorial. Vitelline gland postovarian. Vagina posterior to cirrus pouch. Seminal receptacle present. Uterus first appears as a preovarian, transverse sac, then breaks into egg capsules each with one egg. Parasites of Passeriformes. India.

Type species: *S. microsoma* (Southwell, 1922) Yamaguti, 1959.

10b. **Genital ducts ventral to osmoregulatory canals. Testes posterior and lateral to ovary. Single circle of rostellar hooks** ....
....*Aelurotaenia* **Cameron, 1928. (Fig. 291)**

Diagnosis: Rostellum with a single circle of rosethorn-shaped hooks. Neck long. Proglottids craspedote. Genital ducts pass ventral to osmoregulatory canals. Genital pores preequatorial, unilateral. Cirrus armed. Testes few, posterior and lateral to ovary. Vas deferens convoluted in median, anterior part of segment. Ovary bilobed, median. Vitelline gland compact, between lobes of ovary. Vagina ventral to cirrus, with distal dilation. Uterus first a bilobed sac, later breaking into egg capsules, each usually with a single egg. Parasites of Carnivora (*Felis planiceps*). Trinidad.

Type species: *A. planicipitis* Cameron, 1928.

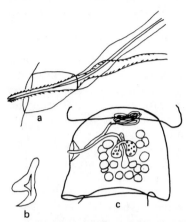

Fig. 291. *Aelurotaenia planicipitis* Cameron, 1928. a. Genital atrium. b. Rostellar hook. c. Proglottid.

11a. **External seminal receptacle absent. Single circle of rostellar hooks** ....*Similuncinus* **Johnston, 1909. (Fig. 292)**

Diagnosis: Rostellum with a single circle of hooks. Neck present or absent. Proglottids craspedote, wider than long. Genital pores unilateral. Cirrus pouch extravascular or crossing ventral to osmoregulatory canals, along with vagina. Cirrus unarmed. Testes surrounding ovary, fewer anteriorly. Ovary rather compact, median or slightly poral. Vitelline gland postovarian. Vagina posterior to cirrus pouch. Seminal receptacle present. Uterus first branched, then breaking into egg capsules. Parasites of Coraciiformes and Charadriiformes. Australia, Asia.

Type species: *S. dacelonis* Johnston, 1909.

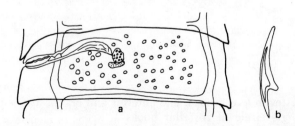

Fig. 292. *Similuncinus dacelonis* Johnston, 1909. a. Proglottid. b. Rostellar hook.

11b. Double circle of rostellar hooks present. Seminal receptacle present ....*Capsulata* **Sandeman, 1959. (Fig. 293)**

Diagnosis: Rostellum armed with a double circle of hooks. Suckers face slightly forward. Neck very short. Segmentation begins in diffuse area near posterior end, with external segmentation appearing last at posterior end. Maturation of genitalia precedes from posterior to anterior; segments then lost from posterior to anterior until only 40 to 50 remain. Mature proglottids acraspedote. Genital pores unilateral. Genital ducts pass between osmoregulatory canals. Genital atrium small. Cirrus pouch exceeds poral canals, and contains coiled ejaculatory duct. Cirrus short, armed. Inner and outer seminal vesicles absent. Testes (30-45) completely surrounding female organs. Vagina opens ventral to cirrus. Seminal receptacle present. Ovary median, of four to nine fanlike lobes. Vitelline gland postovarian. Uterus first reticular, then replaced by a few egg capsules each containing many round eggs. Inner longitudinal muscle bundles numerous (50-60); outer bundles few, small. Charadriiformes. Scotland.

Type species: C. *edonensis* Sandeman, 1959.

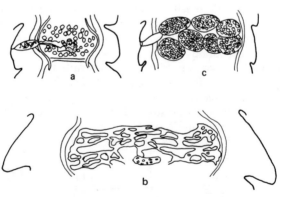

Fig. 293. *Capsulata edonensis* Sandeman, 1959. a. Mature proglottid. b. Early uterus. c. Gravid proglottid.

12a. Testes in two groups, one anterior and one posterior to ovary. Single circle of rostellar hooks ....*Kowalewskiella* **Baczynska, 1914. (Fig. 294)**

Diagnosis: Rostellum with a single circle of hooks. Neck present. Mature proglottids longer than wide. Genital ducts pass between osmoregulatory canals. Genital pores irregularly alternating. Cirrus pouch crosses osmoregulatory canals. Cirrus armed. Testes in two groups, one anterior and one posterior to ovary. Ovary bilobed, median or poral. Vitelline gland compact, postovarian. Vagina posterior to cirrus pouch. Seminal receptacle present. Uterus first saclike, then breaking into capsules, each with one egg. Parasites of Charadriiformes. Russia, Ceylon, North America.
Type species: *K. longiannulata* Baczynska, 1914.

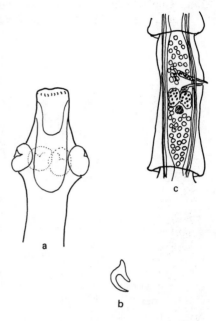

Fig. 294. *Kowalewskiella cingulifera* (Krabbe, 1869) Lopez-Neyra, 1952. After Singh (1952). a. Scolex. b. Rostellar hooks. c. Proglottid.

12b. Testes not as above 13

13a. Testes encircling ovary except on pore side. Single circle of rostellar hooks ....*Onderstepoortia* Ortlepp, 1938.

Diagnosis: Rostellum with a single circle of *Taenia*-like hooks. Proglottids craspedote. Genital ducts pass between osmoregulatory canals. Genital pores irregularly alternating. Cirrus pouch crosses osmoregulatory canals. Testes numerous, surrounding ovary except on poral side. Ovary crescentic, slightly poral. Vitelline gland postovarian. Vagina posterior to cirrus pouch. Seminal receptacle dorsal to ovary. Uterus replaced with egg capsules, each with one egg. Parasites of Charadriiformes. Africa, Ceylon.
Type species: *O. taeniaformis* Ortlepp, 1938.

13b. Testes posterior to ovary 14

14a. Genital ducts passing between osmoregulatory canals ....
....*Choanotaenia* **Railliet, 1896.** (**Fig. 295**)

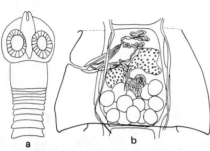

Diagnosis: Rostellum with a single, double, or irregular circle of hooks. Suckers rarely armed. Proglottids craspedote. Genital ducts pass between osmoregulatory canals. Genital pores irregularly alternating. Cirrus pouch extravascular or not. Cirrus armed or not. Testes numerous, mainly posterior to ovary. Ovary bilobed or compact, usually median. Vitelline gland compact, postovarian. Vagina

Fig. 295. *Choanotaenia uncinata* Fuhrmann, 1918. After Burt (1938). a. Scolex. b. Proglottid.

posterior to cirrus pouch. Seminal receptacle present. Uterus sac-like, lobed, or reticular, breaking into egg capsules, each with one egg. Parasites of Accipitriformes, Coraciiformes, Charadriiformes, Galliformes, Passeriformes, Piciformes, Gruiformes, Anseriformes, Strigiformes, Upupiformes. Also, in Insectivora, Rodentia. Cosmopolitan.

Type species: *C. infundibulum* (Bloch, 1779) Railliet, 1896.

14b. Genital ducts dorsal to osmoregulatory canals **15**

15a. Two circles of rostellar hooks ....
....*Panuwa* **Burt, 1940.** (**Fig. 296**)

Diagnosis: Rostellum with two circles of hooks. Proglottids wider than long, craspedote. Genital ducts dorsal to osmoregulatory canals. Genital pores alternating irregularly. Testes numerous, posterior to ovary. Ovary bilobed, equatorial, slightly poral. Vitelline

Fig. 296. *Panuwa lobivanelli* Burt, 1940.

gland postovarian. Vagina posterior to cirrus pouch. Seminal receptacle present. Egg capsules each with one egg. Parasites of Charadriiformes. Ceylon.

Type species: *P. lobivanelli* Burt, 1940.

15b. One circle of rostellar hooks ....
....*Ivritaenia* **Singh, 1962.** (**Fig. 297**)

Diagnosis: Scolex large, well developed. Rostellum armed with single circle of hooks. Neck short. Proglottids acraspedote, broader than long, except gravid ones which are much longer than broad. Genital pores regularly alternating. Genital atrium shallow. Genital ducts dorsal to osmoregulatory canals. Cirrus pouch well developed, extending one-third across proglottid, proximal end curving anteriad. Cirrus small, unarmed, surrounded by hair-like processes which protrude from genital pore. Inner and outer seminal vesicles absent. Testes 15 to 18 in

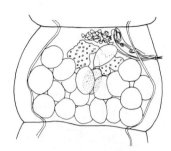

Fig. 297. *Ivritaenia mukteswarensis* Singh, 1962.

number, in one field posterior and lateral to ovary. Vagina posterior to cirrus pouch. Seminal receptacle present. Ovary distinctly bilobed, slightly poral in anterior half of proglottid. Vitelline gland compact, oval, posterior to ovarian isthmus. Uterus saclike, replaced by egg capsules each with one to four eggs. Parasites of Piciformes. India.

Type species: *I. mukteswarensis* Singh, 1962.

Key to the Genera in Dilepidinae

1a. **Genital pores unilateral** 2
1b. **Genital pores alternating** 21
2a. **Rostellum lacking** ....*Arctotaenia* **Baer, 1956. (Fig. 298)**

Diagnosis: Rostellum absent, scolex unarmed. Proglottids craspedote, wider than long. Genital pores unilateral. Genital ducts pass between osmoregulatory canals. Cirrus pouch crosses osmoregulatory canals. Testes 25-30, in single, postovarian field. Ovary anterior, lobated, extending width of medulla. Vitelline gland postovarian, slightly poral. Vagina posterior to cirrus pouch. Uterus first a single sac, becoming lobated when gravid. Parasites of Charadriiformes. Russia, Norway, Greenland.

Type species: *A. tetrabothrioides* (Lönnberg, 1890) Baer, 1956.

2b. **Rostellum present** 3

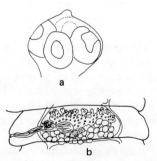

Fig. 298. *Arctotaenia tetrabothrioides* (Lönnberg. 1890) Baer, 1956. a. Scolex. b. Proglottid.

3a. Rostellum long, rod-like, covered uniformly or only at tip (?)
with minute spines ....
..................*Echinorhynchotaenia* Fuhrmann, 1909. (Fig. 299)

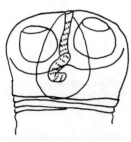

Diagnosis: Rostellum long, rod-like, covered uniformly or only at tip (?) with minute spines. Proglottids craspedote. Genital pores unilateral. Genital ducts pass between osmoregulatory canals. External and internal seminal vesicles present. Cirrus armed. Testes three, posterior to ovary. Ovary bialate, median. Vitelline gland postovarian. Vagina posterior to cirrus pouch. Seminal receptacle present. Uterus an irregular sac. Parasites of Pelecaniformes. Africa, India, Australia.

Fig. 299. *Echinorhynchotaenia tritesticulata* Fuhrmann, 1909.

Type species: *E. tritesticulata* Fuhrmann, 1909.

3b. Rostellum with hooks in circles 4

4a. Cirrus pouch absent, replaced by complex copulatory apparatus. Three testes present. One circle of rostellar hooks ....
.... *Cladogynia* Baer, 1937.

Diagnosis: Rostellum with single circle of hooks. Proglottids craspedote, wider than long. Genital pores unilateral. Genital ducts pass dorsal to osmoregulatory canals. Cirrus pouch replaced by muscular ejaculatory duct within a thin sheath, and a sclerotized stylet opening into atrium. Testes three. Ovary branched, median. Vitelline gland branched, postovarian. Vagina ventral to cirrus apparatus. Seminal receptacle elongate. Uterus reticular. Parasites of flamingo. Africa.

Type species: *C. phoeniconaiadis* (Hudson, 1934) Baer, 1937.

4b. Cirrus pouch present 5

5a. Testes seven or fewer, surrounding ovary. One circle of rostellar hooks ....*Clelandia* Johnston, 1909. (Fig. 300)

Diagnosis: Rostellum with a single circle of hooks. Proglottids craspedote. Genital pores unilateral. Genital ducts dorsal to osmoregulatory canals. Cirrus armed. Testes seven or fewer, surrounding ovary. Ovary bialate, median. Vitelline gland postovarian. Vagina posterior to cirrus pouch. Uterus saclike. Parasites of Ciconiiformes (heron). Australia.
Type species: *C. parva* Johnston, 1909.

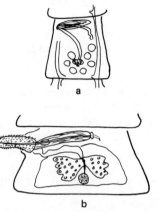

Fig. 300. *Clelandia parva* Johnston, 1909. a. Nearly mature proglottid. b. Nearly gravid proglottid.

5b. Testes more than seven, or if fewer then two circles of rostellar hooks 6

6a. Genital pores submarginal 7

6b. Genital pores marginal 8

7a. Proglottides almost circular in cross-section. Vagina dilated, dorsal to cirrus pouch. Genital atrium present. One circle of rostellar hooks ....*Trichocephaloides* Sinitzin, 1896. (Fig. 301)

Diagnosis: Rostellum slightly bifurcated on the tip, with a single circle of hooks. Proglottids craspedote, nearly cylindrical. Genital pores unilateral, sublateral. Genital ducts dorsal to osmoregulatory canals. Cirrus pouch large, crossing osmoregulatory canals. Testes few, posterior. Ovary median. Vitelline gland postovarian. Vagina dorsal to cirrus pouch,

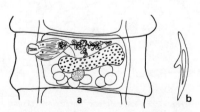

Fig. 301. *Trichocephaloides megalocephala* (Krabbe, 1869) Sinitzen, 1896. a. Proglottid. b. Rostellar hook.

dilated at distal end. Uterus saclike. Parasites of Charadriiformes. Russia, Japan, North America, Europe.
Type species: *T. megalocephala* (Krabbe, 1869) Sinitzen, 1896.

7b. **Proglottids somewhat flattened in cross-section. Vagina posterior to cirrus pouch, opening into shallow groove surrounding opening of cirrus. Genital atrium absent. Two circles of rostellar hooks** .... *Vogea* **Johri, 1959.**

Diagnosis: Scolex with well developed rostellum armed with double circle of large triangular hooks. Suckers unarmed. Neck present. Genital pores unilateral and submarginal. Genital atrium absent. Cirrus opens on circular muscular pad. Vagina opens on groove surrounding pad. Genital ducts dorsal to vessels. Internal and external seminal vesicles absent. Testes numerous (44-51), anterior and posterior to ovary. Ovary transversely elongated, in anterior half of segment, median to osmoregulatory vessels. Vitellaria compact, postovarian. Seminal receptacle present. Uterus a simple transverse sac. Parasites of Passeriformes. India.

Type species: *V. vestibularis* Johri, 1959.

8a. **Genital atrium very large, deep and muscular** 9

8b. **Genital atrium not as above** 10

9a. **Entire genital atrium muscular. No testes anterior to ovary. Two pairs of osmoregulatory canals** ....
....*Valipora* **Linton, 1927. (Fig. 302)**

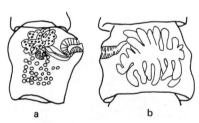

a   b

Fig. 302. a. *Valipora parvispine* Linton, 1927. Mature proglottid. b. *V. mutabilis* Linton, 1927. Gravid proglottid.

Diagnosis: Rostellum with a single circle of hooks. Proglottids craspedote, wider than long. Genital pores unilateral. Genital ducts pass between osmoregulatory canals. Cirrus pouch elongate. Cirrus long, unarmed. Genital atrium with very muscular walls. Testes mainly posterior, none anterior, to ovary. Ovary median, anterior. Vitelline gland postovarian. Vaginal pore posterior to cirrus pore. Seminal receptacle present. Uterus a lobated sac. Parasites of Ciconiiformes (heron), Gaviiformes, Charadriiformes, Anseriformes. Europe, Asia, North America.

Type species: *V. mutabilis* Linton, 1927.

9b. Genital atrium muscular only at proximal end. A few testes anterior to ovary. One pair of osmoregulatory canals ....Mashonalepis Beverly-Burton, 1960. (Fig. 303)

Diagnosis: Scolex with well-developed rostellum bearing single circle of hooks. Suckers weak, unarmed. Neck present. Genital pores unilateral. Genital atrium with powerful interior sphincter. Genital ducts dorsal to vessels. Cirrus pouch weak, not reaching poral vessels. Cirrus unarmed. No internal or external seminal vesicle. Seminal receptacle present. Testes numerous (42-65), surrounding ovary except anterior poral side. Ovary transversely

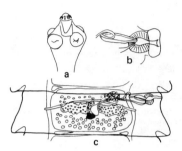

Fig. 303. *Mashonalepis dafyddi* Beverly-Burton, 1960. a. Scolex. b. Genital atrium. c. Proglottid.

elongated. Vitellaria compact, postovarian. Gravid uterus a deeply lobed transverse sac. Only one pair of osmoregulatory canals. Parasites of Ciconiiformes (heron). Africa.

Type species: M. *dafyddi* Beverly-Burton, 1960.

10a. One circle of rostellar hooks 11

10b. Two circles of rostellar hooks 12

11a. Testes mainly antiporal. Uterus reticular. Seminal receptacle huge ....Pseudandrya Fuhrmann, 1943. (Fig. 304)

Diagnosis: Rostellum with a single circle of hooks. Proglottids craspedote, wider than long. Genital pores unilateral. Genital ducts dorsal to osmoregulatory canals. Cirrus pouch crosses osmoregulatory canals. External and internal seminal vesicles present. Testes about 10, mainly antiporal. Ovary

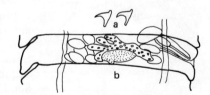

Fig. 304. *Pseudandrya monardi* Fuhrmann, 1943. a. Rostellar hooks. b. Proglottid.

large, lobated, slightly poral. Vitelline gland lobated, postovarian. Vaginal pore posterior to cirrus pore. Seminal receptacle very large. Uterus reticular. Parasites of Carnivora. Africa.

Type species: P. *monardi* Fuhrmann, 1943.

11b.   Testes mainly postovarian. Uterus saclike ....
....................................*Lateriporus* **Fuhrmann, 1907. (Fig. 305)**

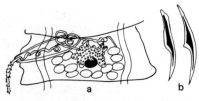

Fig. 305. *Lateriporus clerci* (Johnston, 1912)
Fuhrmann, 1932. After Spassky (1957). a.
Proglottid. b. Rostellar hooks.

Diagnosis: Rostellum with a single circle of hooks. Proglottids craspedote, wider than long. Genital pores unilateral. Genital ducts pass dorsal to osmoregulatory canals. Cirrus pouch crosses osmoregulatory canals. Cirrus armed. Accessory sac may be present. Testes mainly postovarian. Ovary median. Vitelline gland postovarian. Vagina ventral to cirrus pouch. Seminal receptacle present. Uterus saclike. Parasites of Anseriformes. Charadriiformes (gulls and terns), Passeriformes. Greenland, Asia, Europe, Africa, North and South America.

Type species: *L. teres* (Krabbe, 1869) Fuhrmann, 1907.

12a.   Testes completely anterior to ovary ....
....*Proorchida* **Fuhrmann, 1908. (Fig. 306)**

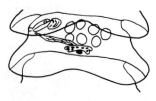

Fig. 306. *Proorchida lobata* Fuhrmann, 1908.

Diagnosis: Rostellum with two circles of hooks. Proglottids craspedote, wider than long. Genital pores unilateral. Genital ducts dorsal to osmoregulatory canals. Testes about seven, anterior to ovary. External seminal vesicle present. Ovary median, posterior. Vitelline gland postovarian. Vagina posterior to cirrus pouch. Seminal receptacle present. Gravid uterus an irregular sac. Parasites of Ciconiiformes. South America.

Type species: *P. lobata* Fuhrmann, 1908.

12b.   Testes lateral and/or posterior to ovary, or surrounding it ..13

13a. Testes only lateral to ovary, three antiporal and one poral ....
....*Paradilepis* **Hsü, 1935.** (Fig. 307)

Diagnosis: Rostellum with
two circles of hooks. Proglottids craspedote. Genital pores
unilateral. Genital ducts dorsal
to osmoregulatory canals. Cirrus armed. Testes four, three
antiporal, one poral. Ovary
about median. Vitelline gland
about postovarian. Vagina ventral to cirrus pouch. Seminal

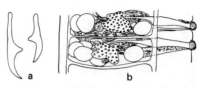

Fig. 307. *Paradilepis simoni* Rausch, 1949.
a. Rostellar hooks. b. Proglottids.

receptacle present. Uterus saclike. Parasites of Pelecaniformes,
Accipitriformes, Ciconiiformes, Galliformes. Asia, Europe, Africa,
Australia, New Guinea, Ceylon, North America.

Type species: *P. scolecina* (Rudolphi, 1819) Hsü, 1935.

13b. Testes not as above ....…..............................14

14a. Genital ducts ventral to osmoregulatory canals ....
....*Metadilepis* **Spassky, 1949.**

Diagnosis: Rostellum sucker-like, without sac. Hooks in two
circles. Neck present. Proglottids craspedote, wider than long.
Genital pores unilateral. Genital ducts ventral to osmoregulatory
canals. Cirrus pouch containing convoluted ejaculatory duct. Testes
in two lateral groups. Ovary median. Vitelline gland postovarian.
Vagina with spinous distal end. Uterus saclike. Parasites of Caprimulgiformes. North and South America.

Type species: *M. globacantha* (Fuhrmann, 1913) Spassky, 1949.

14b. Genital ducts dorsal to or between osmoregulatory canals ..15

15a. Ventral osmoregulatory canal normal in position on poral
side, dorsal to true dorsal canal on antiporal side 16

15b. Osmoregulatory canals normal 17

16a. Genital ducts passing between osmoregulatory canals ....
....*Ophiovalipora* Hsü, 1935. (Fig. 308)

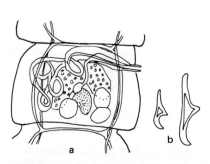

Fig. 308. *Ophiovalipora gorsakii* Yamaguti, 1956. a. Proglottid. b. Rostellar hooks.

Diagnosis: Rostellum with two circles of hooks. Neck short. Proglottids wider than long. Ventral osmoregulatory canal normal in position on poral side, dorsal to true dorsal canal on antiporal side. Genital ducts pass between osmoregulatory canals. Genital pores unilateral. Genital atrium large. Cirrus pouch large, crosses osmoregulatory canals. Vas deferens convoluted near proximal end of cirrus pouch. Testes surrounding ovary except on poral side. Ovary bilobed. Vitelline gland postovarian. Vagina opens ventral to cirrus. Seminal receptacle absent (?). Gravid uterus an irregular sac. Parasites of reptiles, herons. China, Celebes, North and Central America.

Type species: *O. houdemeri* Hsü, 1935.

16b. Genital ducts dorsal to osmoregulatory canals ....
..............................*Dendrouterina* Fuhrmann, 1912. (Fig. 309)

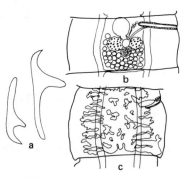

Fig. 309. *Dendrouterina botauri* Rausch, 1948. a. Rostellar hooks. b. Mature proglottid. c. Gravid proglottid.

Diagnosis: Rostellum with two circles of hooks. Ventral osmoregulatory canal normal in position on poral side, dorsal to true dorsal canal on antiporal side. Proglottids craspedote. Genital pores unilateral. Genital ducts dorsal to osmoregulatory canals. Cirrus pouch crosses osmoregulatory canals. Cirrus armed. Testes mainly posterior and lateral to ovary, a few may be anterior. Ovary median. Vitelline gland postovarian. Vagina posterior to cirrus pouch. Seminal receptacle present. Gravid uterus O- or U-shaped, with many branches. Parasites of herons. Africa, North and South America.

Type species: *D. herodiae* Fuhrmann, 1912.

17a. Testes surrounding ovary ....
.... *Cyclorchida* **Fuhrmann, 1907. (Fig. 310)**

Diagnosis: Rostellum with two circles of hooks, each hook with stout handle and small blade. Proglottids craspedote, wider than long. Genital pores unilateral. Genital ducts pass between osmoregulatory canals. Cirrus pouch extravascular. Testes surrounding ovary. Ovary lobated, transversely elongated. Vitelline gland postovarian. Vaginal pore dorsal to cirrus pore. Uterus an irregular, transverse sac. Parasites of Ciconiiformes, Passeriformes, Carnivora (civit). Africa, Asia.

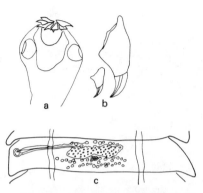

Fig. 310. *Cyclorchida vestibularis* (Johri, 1959) Mathevossian. 1963. a. Scolex. b. Rostellar hooks. c. Proglottid.

Type species: *C. omalancristrota* (Wedl, 1855) Fuhrmann, 1907.

17b. Testes mainly posterior to ovary 18
18a. Genital atrium with two or four spines in special pockets ....
.... *Gryporhynchus* **Nordmann, 1832.**

Diagnosis: Rostellum with two circles of rostellar hooks. Proglottids craspedote, wider than long. Genital pores unilateral. Genital atrium large, with side pockets containing two or more spines. Genital ducts pass between osmoregulatory canals. Cirrus pouch large, reaching median line or farther. Testes few, mainly posterior to ovary. Ovary bilobed, median. Vitelline gland postovarian. Vaginal pore posterior to cirrus pore. Seminal receptacle present. Uterus saclike or U-shaped. Parasites of Ciconiiformes. Asia, Europe, Greenland, Africa, Japan, North America.

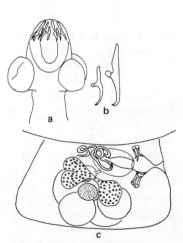

Fig. 311. *Gryporhynchus tetrorchis* Hill, 1941. a. Scolex. b. Rostellar hooks. c. Proglottid.

Type species: *G. pusillum* Nordmann, 1832.

18b. Genital atrium lacking such spines 19

19a. **Genital ducts dorsal to osmoregulatory canals** ....
....*Dilepis* **Weinland, 1858. (Fig. 312)**

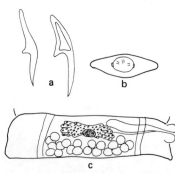

Fig. 312. *Dilepis glareola* Dubinina, 1953. Afer Rybicka (1958). a. Rostellar hooks. b. Egg. c. Proglottid.

Diagnosis: Rostellum with two circles of hooks. Proglottids wider than long, craspedote. Genital pores unilateral. Genital ducts dorsal to osmoregulatory canals. Cirrus pouch long. Testes numerous, mainly posterior to ovary. Ovary median. Vitelline gland posterior to ovary. Vagina variable. Seminal receptacle present. Uterus saclike. Parasites of passeriformes, Accipitriformes, Ciconiiformes, Caprimulgiformes, Charadriiformes, Cypseliformes, Galliformes, Gruiformes, Pelecaniformes, Psittaciformes, Procellariiformes. Also, Insectivora, Primates. Cosmopolitan.

Type species: *D. undula* (Schrank, 1788) Weinland, 1858.

19b. **Genital ducts pass between osmoregulatory canals** **20**

20a. **Testes, ovary and uterus extending laterally beyond osmoregulatory canals. Cirrus pouch extending to aporal osmoregulatory canal** ....*Megacirrus* **Beck, 1951.**

Diagnosis: Rostellum with two circles of hooks. Neck absent. Proglottids craspedote, wider than long. Genital pores unilateral. Genital ducts pass between osmoregulatory canals. Genital atrium small. Cirrus pouch reaching aporal osmoregulatory canal. Cirrus unarmed. Testes numerous, posterior, exceeding osmoregulatory canals. Ovary bilobed, median exceeding osmoregulatory canals laterally. Vitelline gland postovarian. Vagina dorsal to cirrus pouch. Seminal receptacle present. Gravid uterus an irregular sac, extending laterally between osmoregulatory canals. Parasites of Galliformes (*Megapodius*). Palau Islands.

Type species: *M. megapodii* Beck, 1951.

20b. **Testes, ovary and uterus intervascular. Cirrus pouch not extending to median line** ....
.................................*Metabelia* **Mettrick, 1963. (Fig. 313)**

Diagnosis: Medium-sized worms. Rostellum, armed with two circles of hooks. Suckers unarmed. Neck present. Proglottids craspedote. Genital pores unilateral, on middle third of lateral margin. Atrium small. Genital ducts pass between osmoregulatory canals. Cirrus unarmed. Internal and external seminal vesicles absent. Testes 25-34, postoavarian, postvitelline. Vagina

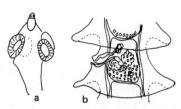

Fig. 313. *Metabelia aetodex* Mettrick, 1963. *a.* Scolex. *b.* Proglottids.

posterior to cirrus pouch. Seminal receptacle present. Ovary median, lobed. Vitelline glnad compact, postovarian. Uterus filling segment, not extending between canals. Parasites of Falconiformes. Africa.

Type species: *M. aetodex* Mettrick, 1963.

21a. Rostellum lacking **22**

21b. Rostellum present, armed or not **23**

22a. Suckers membranous, with marginal hooks arranged like sticks of a fan ....*Cotylorhipis* Blanchard, 1909. (Fig. 314)

Diagnosis: Rostellum absent. Suckers membranous, with long, marginal hooks arranged like sticks of a fan. Proglottids craspedote; gravid segments longer than wide. Genital pores irregularly alternating. Cirrus armed. Other internal organs not described. Parasites of Passeriformes. Argentina.

Type species: *C. furnarii* (del Pont, 1906) Blanchard, 1909.

Fig. 314. *Cotylorhipis furnarii* (Del Pont, 1906) Blanchard, 1909.

22b. Suckers unarmed ....*Ethiopotaenia* **Mettrick, 1961.**

Diagnosis: Scolex unarmed, no restellum. Suckers unarmed. Neck present. Genital pores alternating irregularly. Genital atrium small, on anterior third of margin. Genital ducts passing between osmoregulatory vessels. Cirrus pouch extends beyond poral osmoregulatory canals. Internal seminal vesicle present. External seminal vesicle absent. Testes 20-27, in two lateral groups, sometimes joining posteriorly. Vagina posterior to cirrus. Seminal receptacle present. Ovary lobed, small, median, in anterior half of segment. Vitellaria postovarian. Uterus a deeply lobed transverse sac. Parasites of Passeriformes. Africa.

Type species: *E. trachyphonoides* Mettrick, 1961.

23a. Rostellum unarmed **24**

23b. Rostellum armed **25**

24a. Genital pores alternating regularly. Testes posterior and lateral to ovary ....*Neoangularia* **Singh, 1952. (Fig. 315)**

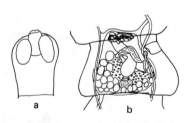

Diagnosis: Rostellum present but unarmed. Proglottids wider than long, craspedote. Genital pores regularly alternating. Testes posterior and lateral to ovary. Vas deferens convoluted near anterior margin of proglottid. Cirrus pouch very large, oblique. Tip of cirrus armed. Ovary bilobed, posterior to cirrus pouch. Vitelline gland postovarian. Vaginal pore anterior to cirrus pore. Vagina swollen, seminal receptacle present. Uterus a lobed sac. Parasites of Apodiformes (swifts). India.

Fig. 315. *Neoangularia ababili* Singh, 1952. a. Scolex. b. Proglottid.

Type species: *N. ababili* Singh, 1952.

24b. Genital pores alternating irregularly. Testes posterior to ovary. ....*Unciunia* **Skrjabin, 1914. (Fig. 316)**

Diagnosis: Rostellum present but unarmed. Proglottids craspedote. Genital pores alternating irregularly. Genital atrium deep, preequatorial. Testes mainly postovarian. Cirrus pouch crosses osmoregulatory canals. Cirrus usually armed. Ovary median. Vitelline gland postovarian. Vagina posterior to cirrus pouch. Seminal receptacle present. Uterus a compartmented sac. Parasites of Falconiformes. Charadriiformes, Anseriformes, Africa, India, South America.

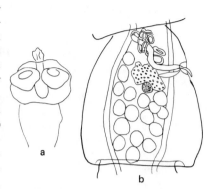

Fig. 316. *Unciunia burmanensis* (Johri, 1951) Mathevossian, 1963. a. Scolex b. Proglottid.

Type species: *U. trichocirrosa* Skrjabin, 1941.

27a. Genital ducts passing between osmoregulatory canals. Cirrus pouch crossing at least half of proglottid ....
....*Bakererpes* Rausch, 1947. (Fig. 317)

Diagnosis: Rostellum with one circle of hooks. Strobila small, with few proglottids. Segments wider than long, strongly convex on poral side. Genital pores alternating regularly. Genital atrium large, with muscular walls lined with small spines. Genital ducts pass between osmoregulatory canals. Cirrus pouch very large, at least reaching median line of segment. Cirrus armed. Testes posterior to ovary.

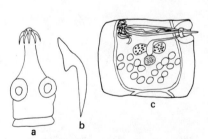

Fig. 317. *Bakererpes fragilis* Rausch, 1947. a. Scolex. b. Rostellar hook. c. Proglottid.

Ovary median. Vitelline gland postovarian. Vagina posterior to cirrus pouch. Seminal receptacle present. Uterus a large sac. Parasites of Charadriiformes. North America.

Type species: *B. fragilis* Rausch, 1947.

27b. Genital ducts dorsal to osmoregulatory canals (between them in *A. setosa* Burt, 1940). Cirrus pouch smaller than above ....*Amoebotaenia* Cohn, 1900. (Fig. 318)

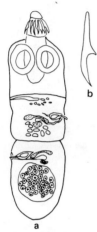

Diagnosis: Rostellum armed with a single circle of hooks. Strobila small, of few segments. Proglottids craspedote or not. Genital pores alternating regularly. Genital ducts dorsal to osmoregulatory canals (between them in *A. setosa* Burt, 1940). Cirrus pouch extravascular. Testes few (6-20), posterior to ovary. Ovary median, usually transversely elongated. Vitelline gland postovarian. Vagina usually posterior to Cirrus pouch. Seminal receptacle present. Uterus an irregular sac. Parasites of Galliformes, Charadriiformes, Piciformes. Cosmopolitan.

Type species: *A. cuneata* (Linstow, 1872) Cohn, 1900.

Fig. 318. *Amoebotaenia lumbrici* (Villot, 1883) Joyeux and Baer, 1939. a. Entire worm. b. Rostellar hook.

28a. Gravid uterus ring-like, surrounding ovary ....*Cyclustera* Fuhrmann, 1901. (Fig. 319)

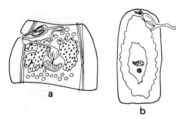

Diagnosis: Rostellum with two circles of hooks. Genital pores regularly alternating. Genital atrium muscular. Genital ducts pass between osmoregulatory canals. Cirrus pouch preequatorial, crossing osmoregulatory canals. Testes surrounding ovary. Ovary lobated, median. Vitelline gland compact, postovarian. Vagina posterior to cirrus pouch. Seminal receptacle present. Gravid uterus ring-like, surrounding remnants of ovary and vitelline gland. Parasites of Ciconiiformes (herons). Europe, Madagascar, North and South America.

Fig. 319. *Cyclustera capito* (Rudolphi, 1819) Fuhrmann, 1901. After Fuhrmann (1909). a. Mature proglottid. b. Gravid proglottid.

Type species: *C. capito* (Rudolphi, 1819) Fuhrmann, 1901.

28b. Gravid uterus saccular, sometimes strongly lobated 29

29a. Gravid uterus strongly lobated ....
....*Liga* **Weinland, 1857.** (**Fig. 320**)
Diagnosis: Rostellum with two circles
of hooks. Suckers armed or not. Strobila
small, of few segments. Proglottids craspedote. Genital pores alternating regularly. Genital ducts dorsal to osmoregulatory canals. Cirrus pouch crosses osmoregulatory canals or not. Testes mainly posterior to ovary. Ovary median,
anterior. Vitelline gland postovarian.
Vagina posterior to cirrus pouch. Seminal receptacle present. Gravid uterus an
irregular sac. External eggshell may
have polar knobs. Parasites of Piciformes, Charadriiformes, Passeriformes,
Gruiformes; also, *Sorex.*

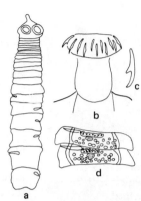

Fig. 320. *Liga brevis* (Linstow, 1884). a. Entire worm. b. Sco-lex. c. Rostellar hook. d. Progl-ottids.

Type species: *L. punctata* (Weinland,
1856) Weinland, 1857.

29b. Gravid uterus not strongly lobated 30
30a. Testes in two groups, anterior and posterior to ovary ....
....*Thaparea* **Johri, 1953.**
Diagnosis: Rostellum with two circles of large and small hooks.
Proglottids craspedote, wider than long. Genital pores alternating
regularly. Genital ducts dorsal to osmoregulatory canals. Cirrus
pouch large, oblique, nearly reaching anterior margin of segment.
Testes in two groups, anterior and posterior to ovary. Internal
seminal vesicle present. Ovary median. Vitelline gland postovarian.
Genital atrium shallow. Seminal receptacle present. Gravid uterus
saclike, extending laterally across osmoregulatory canals. Parasites
of Charadriiformes. India.
Type species: *T. magnivesicula* Johri, 1953.
30b. Testes posterior, lateral and dorsal to ovary 31
31a. Genital ducts dorsal to osmoregulatory canals ....
....*Neoliga* **Singh, 1952.**
Diagnosis: Rostellum with two circles of similar hooks. Neck
and anterior proglottids spinose. Segments craspedote, wider than
long. Genital pores regularly alternating. Genital ducts dorsal to
osmoregulatory canals. Cirrus pouch large, oblique, enclosing
convoluted ejaculatory duct. Cirrus slender, partly armed. Testes
lateral, posterior and dorsal to ovary. Ovary median, bilobed. Vitelline gland postovarian, lobated. Vagina swollen, with sphincter,
opening anterior to cirrus. Seminal receptacle present. Uterus large,
saclike. Parasites of Apodiformes (swift). India.
Type species: *N. diplacantha* Singh, 1952.

31b. Genital ducts pass between osmoregulatory canals ....
....*Chettusiana* **Singh, 1959.** (Fig. 321)

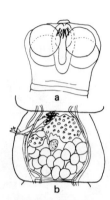

Diagnosis: Scolex globular, sharply demarcated from neck. Suckers large, unarmed. Rostellum bears a double circle of hooks. Neck short. Proglottids somewhat craspedote. Genital pores regularly alternating. Genital atrium small, with hair-like processes protruding from it. Genital ducts passing between osmoregulatory canals. Cirrus pouch extends to near anterior middle of proglottid. Cirrus not described. Internal and external seminal vesicles absent. Vagina posterior to cirrus pouch. Seminal receptacle present. Ovary bilobed, aporal lobe larger; in anterior half of proglotted. Vitellaria compact, irregular, postovarian. Uterus saclike, sometimes extending past osmoregulatory canals. Eggs rounded to oval. Parasites of Charadriiformes. India.

Fig. 321. *Chettusiana indiana* Singh, 1959. a. Scolex. b. Proglottid.

Type species: C. indiana Singh, 1959.

32a. One circle of rostellar hooks 33

32b. Two circles of rostellar hooks 38

33a. Circle of hooks wavy or zigzag 34

33b. Circle of hooks regular 35

34a. Cirrus pouch small, mostly or completely lateral to osmoregulatory canals ....*Angularella* **Strand, 1928.** (Fig. 322)

Diagnosis: Rostellum armed with single, zigzag row of hooks. Proglottids wider than long, craspedote. Genital pores alternating irregularly. Genital ducts dorsal to osmoregulatory canals. Cirrus pouch small, mainly extravascular. Testes numerous, mainly postovarian. Ovary mainly dorsal to cirrus pouch. Seminal receptacle present. Gravid uterus a lobated sac. Parasites of Passeriformes, Apodiformes. Europe, Asia, Ceylon, Taiwan, Central America.

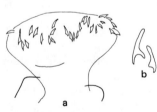

Fig. 322. *Angularella beema* (Clerc, 1906) Strand, 1928. a. Scolex. b. Rostellar hooks.

Type species: A beema (Clerc, 1906) Strand, 1928.

34b. Cirrus pouch large, medial to osmoregulatory canals ....
....*Pseudangularia* **Burt, 1938. (Fig. 323)**

Diagnosis: Rostellum massive, armed with single, zigzag circle of hooks. Proglottids craspedote. Genital pores alternating irregularly. Genital atrium very deep. Genital atrium very deep. Cirrus pouch large, entirely medial to osmoregulatory canals. Cirrus armed basally. Testes numerous, mainly postovarian. Internal and external seminal vesicles present. Ovary large, bialate. Vitellaria postovarian. Distal portion of vagina surrounded by glandular cells, separated from seminal receptacle by powerful sphincter. Uterus a lobated sac. Parasites of Apodiforms, Ceylon, Morocco.

Type species: *P. thompsoni* Burt, 1938.

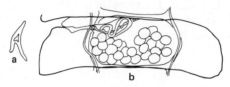

Fig. 323. *Pseudangularella thompsoni* Burt, 1938. a. Rostellar hook. b. Proglottid.

35a. Ovary posterior. Testes in two lateral fields ....
............................*Laterorchites* **Fuhrmann, 1932. (Fig. 324)**

Diagnosis: Rostellum long, slender, with a single circle of hooks. Genital pores alternating irregularly. Proglottids craspedote, wider than long. Testes in two lateral groups. External seminal vesicle present. Cirrus armed. Ovary compact, posterior. Vitelline gland postovarian. Vagina posterior to cirrus pouch. Uterus saclike.

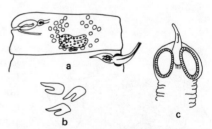

Fig. 324. *Laterorchites bilateralis* (Fuhrmann, 1908) Fuhrmann, 1932. a. Proglottid. b. Rostellar hooks. c. Scolex.

Parasites of Podicipediformes. Central America.

Type species: *L. bilateralis* (Fuhrmann, 1908) Fuhrmann, 1932.

35b. Ovary about central **36**

36a. Uterus reticular ....*Krimi* Burt, 1944. (Fig. 325)

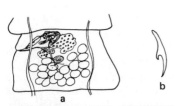

Fig. 325. *Krimi reticulosa* (Singh, 1952) Mathevossian, 1963. a. Proglottid. b. Rostellar hook.

Diagnosis: Rostellum with single circle of hooks. Strobila small, of few segments. Proglottids craspedote. Genital pores irregularly alternating. Genital ducts pass between osmoregulatory canals. Cirrus pouch may cross osmoregulatory canals. Testes numerous, posterior. Vas deferens convoluted near proximal end of cirrus pouch. Ovary compact, anterior. Vitelline gland postovarian. Vagina posterior to cirrus pouch. Seminal receptacle present. Gravid uterus reticular. Parasites of Piciformes, Charadriiformes. Ceylon, North America, India.

    Type species: *K. chrysocolaptis* Burt, 1944.

36b. Uterus saccular 37

37a. Testes in two groups, anterior and posterior to ovary ....
....*Tubanguiella* Yamaguti, 1959. (Fig. 326)

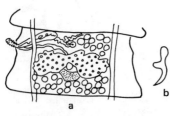

Fig. 326. *Tubanguiella buzzardia* (Tubangui and Masiluñgan, 1937) Yamaguti, 1959. a. Proglottid. b. Rostellar hook.

Diagnosis: Rostellum with single circle of hooks. Proglottids acraspedote, wider than long. Genital pores alternating irregularly. Genital ducts pass between osmoregulatory canals. Cirrus pouch crosses osmoregulatory canals. Testes numerous, in anterior and posterior groups. Ovary bilobed, large. Vitelline gland postovarian. Vagina posterior to cirrus pouch. Seminal receptacle present. Uterus a transversely elongated, lobated sac. Parasites of Accipitriformes (buzzard). Philippines.

    Type species: *T. buzzardia* (Tubangui and Masiluñgan, 1937) Yamaguti, 1959.

37b. Testes posterior to ovary ....
.................................*Sacciuterina* **Mathevossian, 1963. (Fig. 327)**

Diagnosis: Rostellum with single circle of hooks. Proglottids craspedote. Genital pores alternating irregularly. Genital ducts pass between osmoregulatory canals. Cirrus pouch usually crosses osmoregulatory canals. Testes numerous, posterior to ovary. Ovary median, located, preequatorial. Vitelline gland postovarian. Vagina posterior to cirrus pouch. Seminal receptacle present. Uterus saclike. Parasites of Columbiformes, Charadriiformes, Caprimulgiformes, Passeriformes, Accipitriformes. Cosmopolitan.

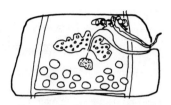

Fig. 327. *Sacciuterina pauciannulata* (Fuhrmann, 1908) Mathevossian, 1963. After Fuhrmann (1932).

Type species: S. *paradoxa* (Rudolphi, 1802) Mathevossian, 1963.

38a. Testes in two fields, anterior and posterior to ovary ....
.................................*Bancroftiella* **Johnston, 1911. (Fig. 328)**
Diagnosis: Rostellum with two circles of hooks. Proglottids craspedote. Genital alternating irregularly. Genital ducts pass between osmoregulatory canals. Cirrus pouch elongate, preequatorial. Testes numerous, in two groups, one anterior and one posterior to ovary. Ovary median, bilobed. Vitelline gland postovarian. Vagina posterior to cirrus pouch. Seminal receptacle present. Uterus an irregular sac. Parasites of Ciconiiformes (herons), Charadriiformes, Passeriformes. Also, kangaroo. Australia, Celebes, Sumatra, Moluccas, Japan, India.

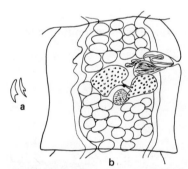

Fig. 328. *Bancroftiella forna* Meggett, 1933. a. Rostellar hooks. b. Proglottid.

Type species: B. *tenuis* Johnston, 1911.

40a. Testes in a transverse band ....
.........................Parorchites Fuhrmann, 1932. (Fig. 329)

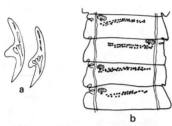

Fig. 329. Parorchites zederi (Baird, 1853) Fuhrmann, 1932. a. Rostellar hook. b. Proglottid.

Diagnosis: Rostellum with two circles of hooks. Neck swollen. Scolex imbedded in gut wall. Proglottids craspedote, wider than long. Genital pores alternating irregularly. Genital ducts dorsal to osmoregulatory canals. Cirrus pouch small, extravascular. Testes numerous, in a continuous band posterior to ovary. Ovary compact, anterior, poral. Vitelline gland postovarian. Uterus saclike. Parasites of penguins. Antarctica.

Type species: *P. zederi* (Baird, 1853) Fuhrmann, 1932.

40b. Testes in two lateral fields 41

41a. Testes extending most of length of proglottid ....
.........................*Laterotaenia* Fuhrmann, 1906. (Fig. 330)

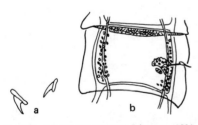

Fig. 330. Laterotaenia nattereri Fuhrmann, 1906. a. Rostellar hooks. b. Proglottid.

Diagnosis: Rostellum small, with two circles of hooks. Proglottids craspedote, wider than long. Genital pores alternating irregularly. Genital ducts pass between osmoregulatory canals. Cirrus pouch small, extravascular. Testes numerous, in two longitudinal, lateral groups, both anterior and posterior to level of ovary. Ovary poral, equatorial. Vitelline gland posterior to ovary. Vagina posterior to cirrus pouch. Seminal receptacle present. Uterus saclike. Parasites of Falconiformes. Brazil.

Type species: *L. nattereri* Fuhrmann, 1906.

41b. Testes postovarian ....
....*Parvirostrum* **Fuhrmann, 1908.** (Fig. 331)

Diagnosis: Rostellum small, with two circles of hooks. Proglottids wider than long, acraspedote. Genital pores alternating irregularly. Cirrus pouch small, extravascular. Testes few, in two lateral groups, not extending length of segment. Ovary small, bilobed, somewhat poral. Vitelline gland postovarian. Va-

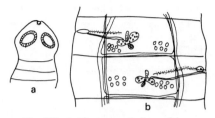

Fig. 331. *Parvirostrum reticulatum* Fuhrmann, 1908. a. Scolex. b. Proglottids.

gina posterior to cirrus pouch. Seminal receptacle small. Uterus saclike. Parasites of Falconiformes, Passeriformes. Brazil, India.
Type species: *P. recticulatum* Fuhrmann, 1908.

42a. Testes and ovary partly cortical ....
...................................*Chitinorecta* **Meggitt, 1927.** (Fig. 332)
Diagnosis: Rostellum with two circles of hooks. Strobila short, of few segments. Proglottids craspedote. Genital pores alternating irregularly. Genital ducts pass between osmoregulatory canals. Cirrus pouch crosses median line of segment. Vas deferens convoluted at anterior margin of proglottid. Testes few, partly cortical, partly medullary. Ovary large, mainly medullary but with ventral, cortical branches. Vitellaria postovarian. Vaginal pore dorsal to cirrus pore. Uterus lobated. Parasites of Charadriiformes. Egypt.
Type species: *C. agnosta* Meggitt, 1927.

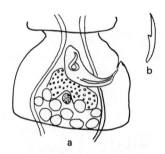

Fig. 332. *Chitinorecta agnosta* Meggett, 1927. a. Proglottid. b. Rostellar hook.

42b. Testes and ovary entirely medullary 43

43a. Uterus reticular ....*Lapwingia* **Singh, 1952.**
Diagnosis: Rostellum with two circles of hooks. Gravid proglottids longer than wide. Genital pore irregularly alternating. Genital atrium spinous. Genital ducts pass between osmoregulatory canals. Cirrus pouch oblique, crossing osmoregulatory canals. Vas deferens

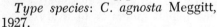

convoluted near proximal end of cirrus pouch. Testes mainly posterior to ovary. Ovary bilobed, preequatorial. Vitelline gland postovarian. Vagina posterior to cirrus pouch. Seminal receptacle present. Uterus reticular, extensive. Parasites of Charadriiformes. India.

Type species: *L. reticulosa* Singh, 1952.

43b. Uterus saccular or horseshoe-shaped 44
44a. Uterus horseshoe-shaped ....
...............................*Proparuterina* **Fuhrmann, 1911.** (**Fig. 333**)

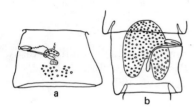

Diagnosis: Rostellum with two circles of hooks. Proglottids craspedote. Genital pores alternating irregularly. Genital ducts pass between osmoregulatory canals. Cirrus pouch small. Testes in a posterior, median group. Ovary small, median. Vitelline gland postovarian. Vagina posterior to cirrus pouch. Seminal receptacle present. Gravid uterus in form of inverted-U. Parasites of Caprimulgiformes. Australasia.

Fig. 333. *Proparuterina aruensis* Fuhrmann, 1911. a. Mature proglottid. b. Gravid proglottid.

Type species: *P. aruensis* Fuhrman, 1911.

44b. Uterus saccular 45
45a. Testes partly anterior to ovary. Cirrus pouch mainly medial to osmoregulatory canals ....
....*Parvitaenia* **Burt, 1940.** (**Fig. 334**)

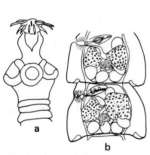

Diagnosis: Rostellum with two circles of hooks. Gravid proglottids longer than wide. Segments craspedote. Genital ducts pass between osmoregulatory canals. Genital pores alternate irregularly. Genital atrium deep. Cirrus armed or not. Cirrus pouch large, mostly or entirely intervascular. Testes few, mainly posterior to ovary but a few dorsal and anterior to ovary. Ovary bilobed, large. Vitelline gland postovarian. Vagina posterior to cirrus pouch. Seminal receptacle present. Uterus first bilobed, then saclike. Parasites of Ciconiiformes. Ceylon, Celebes, Japan, Java, Mexico, South America.

Fig. 334. *Parvitaenia ardeolae* Burt, 1940. a. Scolex. b. Proglottids.

Type species: *P. ardeolae* Burt, 1940.

45b. No testes anterior to ovary. Cirrus pouch crosses osmoregulatory canals ....*Anomotaenia* Cohn, 1900. (Fig. 335)

Diagnosis: Rostellum with two circles of hooks. Proglottids craspedote, wider than long or longer than wide. Genital pores irregularly alternating. Genital ducts pass between osmoregulatory canals. Cirrus pouch crosses osmoregulatory canals. Testes numerous, mainly posterior to ovary. Ovary median. Vitelline gland postovarian. Vagina posterior to cirrus pouch. Seminal vesicle present. Uterus an irregular sac. Parasites of Chara-

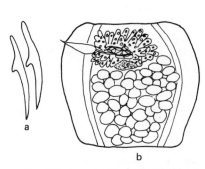

Fig. 335. *Anomotaenia nymphaea* (Schrank, 1790) Fuhrmann, 1908. After Dubinina (1953). a. Rostellar hooks. b. Proglottid.

driiformes, Falconiformes, Cuculiformes, Passeriformes, Ciconiiformes, Trogoniformes, Piciformes, Anseriformes, Galliformes, Gruiformes, Strigiformes, Apterygiformes, Cypseliformes. Also, in *Sorex.* Cosmopolitan.

Type species: A. microrhyncha (Krabbe, 1869) Cohn, 1900.

Table of characters of most species: Mathevossian (1963), Mettrick (1958), Singh (1959).

Key to the Subfamilies of Anoplocephalidae

1a. Uterus with one or more paruterine organs ....
.............................Thysanosomatinae Skrjabin, 1933. (P. 218)

1b. Uterus without paruterine organs 2

2a. Cirrus pouch absent ....Rajotaeniinae Yamaguti, 1959. (P. 222)
2b. Cirrus pouch present 3

3a. Gravid uterus tubular, saccular, lobed or reticular, never breaking into egg capsules ....
.............................Anoplocephalinae Blanchard, 1891. (P. 222)

3b. Gravid uterus breaking into egg capsules 4

4a. Egg capsules each with a single egg ....
.............................Linstowiinae Fuhrmann, 1907. (P. 238)

4b. Egg capsules each with several eggs ....
.............................Inermicapsiferinae López-Neyra, 1943. (P. 243)

Key to the Genera of Thysanosomatinae

1a. Posterior margin of proglottid fringed ....
.................................*Thysanosoma* Diesing, 1835. (Fig. 336)

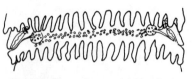

Diagnosis: Posterior margin of each proglottid with fringe-like outgrowths. Two sets of reproductive organs per proglottid. Genital pores bilateral. Cirrus pouch small, cylindrical. Cirrus slender, unarmed (?). Testes numerous, between two ovaries. Seminal vesicles ab-

Fig. 336. *Thysanosoma actinioides* Diesing, 1834. After Spassky (1951).

sent. Ovary and vitellaria mixed into a compound germovitellarium which is poral. Vagina posterior to cirrus pouch. Seminal receptacle small. Uterus a sinuous tube which breaks into many paruterine organs, each with several eggs. Eggs lacking pyriform apparatus. Parasites of ruminents. North and South America.

Type species: *T. actinioides* Diesing, 1835.

1b. Posterior margin of proglottid not fringed ....…...............2

2a. Reproductive organs doubled in each proglottid ....
....*Wyominia* Scott, 1941. (Fig. 337)

Diagnosis: Suckers pedunculated. Posterior margins of proglottides not fringed. Double set of reproductive organs in each segment. Genital ducts passing between osmoregulatory canals. Genital ducts bilateral; male pore anterior, lateral, female pore posterior, somewhat dorsal. Cirrus pouch narrow, reaching ventral osmoregulatory canal. Cirrus unarmed. Testes 50-62, in single row in posterior two-thirds of proglottid. Seminal vesicles absent. Ovary

Fig. 337. *Wyominia tetoni* Scott, 1941. Scolex.

and vitelline gland poral. Seminal receptacle large, between ovary and vitelline gland. Uterus first a transverse tube anterior to testes, then breaking into paruterine organs each with about six eggs. Parasites of ruminants (mountain sheep). North America.

Type species: *W. tetoni* Scott, 1941.

2b. Reproductive organs single in each proglottid 3

3a. Two paruterine organs per proglottid ....
.... *Stilesia* Railliet, 1893. (Fig. 338)

Diagnosis: Proglottids wider
than long, craspedote. Genital
pores unilateral, irregularly alternating. Genital atrium deep.
Cirrus pouch small. Testes few,
in two lateral fields. Seminal
vesicles absent. Ovary and vitellaria united into poral germovitellarium. Vaginal pore dor-

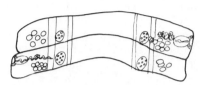

Fig. 338. *Stilesia vittata* Railliet, 1896.

soposterior to cirrus pore. Uterus first a bilobed sac with slender
isthmus, then replaced by two paruterine organs. Parasites of
ruminants. Asia, Africa, Europe.
Type species: S. *globipunctata* (Rivolta, 1874) Railliet, 1893.

3b. One or several paruterine organs per proglottid 4

4a. One paruterine organ per proglottid ....…..............5

4b. Several paruterine organs per proglottid ....…......7

5a. Ovary and vitelline gland united into single germovitellarium
....….............*Avitellina* Gough, 1911. (Fig. 339)

Diagnosis: Strobila large, narrow, proglottids wider than long.
External   metamerism   poorly
marked or absent in anterior half
of strobila. Dorsal osmoregulatory
canals liable to atrophy in posterior half of strobila. Genital
pores irregularly alternating. Osmoregulatory canals ventral to
genital ducts. Cirrus pouch small.
Seminal vesicles absent. Testes in
two lateral groups, each subdivided by osmoregulatory canals.

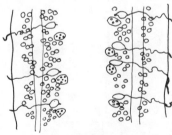

Fig. 339. *Avitellina arctica* Kolmakov,
1938.

Ovary and vitellaria united into poral germovitellarium. Seminal
receptacle present. Paruterine organ single, containing fibrous
capsules each with several eggs. Parasites of ruminants. Europe,
Asia, Africa, Philippines.
Type species: A. *centripunctata* (Rivolta, 1874) Gough, 1911.
Key to species: Spassky (1951).

5b. **Ovary and vitelline gland separate, although ovary may sur-
round vitelline gland** 6

6a. Proglottids narrower than scolex. External seminal vesicle absent ....*Mogheia* **Lopez-Neyra, 1944.**

Diagnosis: Scolex large, neck absent. Proglottids wider than long, narrower than scolex. Genital pores irregularly alternating. Genital ducts passing between osmoregulatory canals. Cirrus pouch small. Testes few, antiporal. Seminal vesicles absent. Ovary slightly poral. Vitelline gland posteromedial to ovary. Vagina posterior to cirrus. Seminal receptacle small. Uterus persistant as a spherical sac filling nearly entire length of segment, with single spherical paruterine organ. Eggs without pyriform apparatus. Parasites of Passeriformes (Turdidae), India.

Type species: M. *orbiuterina* (Moghe, 1933) Lopez-Neyra, 1944.

6b. Proglottids wider than scolex. External seminal vesicle present. Testes both poral and antiporal to ovary ....
.... *Columbia* **Srivastava and Capoor, 1965. (Fig. 340)**

Diagnosis: Scolex simple, narrower than strobila. Proglottids wider than long. Genital pores irregularly alternating. Cirrus pouch not reaching osmoregulatory canals. Testes in poral and antiporal groups. Internal and external (?) seminal vesicles present. Ovary bilobed, poral. Vitelline gland compact, transversely elongated, postovarian. Vagina irregularly dorsal and ventral to cirrus pouch. Uterus a transverse, lobulated sac. Paruterine organ single. Parasites of columbiformes. India.

Type species: C. *allahabadi* Srivastava and Capoor, 1965.

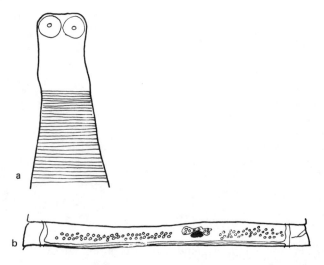

Fig. 340. *Columbia allahabadi* Srivastava and Capoor, 1965. a. Scolex. b. Proglottid.

7a. About 300 paruterine organs per proglottid ....
...........................*Thysaniezia* Skrjabin, 1926. (Fig. 341)

Diagnosis: Proglottids wider than long. Genital pores irregularly alternating. Cirrus pouch oblique, small. Cirrus armed. Testes numerous in two lateral, extravascular fields. Genital ducts passing between osmoregulatory canals. Vas deferens convoluted anterior to cirrus pouch, lateral to poral osmoregulatory canals. Ovary lobated, poral. Vitelline gland

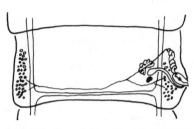

Fig. 341. *Thysaniezia ovilla* (Rivolta, 1878) Skrjabin, 1926. After Mathevossian (1938).

compact, postovarian. Vagina posterior to cirrus pouch. Seminal receptacle present. Uterus first a transverse tube, replaced by numerous (300) paruterine organs. Parasites of ruminants. Europe. Asia, Africa, Australia, Argentina.
Type species: *T. ovilla* (Rivolta, 1878) Skrjabin, 1926.

7b. Eight to twelve paruterine organs per proglottid ....
....*Ascotaenia* Baer, 1927.

Diagnosis: Proglottids wider than long. External metamerism indistinct in anterior half of proglottid. Genital pores irregularly alternating. Cirrus pouch small. Testes few, in two fields separated by ovary. Osmoregulatory canals ventral to genital ducts. Ovary poral. Vitelline gland rudimentary. Uterus first a transverse tube, then replaced by 8-12 paruterine organs, each with several eggs. Parasites of ruminants. Russia.
Type species: *A. pygargi* (Cholodkovsky, 1902) Baer, 1927.

DIAGNOSIS OF THE ONLY GENUS IN RAJOTAENIINAE
Rajotaenia Wertheim, 1954 (Fig. 342)

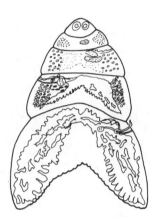

Fig. 342. *Rajotaenia gerbilli* Wertheim, 1954. Entire worm.

Diagnosis: Scolex with convex base. Strobila with three or four proglottids, each much wider than long. Terminal segment with serrated, concave posterior border. Osmoregulatory system with 20 longitudinal canals. Genital pores preequatorial, regularly alternating. Cirrus pouch and cirrus lacking. Testes about 100, in two lateral groups; poral group not extending anterior to genital ducts. Ovary multilobate, medial. Vitelline gland (?). Vaginal pore posterior to male pore. Seminal receptacle anterior to ovary. Uterus appears as several transverse tubes with lateral outpocketings. Eggs with pyriform apparatus (?). Parasites of Rodentia (gerbil). Israel.

Type species: *R. gerbilli* Wertheim, 1954. (Exact identity uncertain).

Key to the Genera of Anoplocephalinae

1a. Parasites of birds 2
1b. Parasites of mammals 15
2a. Two sets of reproductive organs in each proglottid 3
2b. One set of reproductive organs in each proglottid 7
3a. Scolex rudimentary, without suckers. Strobila wider than long
....*Eurycestus* Clark, 1954.

Diagnosis: Scolex rudimentary, lacking suckers. Proglottids very wide and very short, acraspedote. Two sets of reproductive organs per proglottid. Genital pores marginal, preequatorial. Cirrus pouch cylindrical. Cirrus long, armed. Testes in two posterolateral groups, overlapping poral wing of ovary. Ovary bialate, medial to testes. Vitelline gland postovarian. Vagina posterior to cirrus pouch, coiled. Seminal receptacle slender. Uterus a transverse tube with sac-like outgrowths. Osmoregulatory canals reticular. Parasites of Charadriiformes (avocet). North America.

Type species: *E. avoceti* Clark, 1954. (Exact identity uncertain).

3b. **Scolex normal, with suckers. Strobila longer than wide** 4

4a. Suckers each with two muscular projections 5

4b. Suckers without muscular projections 6

5a. Small glands present anterior to each sucker. Uterus simple ....*Moniezioides* Fuhrmann, 1918. (Fig. 343)

Diagnosis: Scolex with four suckers, each with two protuberances. Four groups of small glands present between suckers. Neck absent. Proglottids wider than long, craspedote. Two sets of reproductive organs in each segment, except for uterus which is single. Genital pores lateral. Cirrus pouch slender, crossing osmoregulatory canals. Testes in single, dorsal, medullary field, median and posterior to ovaries. Ovaries bialate, submedian. Vitelline glands compact, submedian. Vaginas posterior to cirrus pouches. Seminal receptacles present. Uterus first a single, transverse tube, assuming two swellings when gravid. Parasites of parrots. New Caledonia.

Type species: M. rouxi Fuhrmann, 1918.

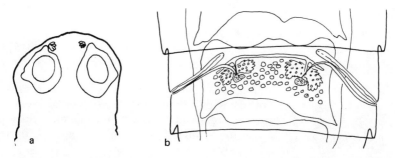

Fig. 343. *Moniezioides rouxi* Fuhrmann, 1918. After Fuhrmann (1932). a. Scolex. b. Proglottid.

5b. Glands not present anterior to suckers. Uterus with posterior outpocketings ....*Coelodela* Shipley, 1900.

Diagnosis: Scolex with four suckers, each with two lateral, muscular projections. Proglottids wider than long, craspedote. Each segment with double sets of reproductive organs except uterus, which is single. Genital pores lateral. Cirrus pouch bulbous. Genital atrium deep. External and internal seminal vesicles present. Testes numerous in single anterior field. Ovaries lobated, in lateral medulla. Vitelline glands postovarian. Vagina opens anterior to cirrus. Seminal receptacle present. Uterus a transverse tube with posterior outpocketings. Parasites of Columbiformes. New Guinea.

Type species: C. kuvaria Shipley, 1900.

6a. Gravid uterus reticular ....*Cittotaenia* Riehm, 1881. (Fig. 344)

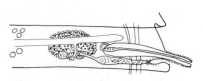

Fig. 344. *Cittotaenia avicola* Fuhrmann, 1897.

Diagnosis: Suckers simple. Proglottids much wider than long, craspedote. Two sets of reproductive organs per segment. Genital pores marginal. Genital ducts dorsal to osmoregulatory canals. Cirrus pouch muscular. Testes scattered throughout medulla. Internal seminal vesicle present; external seminal vesicle absent. Ovary multilobate, poral. Vitelline gland compact, postovarian. Vagina posterior to cirrus pouch. Seminal receptacle present. Uterus reticular. Eggs with pyriform apparatus. Parasites of rodents, lagomorphs, artiodactyles, monotreme (echidna); Psittaciformes, anseriformes, Rheiformes. Cosmopolitan.

Type species: *C. denticulata* (Rudolphi, 1804) Riehm, 1881.

6b. **Gravid uterus horseshoe-shaped** ....
....*Paronia* Diamare, 1900. (Fig. 345)

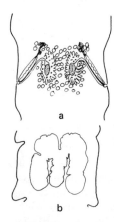

Fig. 345. *Paronia coryllidis* Burt, 1939.
a. Mature proglottid.
b. Gravid proglottid.

Diagnosis: Suckers simple. Neck absent. Proglottids wider than long. Two sets of reproductive organs in each segment. Genital ducts dorsal to osmoregulatory canals. Ventral canals commonly with valves at origins of transverse anastomoses. Cirrus pouch elongate, crossing osmoregulatory canals. Testes numerous, in dorsal intervascular field. Internal seminal vesicle present. External seminal vesicle absent. Ovaries multilobate, submedian. Vitelline glands compact, interovarian. Vagina ventral, dorsal or posterior to cirrus pouch. Seminal receptacle present. Uteri horseshoe-shaped, sometimes with outgrowths or joined by dorsal branches. Parasites of Passeriformes, Piciformes, Columbiformes, Rhamphastiformes. Australia, New Guinea, Africa, South America, Ceylon, Thailand, India, Taiwan, Sumatra.

Type species: *P. trichoglossi* (Linstow, 1888) Diamare, 1900.
Key to species: Spassky (1951).

7a. Gravid uterus a three-lobed sac ....
....*Triuterina* **Fuhrmann, 1921.** (Fig. 346)

Diagnosis: Scolex unknown. Proglottids somewhat wider than long. Single set of reproductive organs per segment. Genital pores irregularly alternating. Genital ducts passing between osmoregulatory canals. Cirrus pouch crosses ventral osmoregulatory canal, very muscular, with strong sphincter at base. Testes numerous, occupying most of medulla. Ovary lobated, poral.

Fig. 346. *Triuterina anoplocephaloides* (Fuhrmann, 1902) Fuhrmann, 1921. Gravid uterus.

Vitelline gland postovarian. Vagina ventral to cirrus, with distal sphincter. Seminal receptacle present. Uterus a three-lobed sac, two lobes lateral, one lobe anterior. Parasites of parrots. Africa.
    Type species: *T. anoplocephaloides* (Fuhrmann, 1902) Fuhrmann, 1921.

7b. Gravid uterus a transverse sac or tube, or reticular 8

8a. Cirrovaginal atrium atrophied, genital pores absent in mature and gravid proglottids but present in immature ones ....
....*Aporina* **Fuhrmann, 1902.** (Fig. 347)

Diagnosis: Single set of reproductive organs per segment. Genital pores irregularly alternating in immature proglottids, atrophied in mature and gravid ones. Genital ducts passing dorsal to osmoregulatory canals. Cirrus pouch small, poorly developed.

Fig. 347. *Aporina alba* Fuhrmann, 1902.

Testes numerous, surrounding ovary. Ovary large, fan-shaped, median. Vitelline gland postovarian, somewhat poral. Vagina posterior to cirrus pouch. Uterus a transverse sac that overreaches osmoregulatory canals laterally, then bends forward. Parasites of Psittaciformes. Brazil, India.
    Type species: *A. alba* Fuhrmann, 1902.

8b. Genital pores present on all proglottids 9

9a. **Vitelline gland anterior to ovary** ....*Arostellina* **Neiland, 1955.**

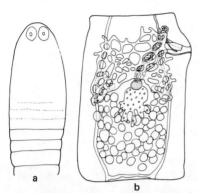

Diagnosis: Scolex small, not demarcated from wider neck. Most proglottids longer than wide, acraspedote. One set of reproductive organs per proglottid. Genital ducts dorsal to osmoregulatory canals. Genital pores irregularly alternating. Testes posterior and lateral to ovary. Seminal vesicles absent. Cirrus pouch small, not reaching osmoregulatory canals. Ovary lobulated, median. Vitelline gland compact, preovarian. Vagina opening posterior to cirrus. Seminal receptacle present. Uterus reticular, arising anterior to ovary, occupying entire proglottid when gravid. Parasites of hummingbird. Nicaragua, Brazil.

Fig. 348. *Arostellina reticulata* Neiland, 1955. a. Scolex. b. Proglottid.

Type species: *A. reticulata* Neiland, 1955.

9b. **Vitellaria posterior to ovary** 10

10a. **Testes in continuous transverse band anterior to ovary** ....
....*Taufikia* **Woodland, 1928.**

Diagnosis: Scolex with four large suckers. Proglottids wider than long, craspedote. Single set of reproductive organs per proglottid. Dorsal osmoregulatory canals absent. Genital pores irregulatory canal. Testes few, in single, preovarian field. Internal seminal vesicle present, external absent. Ovary bilobed, slightly poral. Vitelline gland postovarian.

Fig. 349. *Taufikia edmondi* Woodland, 1928. After Fuhrmann (1932).

Vagina posterior to cirrus pouch. Uterus saccular. Parasites of Accipitriformes. Africa.

Type species: *T. edmondi* Woodland, 1928.

10b. **Testes not as above** 11

11a. Uterus first appears reticular ....
.....................................*Monoecocestus* **Beddard, 1914. (Fig. 350)**

Diagnosis: Neck absent. Scolex simple. Proglottids wider than long, craspedote. Single set of reproductive
organs per segment. Genital pores
unilateral or irregularly alternating.
Cirrus pouch well developed. Cirrus
armed. Testes numerous, in posterior
medulla. External and internal seminal
vesicles present. Ovary medial or poral.
Vitelline gland postovarian. Vaginal
pore anterior to cirrus pore. Seminal
receptacle present. Uterus first appears

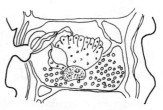

Fig. 350. *Monoecocestus anoplocephaloides* (Douthitt, 1915) Harke-
ma, 1936. After Baer (1927).

reticular, later becomes saccular. Eggs with pyriform apparatus.
Parasites of Struthioniformes, Rodentia, Artiodactyla (peccary).
North and South America.

Type species: *M. decrescens* (Diesing, 1856) Beddard, 1914.
Key to North American species: Wardle and McCleod (1952).

11b. Uterus always a transverse tube or sac 12

12a. Gravid uterus horseshoe-shaped, with outgrowths ....
...............................*Hemiparonia* **Baer, 1925. (Fig. 351)**

Diagnosis: Scolex long, not set off from
neck. Proglottids not much wider than
long, craspedote. Single set of reproductive
organs per segment. Genital pores unilateral. Cirrus pouch long. Testes in single
field posterior and antiporal to ovary. Internal and external seminal vesicles absent.
Genital ducts dorsal to osmoregulatory
canals. Ovary median. Vitelline gland postovarian. Vagina ventral to cirrus pouch.
Seminal receptacle present. Uterus horseshoe-shaped, with convexity directed anteriorly.

Type species: *H. cacatuae* (Maplestone,
1922) Baer, 1925.

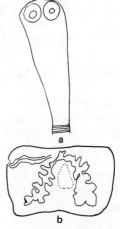

Fig. 351. *Hemiparonia ca-
catuae* (Maplestone, 1922)
Baer, 1925. a. Scolex. b.
Gravid proglottid.

12b. Gravid uterus not horseshoe-shaped 13

13a. **Testes mainly lateral to ovary** .... *Killigrewia* **Meggitt, 1927.**
Diagnosis: Proglottids wider than long. Single set of reproductive organs per segment. Genital pores irregularly alternating, persisting throughout strobila. Osmoregulatory canals ventral to genital ducts. Cirrus pouch small. Testes in poral and antiporal groups. Ovary slightly poral. Vitelline gland postovarian. External and internal seminal vesicles present. Seminal receptacle present. Uterus a transverse sac with outgrowths. Parasites of Columbiformes. Asia, Taiwan, Europe, Africa, Australia, North and South America.
Type species: *K. frivola* Meggitt, 1927.

13b. **Testes mainly anterior and lateral to ovary** 14

14a. **Ovary fan-shaped. Seminal receptacle present** ....
....*Pulluterina* **Smithers, 1954.**
Diagnosis: Scolex unknown. Proglottids wider than long. Single set of reproductive organs per segment. Dorsal osmoregulatory canals absent. Genital pores irregularly alternating. Cirrus pouch crosses dorsal to osmoregulatory canal. Testes numerous, mainly lateral to ovary but several anterior and posterior to it. Internal seminal vesicle present. Ovary fan-shaped, nearly length of proglottid. Vitelline gland postovarian. Vagina ventral to cirrus pouch. Seminal receptacle present. Uterus a transverse sac with anterior and posterior branches. Eggs with polar points on middle shell. Parasites of parrots. New Zealand.
Type species: *P. nestoris* Smithers, 1954.

14b. **Ovary bilobed. Seminal receptacle absent** ....
....*Gidhaia* **Johri, 1934.**
Diagnosis: Scolex unknown. Dorsal osmoregulatory canals absent. Genital pores irregularly alternating. Reproductive organs single. Genital ducts dorsal to osmoregulatory canal. Cirrus pouch not reaching osmoregulatory canal. Testes few, mainly anterior and lateral to ovary. Ovary bilobed, nearly median. Vitelline gland postovarian. Vagina posterior to cirrus pouch. Seminal receptacle absent. Uterus a transverse sac with lateral ends subdivided. Parasites of vulture. India.
Type species: *G. indica* Johri, 1934.

15a. **One set of reproductive organs in each proglottid** 16

15b. **Two sets of reproductive organs in each proglottid** 30

16a. Uterus reticular 17

16b. Uterus a transverse sac or tube 20

17a. Vagina anterior to cirrus pouch ....
..................*Monoecocestus* Beddard, 1914. (See page 227).

17b. Vagina posterior to cirrus pouch 18

18a. External seminal vesicle absent. Prostate gland present ....
....*Andrya* Railliet, 1893. (Fig. 352)

Diagnosis: Scolex spheroid. Neck short. Proglottids wider than long, craspedote. Single set of reproductive organs per segment. Genital pores unilateral or irregularly alternating. Genital ducts dorsal to osmoregulatory canals. Distinct prostate gland present close to cirrus pouch, with duct joining vas deferens before entering cirrus pouch. Testes numerous, mainly antiporal and anterior to ovary. Ovary multilobulate, poral or median. Vitelline gland compact, postovarian. External seminal vesicle absent, internal seminal vesicle present. Vaginal pore posterior to cirrus pouch. Seminal receptacle present, large. Uterus first reticular, then saclike, lobated. Eggs with pyriform appa-

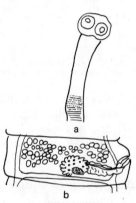

Fig. 352. *Andrya cuniculi* (Blanchard, 1891) Railliet, 1893. a. Scolex. b. Proglottid.

ratus. Parasites of Rodentia. Europe, Africa, North America, Russia.
Type species: *A. rhopalocephala* (Riehm, 1881) Railliet, 1893.

18b. External seminal vesicle present. Prostate gland absent 19

19a. Seven to 15 testes. Eggs with polar filaments ....
..................................*Hymenandrya* Smith, 1954.

Diagnosis: Proglottids wider than long, craspedote. Single set of reproductive organs per segment. Genital pores unilateral. Cirrus pouch crosses poral osmoregulatory canals. External and internal seminal vesicles present. Testes few (7-15) divided by ovary into poral and antiporal groups. Ovary lobated, slightly poral. Vitelline gland postovarian. Vagina posterior to cirrus pouch. Uterus reticular. Middle egg membrane with polar filament on each end. Parasites of Rodentia (pocket gopher). North America.
Type species: *H. thomomyis* Smith, 1954.

19b. **Testes more numerous. Eggs with pyriform apparatus** ....
............*Aprostatandrya* **(Kirschenblat, 1938) Spassky, 1951.**

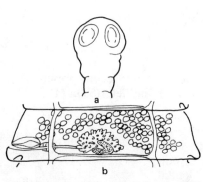

Diagnosis: Scolex wider than neck. Proglottids wider than long, craspedote. Single set of reproductive organs per segment. Genital pores unilateral. Cirrus pouch crosses poral osmoregulatory canals. Testes numerous, antiporal, anterior or posterior to ovary. External and internal seminal vesicle present. Prostate gland absent. Ovary lobated, median or poral. Vitelline gland posterior to or overlapping ovary. Vaginal pore posterior to cirrus pore. Seminal receptacle present, large. Uterus reticular. Eggs with pyriform apparatus. Parasites of Rodentia. Africa, Russia, North America.

Fig. 353. *Aprostatandrya sciuri* (Rausch, 1947) Spassky, 1951. a. Scolex. b. Proglottid.

Type species: A. *macrocephala* (Douthitt, 1915) Spassky, 1951.

20a. **Ovary in antiporal half of proglottid** ....
.....................................*Parabertiella* **Nybelin, 1917. (Fig. 354)**

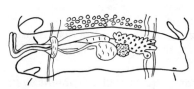

Diagnosis: Suckers on small elevations, separated by deep grooves. Proglottids wider than long, craspedote. Single set of reproductive organs per proglottid. Genital pores irregularly alternating. Genital ducts dorsal to osmoregulatory canals. Genital cloaca has a strong sphincter. Cirrus pouch reaches median line. Cirrus long, armed. Internal seminal vesicle absent. Testes numerous, in single anterior, intervascular field. Ovary aporal, multilobed. Vitelline gland compact, postovarian. Vagina posterior to cirrus pouch. Seminal receptacle present, poral to ovary. Uterus a transverse sac, exceeding osmoregulatory canals. Eggs with pyriform apparatus. Parasites of marsupials. Australia.

Fig. 354. *Parabertiella campanulata* Nybelin, 1917. After Baer (1927).

Type species: P. *campanulata* Nybelin, 1917.

20b. **Ovary median or nearly median, or poral** **21**

21a. Ovary extending entire width of medulla. Genital pores unilateral ....*Anoplocephala* Blanchard, 1848. (Fig. 355)

Diagnosis: Proglottids wider than long, craspedote. Single set of reproductive organs per segment. Genital pores unilateral. Genital ducts dorsal to osmoregulatory canals. Scolex may have a pair of lappets on each side. Cirrus pouch well developed. Testes numerous, medullary. Ovary multilobate,

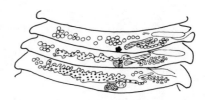

Fig. 355. *Anoplocephala spatula* (Linstow, 1901) Janicki, 1910. After Bischoff (1913).

slightly poral, filling most of medullary width. Vitelline gland postovarian. Vagina ventroanterior to cirrus pouch. Seminal receptacle present. Uterus a transverse sac. Eggs with pyriform apparatus. Parasites of Hyracoidea, Perissodactyla, gorilla. Cosmopolitan.

Type species: *A. perfoliata* (Goeze, 1782) Blanchard, 1848.

21b. Ovary not extending entire width of medulla. Genital pores unilateral or alternating 22

22a. Testes in two fields anterior to ovary. Proglottids very much wider than long ....*Meggittina* Lynsdale, 1953.

Diagnosis: Scolex very small, with four minute suckers. Neck very wide. Strobila consisting of not more than two very wide, very short proglottids. Single set of reproductive organs per segment. Genital pores alternating, on anterior face of free border of proglottid. Cirrus pouch curved. Testes numerous (250-350) in two fields anterior to ovary, most numerous on aporal side. External and internal seminal vesicles absent. Ovary poral, transversely elongated. Vitelline gland compact, medial to ovary. Seminal vesicle present. Uterus an irregular, transverse sac. Eggs lacking pyriform apparatus. Parasites of domestic rodents. Africa.

Type species: *M. baeri* Lynsdale, 1953.

22b. Testes not as above 23

23a. **Testes occupying entire width of medulla** ....
...............................*Pseudanoplocephala* **Baylis, 1927.** (**Fig. 356**)

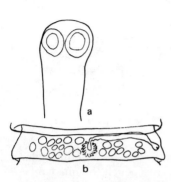

Diagnosis: Scolex small. Neck narrow. Proglottids wider than long, craspedote. Genital pores unilateral. Dorsal osmoregulatory canals absent. Cirrus pouch elongate. Internal and external seminal vesicles present. Testes in two groups, one on each side of ovary. Ovary median. Vitelline gland postovarian. Vagina ventral to cirrus pouch. Seminal receptacle present. Uterus a transversely elongate sac with numerous outgrowths. Eggs lacking pyriform apparatus. Parasites of wild and domestic swine. Ceylon.

Fig. 356. *Pseudanoplocephala craw-fordi* Baylis, 1927. After Medaliar and Iyer (1938). a. Scolex, b. Proglottid.

Type species: P. crawfordi Baylis, 1927.

23b. **Testes not as above** 24

24a. **Testes antiporal to ovary** ....
...............................*Paranoplocephala* **Lühe, 1910.** (**Fig. 357**)

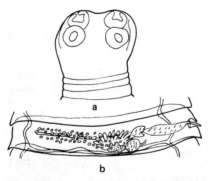

Diagnosis: Proglottids wider than long, craspedote. Single set of reproductive organs per proglottid. Genital pores unilateral or irregularly alternating. Genital ducts dorsal to osmoregulatory canals. Cirrus pouch well developed. Internal and external seminal vesicles present. Testes numerous, in single field aporal to ovary. Ovary lobated, poral. Vitelline gland postovarian. Vagina posterior to cirrus pouch. Seminal receptacle present. Uterus an irregular transverse sac. Eggs with pyriform apparatus. Parasites of Rodentia, Perissodactyla. Europe, Asia, North and South America.

Fig. 357. *Paranoplocephala mamillana* (Mehlis, 1831) Baer, 1927. After Spassky (1951). a. Scolex. b. Proglottid.

Type species: P. omphalodes (Hermann, 1783) Lühe, 1910.

Key to species: Spassky (1951).

24b. **Testes not as above** 25

25a. Genital pores unilateral ....
.... *Flabelloskrjabina* **Spassky, 1951. (Fig. 358)**
Diagnosis: Neck absent. Proglottids wider than long, craspedote. Single set of reproductive organs per segment. Genital pores unilateral. Cirrus pouch crosses osmoregulatory canals. Cirrus long. Testes numerous, mainly antiporal. Ovary fanshaped, median. Vitelline gland postovarian. Seminal receptacle present. Uterus an irregular, transverse sac anterior to vitellaria and seminal receptacle. Eggs with pyriform apparatus. Parasites of tapirs. Philippines (?), Brazil.
Type species: *F. tapirus* (Chin, 1938) Spassky, 1951.

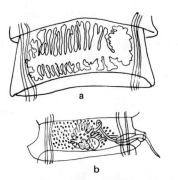

Fig. 358. *Flabelloskrjabinia tapirus* (Chin. 1938) Spassky, 1951. a. Gravid proglottid. b. Mature proglottid.

25b. Genital pores alternating 26

26a. Genital pores alternating regularly. Ovary median ....
....*Perutaenia* **Parra, 1953.**

Diagnosis: Neck absent. Proglottids wider than long, craspedote. Single set of reproductive organs per proglottid. Genital pores regularly alternating. Genital ducts dorsal to osmoregulatory canals. Cirrus pouch crossing osmoregulatory canals. Cirrus armed. Testes few (15-20) dorsal, mainly preovarian. Internal and external seminal vesicles present. Ovary median, bilobed. Vitelline gland postovarian. Vagina ventroanterior to cirrus pouch. Seminal receptacle (?). Uterus an irregular, transverse sac. Eggs with pyriform apparatus. Parasites of Rodentia (Mountain chinchilla). Peru.
Type species: *P. threlkeldi* (Parra, 1952), Parra, 1953.

26b. Genital pores irregularly alternating 27

27a. Vitelline gland poral to ovary ....
....*Lentiella* **Rêgo, 1964. (Fig. 359)**
Diagnosis: Scolex small, simple. Neck absent. Proglottids few (24-28), wider than long. Single set of reproductive organs per segment. Genital pores irregularly alternating. Cirrus pouch well

developed, containing armed cirrus. Testes few, in a single field posterior to ovary and vitellaria. Ovary lobated, slightly aporal. Vitelline gland compact, mainly poral to ovary. Vagina ventral to cirrus pouch. Seminal receptacle small. Uterus an irregular, transverse sac, mainly preequatorial. Eggs with pyriform apparatus. Osmoregulatory system not described. Parasites of rodents. Brazil. *Type species: L. machadoi* Rêgo, 1964.

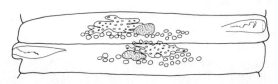

Fig. 359. *Lentiella machadoi* Rêgo, 1964.

27b. Vitelline gland median to ovary 28

28a. Ovary poral. Testes mainly in anterior half of proglottid ....
.........................*Bertiella* Stiles and Hassal, 1902. (Fig. 360)

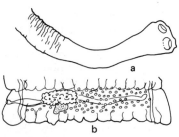

Fig. 360. *Bertiella hamadryadis* Pieran-toni, 1928. a. Scolex. b. Proglottid.

Diagnosis: suckers often on stalk-like outgrowths. Neck short. Proglottids wider than long, craspedote. Single set of reproductive organs per segment. Genital pores irregularly alternating. Genital ducts dorsal to osmoregulatory canals. Cirrus pouch developed. Testes numerous, in single field, mainly preovarian. Internal seminal vesicle present. Ovary lobated, slightly poral. Vitelline gland postovarian. Vaginal pore posterior or dorsal to cirrus pouch. Seminal receptacle present. Uterus an irregular, transverse sac. Eggs with pyriform apparatus. Parasites of primates (including man), Rodentia, Marsupialia. Australia, Asia, Europe, Africa, Oceanica, North and South America, Japan.

Type species: B. studeri (Blanchard, 1891) Stiles and Hassal, 1902.

Key to species: Spassky (1951).

28b. Ovary median 29

29a. Testes in two groups, mainly in posterior half of proglottid
....*Schizorchis* Hansen, 1948. (Fig. 361)

Diagnosis: Scolex small. Short
neck present. Proglottids wider than
long, craspedote. Single set of reproductive organs per segment.
Genital pores irregularly alternating.
Cirrus pouch crosses poral osmoregulatory canals. Cirrus unarmed.
Internal seminal vesicle present,
external seminal vesicle absent.
Testes numerous, in two lateral
groups in posterior half of proglot-

Fig. 361. *Schizorchis altaica* Gvos-
dev, 1951.

tid. Ovary slightly poral or median. Vitelline gland postovarian.
Vaginal pore posterior or ventral to cirrus. Seminal receptacle
visible only in gravid proglottids. Uterus an irregular, transverse
sac. Eggs with pyriform apparatus. Parasites of rodents (pika).
North America, Russia.

Type species: *S. ochotonae* Hansen, 1948.

29b. Testes in single group, mainly in anterior half of proglottid
....*Indotaenia* Singh, 1962. (Fig. 362)

Diagnosis: Scolex unarmed.
Suckers weakly developed.
Neck short. Proglottids slightly craspedote, wider than
long. Genital pores irregularly alternating. Genital atrium
shallow. Genital ducts pass
dorsal to osmoregulatory canals. Cirrus pouch cylindrical.
Cirrus unarmed. Internal and

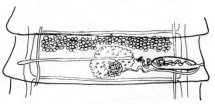

Fig. 362. *Indotaenia indica* Singh, 1962.

external seminal vesicles absent. Testes numerous (103-121), in a
single group anterior to all other genitalia. Vagina opens posterior
to cirrus. Seminal receptacle absent. Ovary median, fan-shaped,
near rear of proglottid. Vitellaria compact, overlapping posterior
third of ovary. Uterus a transverse sac with shallow diverticula,
exceeding osmoregulatory canals. Pyriform apparatus on eggs well
developed. Parasites of rodents (flying squirrel). India.

Type species: *I. indica* Singh, 1962.

31a. Interproglottid glands absent ....
....*Fuhrmannella* Baer, 1925. (Fig. 363)

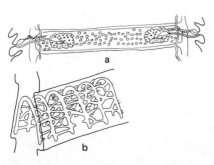

Fig. 363. *Fuhrmannella transvaalensis* Baer, 1925. After Fuhrmann (1932). a. Mature proglottid. b. Uterus.

Diagnosis: Scolex not described. Proglottids wider than long, craspedote. Double set of reproductive organs per segment. Genital pores marginal. No interproglottid glands. Genital ducts pass dorsal to osmoregulatory canals. Cirrus pouch not reaching osmoregulatory canals. Cirrus unarmed. Testes numerous, in single field between ovaries and occasionally extending lateral to ovaries. Ovaries compact, poral. Vitelline gland dorsal to ovary. Vaginal pore ventral to cirrus pore. Seminal receptacle present. Uterus reticular, arching anteriorly over genital glands. Eggs with pyriform apparatus. Parasites of rodents. Africa.

Type species: *F. transvaalensis* Baer, 1925.

31b. Interproglottid glands present 32

32a. Genital pores in hind quarter of margin of proglottid. Prostate gland present ....*Diandrya* Darrah, 1930. (Fig. 364)

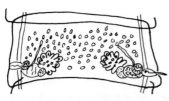

Fig. 364. *Diandrya composita* Darrah, 1930. After Fuhrmann (1932).

Diagnosis: Scolex simple. Proglottids wider than long, craspedote. Double set of reproductive organs per segment. Interproglottid glands present. Genital pores marginal, postequatorial. Cirrus pouch crosses osmoregulatory canals. Cirrus armed. Prostate gland with duct to vas deferens present. Testes numerous, in single intervascular field. Internal seminal vesicle present, external seminal vesicle absent. Ovary fan-shaped, poral. Vitelline gland postovarian. Vagina posteroventral to cirrus pouch. Seminal receptacle elongate. Uterus first reticular, ventral to testes, then filling entire segment. Parasites of Rodentia (marmot). North America.

Type species: *D. composita* Darrah, 1930.

32b. Genital pores in middle of margin of proglottid. Prostate gland absent ....*Moniezia* **Blanchard, 1891. (Fig. 365)**

Diagnosis: Scolex simple. Strobila very long. Proglottids wider than long, craspedote. Interproglottid glands present. Genital pores marginal, equatorial. Genital ducts dorsal to osmoregulatory canals. Cirrus pouch reaches poral osmoregulatory canal. Internal seminal vesicle present. Cirrus armed with minute spines. Testes in single, intervascular field, mainly posterior to and between ovaries. Ovary fan-shaped, poral. Vitelline gland compact, postovarian. Vagina posteroventral to cirrus pouch on one side and posterdorsal to cirrus pouch on the other. Seminal receptacle present. Uterus first reticular, then filling entire proglottid. Eggs with pyriform apparatus. Parasites of Perissodactyla, Artiodactyla, Primates (including man). Cosmopolitan.

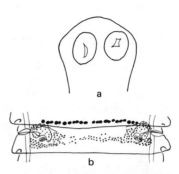

Fig. 365. *Moniezia expansa* (Rudolphi, 1910) Blanchard, 1891. After Mathevossian (1938). a. Scolex. b. Proglottid.

Type species: M. expansa (Rudolphi, 1805) Blanchard, 1891.
Key to species: Spassky (1951).

33a. Testes scattered throughout medulla ....
....*Cittotaenia* **Riehm, 1881. (See P. 224)**

33b. Testes not scattered throughout medulla **34**

34a. Testes divided into two groups in front of ovaries ....
....*Progamotaenia* **Nybelin, 1917. (Fig. 366)**

Diagnosis: Scolex simple. Neck absent. Proglottids wider than long, craspedote. Posterior edge of velum fringed or not. Two sets of reproductive organs per segment. Genital pores marginal. Genital ducts dorsal to osmoregulatory canals. Cirrus pouch large. Internal seminal vesicle present. Testes numerous, in two lateral, preovarian fields. Ovaries poral, posterior. Vitelline glands postequatorial. Vagina posterior to cirrus pouch. Seminal receptacle present.

Fig. 366. *Progamotaenia diaphana* (Zschokke, 1907) Baer, 1927.

Uterus paired or single, becoming sac-like when gravid. Eggs with or without (?) pyriform apparatus. Parasites of marsupials. Australia, New Guinea.
Type species: P. bancrofti (Johnston, 1912) Nybelin, 1917.
Key to species: Spassky (1951).

34b. Testes in band across medulla **35**

35a. Testes postuterine ....*Mosgovoyia* **Spassky, 1951. (Fig. 367)**
Diagnosis: Scolex with four, simple suckers. Neck indistinct. Strobila large. Proglottids wider than long, craspedote. Two sets of reproductive organs present. Genital pores bilateral. Genital ducts pass dorsal to osmoregulatory canals. Cirrus pouch crosses osmoregulatory canals. Slender internal seminal vesicle present, external seminal vesicle absent. Testes numerous, in single or double postequatorial, intervascular fields. Ovary poral, vitelline gland postovarian. Vagina ventral to cirrus pouch. Seminal receptacle present. Uterus first a simple sac, developing outgrowths when gravid. Eggs with well-developed pyriform apparatus. Parasites of Lagomorpha.
Type species: M. pectinata (Goeze, 1782) Spassky, 1951.

Fig. 367.   Mosgovoyia *pectinata* (Goeze, 1782) Spassky, 1951.

35b. Testes preovarian **36**

36a. Uterus double. Scolex cross-shaped. Eggs with pyriform apparatus ....*Fuhrmannodes* **Strand, 1942. (Fig. 368)**

Fig. 368. *Fuhrmannodes proterogyna* (Fuhrmann, 1932) Strand, 1942.

Diagnosis: Scolex large, cross-shaped, with prominent suckers. Neck short. Proglottids wider than long, craspedote, with lobed velum. Two sets of proterogynous reproductive organs per segment. Genital pores bilateral. Cirrus pouch small. Testes numerous, in continuous, preequatorial band. Internal and external seminal vesicles present. Ovary compact, transversely elongated. Vitelline gland postovarian. Seminal receptacle present. Vagina? Uterus double, lobated, filling entire medulla when gravid. Eggs with pyriform apparatus. Parasites of kangaroo. Australia.
Type species: F. proterogyna (Fuhrmann, 1932) Strand, 1942.

36b. Uterus single. Scolex not cross-shaped. Eggs without pyriform apparatus ......*Paramoniezia* Maplestone and Southwell, 1923. *Diagnosis*: Scolex small, with four very small suckers. Neck absent. Proglottids wider than long, craspedote. Two sets of reproductive organs per segment. Genital pores bilateral. Genital ducts dorsal to osmoregulatory canals. Cirrus pouch tubular, short. Internal seminal vesicle present. External seminal vesicle absent. Cirrus unarmed. Testes numerous (300), in single field anterior to uterus. Ovary poral. Vagina ventral to cirrus pouch on the right, variable on the left. Seminal receptacle present. Uterus a single, transverse tube. Eggs without pyriform apparatus. Parasites of domestic pig (?), wart hog. Australia, Africa.

Type species: *P. suis* Maplestone and Southwell, 1923.

Key to the Genera of Linstowiinae

1a. Parasites of reptiles 2
1b. Parasites of birds or mammals 5
2a. Two sets of reproductive organs per segment ....
....*Panceriella* Stunkard, 1969. (Fig. 369)

Diagnosis: Scolex simple, neck absent. Gravid proglottids may be longer than wide. Two sets of reproductive organs per segment. Genital pores bilateral. Cirrus pouch well developed. Seminal vesicles absent. Testes in two lateral groups, each surrounding ovary except on poral side. Genital ducts passing between osmoregulatory canals. Ovaries compact or bilobed, poral. Vitelline glands postovarian. Two uteri formed, each breaking into egg capsules each with one egg. Parasites of varanid lizard. Africa, Palestine.

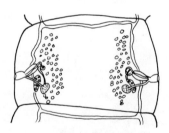

Fig. 369. *Panceriella varani* (Stossich, 1895) Stunkard, 1969.

Type species: *P. varani* (Stossich, 1895) Stunkard, 1969.

2b. One set of reproductive organs per segment 3

3a. Gravid proglottids two to six times as long as broad. Anterior two-fifths of mature proglottid free of reproductive organs ....
.... *Diochetos* Harwood, 1932.

Diagnosis: Scolex small, neck present. Strobila of few proglottids. Mature and gravid segments two to six times as long as wide. Genital pores irregularly alternating, preequatorial. Osmoregulatory canals two, poral one ventral to genital ducts. Testes numerous, tending to be arranged in two lateral groups. Ovary and postovarian vitelline gland small, median. Anterior two-fifths of mature proglottid free of reproductive organs. Uterus breaking into sparce egg capsules, each with single egg. Parasites of phrynosomid lizards. North America.

Type species: *D. phrynosomatis* Harwood, 1932.

3b. **Gravid proglottids not over twice as long as broad. Anterior two-fifths of mature proglottid not free of reproductive organs** **4**

4a. **Vaginal sphincter present. Cirrus pouch very long** ....
.... *Semenoviella* **Spassky, 1951. (Fig. 370)**

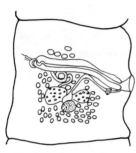

Diagnosis: Proglottids longer than wide, acraspedote. Genital pores irregularly alternating. Genital ducts passing between osmoregulatory canals. Cirrus pouch very large, passing median line of segment. Seminal vesicles absent. Testes encircling ovary. Ovary bilobed, median. Vitelline gland postovarian. Vagina posterior to cirrus pouch, with distal sphincter. Uterus breaks into egg capsules, each with single egg. Parasites of worm lizards. South America.

Fig. 370. *Semenoviella amphisbaenae* (Rudolphi, 1819) Spassky, 1951.

Type species: *S. amphisbaenae* (Rudolphi, 1819) Spassky, 1951.

4b. **Vaginal sphincter absent. Cirrus pouch not particularly long** .... *Oochoristica* **Lühe, 1898. (Fig. 371)**

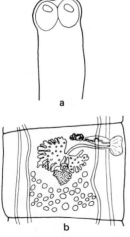

a

b

Fig. 371. *Oochoristica indica* Mizra, 1945. a. Scolex. b. Proglottid.

Diagnosis: Proglottids acraspedote, gravid segments usually longer than wide. Genital pores irregularly alternating. Genital atrium usually muscular. Genital ducts passing between or dorsal to osmoregulatory canals. Testes few or many. Cirrus pouch small. Seminal vesicles absent. Ovary bilobed, median or slightly poral. Vitelline gland postovarian. Vagina posterior to cirrus pouch, lacking sphincter. Seminal receptacle present. Uterus rapidly breaking into egg capsules containing single egg. Parasites of lizards, snakes and turtles. Africa, Europe, North and South America, Asia, Ceylon, Java, Australia, Macassar, Celebes, Philippines.

Type species: *O. tuberculata* (Rudolphi, 1819) Lühe, 1898.

5a. Testes separated into anterior and posterior groups ....
.... *Cycloskrjabinia* Spassky, 1951. (Fig. 372)

Diagnosis: Proglottids longer than wide. Genital pores irregularly alternating. Cirrus pouch spherical. Testes in preovarian and postovarian fields. Seminal vesicles absent. Ovary and vitelline gland bilobed, median. Vagina posterior to cirrus pouch. Uterus not described; eggs scattered in parenchyma. Parasites of Chiroptera. North America.

Type species: *C. taborensis* (Loewen, 1934) Spassky, 1951.

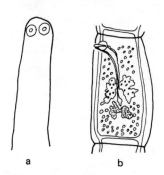

Fig. 372. *Cycloskrjabinia taborensis* (Loewen, 1934) Spassky, 1951. a. Scolex. b. Proglottid.

5b. Testes not separated into anterior and posterior groups 6

6a. Genital pores unilateral 7

6b. Genital pores irregularly alternating 9

7a. No testes anterior to ovary ....
.... *Oschmarenia* Spassky, 1951. (Fig. 373)

Diagnosis: Proglottids craspedote, wider than long. Genital pores unilateral. Cirrus pouch small. Seminal vesicles absent. Testes in single or double field behind or lateral to ovary. Ovary and vitelline gland median or submedian. Vagina posterior to cirrus pouch. Uterus? Eggs scattered singly in parenchyma. Parasites of Marsupialia, Mustelidae, Canidae (fox). Burma, Africa, North America.

Type species: *O. incognita* (Meggitt, 1927) Spassky, 1951.

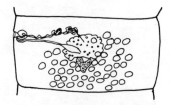

Fig. 373. *Oshmarenia oklahomensis* (Peery, 1939) Spassky, 1951.

7b. A few or many testes anterior to ovary 8
8a. Ovary between dorsal and ventral osmoregulatory canals ......
.... *Multicapsiferina* Fuhrmann, 1921.

Diagnosis: Genital pores unilateral. Genital ducts passing between osmoregulatory canals. Cirrus pouch small. Testes numerous, lateral, posterior and anterior to ovary. Ovary poral, between poral osmoregulatory canals. Vitelline gland lateral or posterior to ovary. Vagina posterior to cirrus pouch. Seminal receptacle long. Uterus breaking into egg capsules, each with single egg. Parasites of Galliformes (*Numida*). Africa.

Type species: *M. linstowi* (Parona, 1885) Fuhrmann, 1921.

8b.   Ovary medial to excretory canals ....*Sobolevina* **Spassky, 1951. (Fig. 374)**

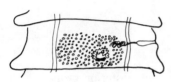

Fig. 374. *Sobolevina otidis* (Meggitt, 1927) Spassky, 1951.

Diagnosis: Proglottids craspedote, wider than long. Genital pores unilateral. Cirrus pouch small. Seminal vesicles absent. Testes numerous, in single field surrounding ovary, median to osmoregulatory canals. Ovary and postovarian vitelline gland slightly poral. Uterus not described. Eggs lie singly in parenchyma. Parasites of Otidiformes. Egypt.

Type species: *S. otidis* (Meggitt, 1927) Spassky, 1951.

9a.   Seminal receptacle absent ....*Mathevotaenia* **Akhumian, 1946. (Fig. 375)**

Fig. 375. *Mathevotaenia symmetrica* (Baylis, 1927) Akhumian, 1946.

Diagnosis: Proglottids craspedote, wider than long. Genital pores irregularly alternating. Genital ducts passing between or dorsal to osmoregulatory canals. Genital atrium is not sucker-like. Testes numerous, lateral and posterior to ovary. Seminal vesicles absent. Ovary and postovarian vitelline gland median. Vagina posterior to cirrus pouch. Seminal receptacle absent. Uterus replaced by thin egg capsules each with single egg. Parasites of rodents, marsupials, insectivores, viverrids, mustelids, lemurs, monkeys. Europe, Asia, Japan, North and South America, Africa, Panama, Tasmania.

Type species: *M. symmetrica* (Baylis, 1927) Akhumian, 1946. *Key to species*: Spassky (1951).

9b.   Seminal receptacle present **10**

10a. Genital ducts pass ventral to excretory vessels ....
.... *Linstowia* **Zschokke, 1899.** (Fig. 376)

Diagnosis: Proglottids numerous, craspedote, wider than long. Genital pores irregularly alternating. Cirrus pouch long or short. Seminal vesicles absent. Testes numerous in continuous, extensive field. Genital ducts passing ventral to osmoregulatory canals. Ovary and postovarian vitelline gland median. Vagina posterior or ventral to

Fig. 376. *Linstowia semoni* (Zschokke, 1846) Zschokke, 1899. After Baer (1927).

cirrus pouch. Seminal receptacle present. Uterus first a transverse tube, then breaking into egg capsules, each with one egg. Pyriform apparatus absent. Parasites of monotremes and marsupials. Australia, Tasmania, Brazil.

Type species: L. echidnae (Thompson, 1893) Zschokke, 1899.
Key to species: Spassky (1951).

10b. Genital ducts pass between or dorsal to excretory vessels ..11

11a. Vaginal sphincter present ....
....................................*Paratriotaenia* **Stunkard, 1965.** (Fig. 377)

Diagnosis: Scolex simple, neck present. Proglottids about as long as wide, slightly craspedote. Genital pores irregularly alternating. Genital atrium large, protrusible. Cirrus pouch small. Seminal vesicles absent. Testes numerous, in continuous field lateral and posterior to ovary. Lobated ovary and postovarian vitelline gland median. Vagina posterior to cirrus pouch, with powerful distal sphincter. Seminal receptacle present. Uterus not observed. Eggs single in parenchyma; pyriform apparatus absent. Parasites of Primates (marmoset). South America.

Type species: P. oedipomidatis Stunkard, 1965.

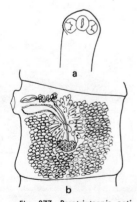

Fig. 377. *Paratriotaenia aetipomidatis* Stunkard, 1965. a. Scolex. b. Proglottid.

11b. Vaginal sphincter absent ....
................................*Atriotaenia* **Sandground, 1926.** (Fig. 378)

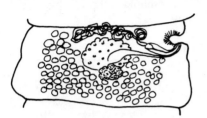

Fig. 378. *Atriotaenia incisa* (Railliet, 1899)
Spassky, 1951. After Joyeux and Baer (1936).

Diagnosis: Proglottids wider than long, craspedote. Genital pores irregularly alternating. Genital atrium may form large, sucker-like organ. Genital ducts passing dorsal to osmoregulatory canals. Testes mainly posterior and lateral to ovary, occasionally a few anterior. Seminal vesicles absent. Ovary and vitelline gland median. Vagina posterior to cirrus pouch, lacking sphincter. Seminal receptacle present. Uterus not observed. Eggs scattered singly in parenchyma. Parasites of mustelids and procyonids. Europe, Asia, Brazil, North America.

Type species: *A. sandgroundi* (Baer, 1935) Spassky, 1951.

Key to the Genera of Inermicapsiferinae

1a. Ovary and vitelline gland median or nearly median 2

1b. Ovary and vitelline gland definitely poral 3

2a. Genital pores unilateral ....
.... *Thysanotaenia* Beddard, 1911. (Fig. 379)

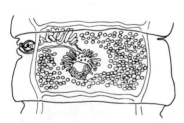

Fig. 379. *Thysanotaenia lemuris* Beddard, 1911. After Deblock and Diaouré (1962).

Diagnosis: Proglottids craspedote, wider than long. Genital pores unilateral, preequatorial. Cirrus pouch pyriform. Cirrus armed. Osmoregulatory canals ventral to genital ducts. Testes numerous (100-190), lateral and posterior to ovary; sometimes anterior to ovary on antiporal side. Vas deferens wide, convoluted. Ovary about median, bilate. Vitelline gland compact, postovarian. Vagina opening behind cirrus. Seminal receptacle proximal. Uterus first a transverse tube, rapidly breaking down into egg capsules, each with several eggs. Parasites of lemur, man. Malagasy, Cuba.

Type species: *T. lemuris* Beddard, 1911.

2b. Genital pores irregularly alternating ....
.... *Megacapsula* **Wahid, 1961. (Fig. 380)**

Diagnosis: Scolex not separated from neck by constriction. Neck short. Proglottids acraspedote, broader than long. Genital pores irregularly alternating. Genital atrium small. Genital ducts (?). Cirrus pouch robust, reaching poral osmoregulatory canals. Cirrus not described. Inner and outer seminal vesicles absent. Testes (26-30) in small postovarian field. Vagina posterior to cirrus pouch. Seminal receptacle present. Ovary median or very slightly poral, bilobed. Vitelline gland median, postovarian. Uterus first a transverse sac, then replaced by egg capsules each containing several eggs. Parasites of lizards. Africa.

Type species: *M. leiperi* Wahid, 1961.

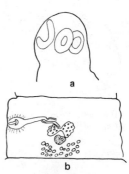

Fig. 380. *Megacapsula leiperi* Wahid, 1961. *a.* Scolex. *b.* Proglottid.

3a. No testes poral to vitelline gland ....
....*Metacapsifer* **Spassky, 1951.**

Diagnosis: Proglottids wider than long, except for gravid ones which may be as long as wide; craspedote. Genital pores unilateral. Testes few (6-8) in antiporal half of segment. Cirrus pouch small. Ovary and postovarian vitelline gland poral. Uterus breaks down into egg capsules, each with several eggs. Parasites of Rodentia (Muridae). Africa.

Type species: *M. aberratus* (Baer, 1924) Spassky, 1951.

3b. Testes present poral to vitelline gland 4

4a. Testes absent anterior to ovary on poral side ....
..................................*Inermercapsifer* **Janicki, 1910. (Fig. 381)**

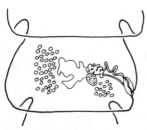

Fig. 381. *Inermercapsifer settii*
Janicki, 1910.

Diagnosis: Proglottides craspedote, wider than long, except for gravid ones. Genital pores unilateral. Cirrus pouch small. Genital ducts passing between osmoregulatory canals. Testes numerous, in single or double field but absent anterior to vagina on poral side. Ovary and postovarian vitelline gland poral. Vagina posterior to cirrus pouch. Seminal receptacle small. Uterus breaks down into egg capsules each containing several eggs. Parasites of Rodentia, Hyracoidea, and accidentally in man. Africa, Syria, Brazil, Sinai.

Type species: *I. hyracis* (Rudolphi, 1808) Janicki, 1910.

4b. **Testes present anterior to ovary on poral side** ....
....*Pericapsifer* **Spassky, 1951. (Fig. 382)**

Fig. 382. *Pericapsifer pagenstecheri* (Setti, 1897) Spassky, 1951. After Bischoff (1913).

Diagnosis: Proglottids wider than long, craspedote. Genital pores unilateral. Cirrus pouch small. Testes numerous, distributed throughout medulla, both before and behind vagina. Ovary and postovarian vitelline gland poral. Vagina posterior to cirrus pouch. Seminal receptacle present. Uterus forming egg capsules, each with several eggs. Parasites of Hyracoidea. Africa.

Type species: *P. pagenstecheri* (Setti, 1897) Spassky, 1951.

Key to the Orders in Subclass Cestodaria

1a. **Genital pores at or near posterior end. Uterine pore anterior**
....**Amphilinidea Poche, 1922.**
Diagnosis: Body flattened, elongated, with indistinct hold-fast mechanism at anterior end. Genital pores near posterior end. Testes in two lateral, preovarian fields. Ovary posterior. Vitelline glands lateral. Uterus N-shaped or looped. Uterine pore near anterior end. Parasites of fishes and turtles. (P. 247)

1b. **Genital and uterine pores in anterior fourth of body** ....
....**Gyrocotylidea Poche, 1926.**
Diagnosis: Body flattened, elongated, with indistinct holdfast mechanism at anterior end. Posterior forming a crenulated rosette or a long, slender cylinder. Male pore anterior, ventral. Testes an-

terior, in two lateral fields. Ovary posterior. Vaginal pore anterior, dorsal. Vitellaria follicular, lateral. Uterine pore anterior, ventral. Parasites of marine fishes. (P. 251)

Key to Families of Amphilinidea

1a. Uterus N-shaped, with terminal ascending limb lateral ....
......................................Amphilinidae Claus, 1879. (P. 247)
Diagnosis: Small proboscis-like or sucker-like apical organ present at anterior end. Body flat, elongate, with rounded margins. Testes numerous, in two lateral fields or scattered throughout body. Cirrus and vaginal pores at or near posterior end of body, opening separately or in common atrium. Ovary posterior. Vitellaria follicular, in lateral fields. Uterus slender, N-shaped, with descending limb median. Uterine pore anterior. Osmoregulatory canals two, with common posterior pore. Parasites of coelomic cavity of Teleostei, Chondrostei and Chelonia.
Type genus: *Amphilina* Wagener, 1858.

1b. Uterus looped, with terminal ascending limb median ....
......................Austramphilinidae Johnston, 1931. (P. 250)
Diagnosis: Rostellum-like organ with sheath at anterior end. Body flat, slender. Testes numerous, mostly lateral. Cirrus and vaginal pores at or near posterior end of body, opening separately. Ovary posterior. Vitellaria lateral. Seminal receptacle large, median. Uterus with terminal ascending limb median. Uterine pore anterior. Parasites of Chelonia and fishes.
Type genus: *Austramphilinia* Johnston, 1931.

Key to Genera of Amphilinidae

1a. Vaginal pore marginal .....*Amphilina* Wagener, 1858. (Fig. 383)
Diagnosis: Body leaf-shaped, flattened. Anterior end bluntly pointed, with sucker-like depression. Posterior end rounded or slightly concave. Testes numerous, scattered throughout body. Cirrus long, slender, armed with hooks at the end, opening at posterior end of body. Ovary lobated, irregular, in posterior third of body. Vitellaria lateral. Vagina crossing vas deferens, opening on margin of body near posterior end. Accessory seminal receptacle absent. Descending and first ascending limbs of uterus mostly on same side of body. Uterine pore near anterior end. Parasites of sturgeons. Europe, Japan, North America.
Type species: *A. foliacea* (Rudolphi, 1819) Wagner, 1858.

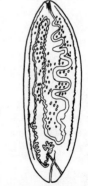

Fig. 383. *Amphilina foliacea* (Rudolphi, 1819) Wagener, 1858. After Hein *in* Fuhrmann (1930).

1b. Vaginal pore medial 2
2a. Seminal receptacle absent 3
2b. Seminal receptacle present 4
3a. Cirrus opening at posterior end of body ....
....*Gephyrolina* Poche, 1926. (Fig. 384)

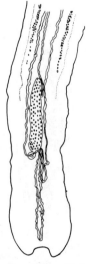

Diagnosis: Anterior end bluntly pointed, with protrusible proboscis. Posterior end rounded except for notches at genital pores. Body elongate, flattened. Testes in lateral fields. Cirrus short, unarmed, opening at posterior end. Ovary elongate, not lobated, near posterior end of body. Vitellaria lateral. Vagina not crossing vas deferens, opening dorsal to cirrus at posterior end of body. Accessory seminal receptacle absent. Descending limb of uterus mostly on same side of body as first ascending limb. Uterine pore anterior, beside proboscis. Eggs with short polar processes. Parasites of siluroid fishes. India.

Type species: G. paragonopora Woodland, 1923.

Fig. 384. Gephyro-
lina   paragonopora
Woodland, 1923.

3b. Cirrus opening at level of posterior end of ovary ....
....*Hunteroides* Johri, 1959. (Fig. 385)

Diagnosis: Scolex well developed, highly muscular, wtih constriction separating it from rest of body. Body large (60 mm) mostly covered with glandular cells. Column of muscles continue from scolex deep into body, bifurcating most of the way. Vitellaria in two narrow lateral fields, extending posteriorly to ovary, apparently in cortical parenchyma. Ovary an elongate mass, medullary, in longitudinal axis of body. Vaginal opening slightly anterior to cirrus opening. Descending limb of uterus median. Uterine pore apparently anterior. Vagina makes a long posterior loop almost to posterior margin of body. Cirrus sac oval, posterior to ovary, slightly left of median line. Testes extend from 6 mm behind scolex to just in front of ovary, lateral to uterine loops, medial to vitellaria. Parasites of siluroid fish. India.

Type species: H. mystei Johri, 1959.

Fig. 385. Hunter-
oides   mystei   Johri,
1959. Posterior end.

4a. Vaginal pore single .... *Gigantolina* **Poche, 1922.** (Fig. 386)

Diagnosis: Both ends blunt. Body very long (38 cm), flattened. Cuticle with reticular sculpturing. Testes very numerous, in lateral fields. Cirrus short, opening at posterior end of body. Ovary bilobed, each dendritic. Vitellaria lateral. Vagina opens dorsally, anterior to cirrus, with distal sphincter. Large seminal receptacle present. Descending limb of uterus median, ascending limbs lateral. Uterine pore ventral, near anterior end. Eggs lacking polar processes. Parasites of marine teleosts. Ceylon.

Type species: *G. magna* Southwell, 1915.

Fig. 386. *Gigantolina magna* Southwell, 1915. Posterior end.

4b. Vaginal pore double 5
5a. Seminal receptacle about one-third as long as body ....
....*Schizochoerus* **Poche, 1922.**

Diagnosis: Body long, narrow, flattened. Ends bluntly pointed. Retractile proboscis on anterior end. Testes numerous, lateral. Cirrus opens at posterior end of body. Ovary round, near posterior end. Vitellaria lateral. Vagina with double opening anterior to cirrus; sphincter absent. Seminal receptacle about one-third body length. Descending limb of uterus on same side of body as last ascending limb. Uterine pore near anterior end. Eggs lacking polar processes. Parasites of teleosts. Brazil.

Type species: *S. liguloides* (Diesing, 1850) Poche, 1922.

5b. Seminal receptacle about one-sixth as long as body ....
....*Nesolecithus* **Poche, 1922.** (Fig. 387)

Diagnosis: Body leaf-shaped, flattened, with rather pointed ends. Proboscis with short retractor muscle. Testes numerous, lateral. Cirrus opens at posterior end of body. Ovary round, near posterior end of body. Vitellaria lateral. Vagina with double opening slightly anterior to cirrus pore. Seminal receptacle one-twelfth to one-sixth length of body. Uterus with descending limb on same side of body as ascending limb. Uterine pore at anterior end of body. Parasites of teleosts. Brazil, Africa.

Type species: *N. janicki* Poche, 1922.

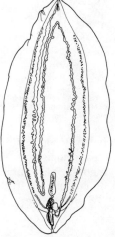

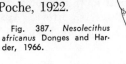

Fig. 387. *Nesolecithus africanus* Donges and Harder, 1966.

Key to Genera of Austramphilinidae

1a. Vaginal pore separated from male pore ....
....*Gyrometra* Yamaguti, 1954. (Fig. 388)

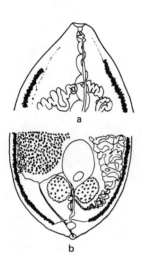

Fig. 388. *Gyrometra albotaenia* Yamaguti, 1954. a. Anterior end. b. Posterior end.

Diagnosis: Body long, ribbonlike. Anterior end conical, with apical pit; posterior end rounded, with button-like papilla. Testes, small, numerous, in two narrow lateral bands beginning at different levels shortly behind anterior end and ending at level of ovary or anterior to it. Male pore on posterior papilla. Ovary bilobed, near posterior end. Vaginal pore middorsal, slightly anterior to male pore. Vagina with distal sphincter. Very large seminal receptacle anterior to ovary, with small accessory receptacle ventral near its posterior end. Vitellaria in two lateral narrow bands from near anterior end to level of vaginal pore. Terminal ascending limb of uterus median, laterally coiled, opening into apical pit along with frontal glands. Parasites of coelom of pristopomid fishes. Macassar, Celebes.

Type species: *G. albotaenia* Yamaguti, 1954.

1b. Vaginal pore joined with male pore ....
.............................*Austramphilina* Johnston, 1931. (Fig. 389)

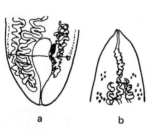

Fig. 389. *Austramphilina elongata* Johnston, 1931. a. Posterior end. b. Anterior end.

Diagnosis: Body long, thin, pointed on anterior end, with apical pit; rounded at posterior end. Cuticle pitted. Testes numerous, lateral, extending from near where median limb of uterus crosses other limbs to just anterior to level of ovary. Male genital pore at posterior end of body. Ovary compact, not bilobed, near posterior end of body at base of seminal receptacle. Vitellaria in narrow lateral bands. Vagina opening together with male pore. Distal end of vagina ciliated, with diverticulum halfway along its length. Seminal receptacle very large, with two small accessory receptacles. Terminal ascending limb of uterus median, with lateral loops, opening at base of apical pit. Parasites of coelom of freshwater tortoise. Australia.

Type species: *A. elongata* Johnston, 1931.

DIAGNOSIS OF THE ONLY FAMILY IN GYROCOTYLIDEA
Gyrocotylidae Benham, 1901

Diagnosis: Anterior end provided with holdfast mechanism. Posterior end with cylindrical or funnel-like opening which may be frilled. Body elongate, may have crenulated margins. Testes lateral, anterior. Cirrus pore ventral, submedian, near anterior end. Vaginal pore dorsal, submedian near anterior end. Ovary follicular, posterior to uterus. Vitellaria follicular, lateral. Uterine pore preequatorial, ventral. Eggs operculate, unembryonated. Parasites of Chondrichthyes, mainly Holocephali.

Type genus: Gyrocotyle Diesing, 1850.

Key to the Genera of Gyrocotylidae

1a. Body margins crenulated, posterior end with ruffle ....
....Gyrocotyle Diesing, 1850. (Fig. 390)

Diagnosis: Body elongate, flattened, with spinous cuticle and crinkled margins. Anterior end with cone containing sucker-like cavity. Posterior end with rosette-like adhesive organ, variably crenulated according to state of contraction. Testes mainly lateral, in anterior part of body. Male genital pore anterior, submedial, ventral. Ovary midequatorial. Vitellaria lateral anterior to ovary, confluent posterior to ovary. Vaginal pore anterior, submedial, dorsal. Vagina long, mainly median. Seminal receptacle present. Uterus preovarian, median with lateral loops, large uterine sac present. Uterine pore midventral, posterior to male pore. Parasites of Chondrichthyes, mainly Holocephali. Cosmopolitan.

Type species: G. rugosa Diesing, 1850.

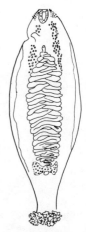

Fig. 390. *Gyrocotyle rugosa* Diesing, 1850. After Manter (1953).

1b. Body margins not crenulated, posterior end a long, cylindrical tube ....Gyrocotyloides Fuhrmann, 1931. (Fig. 391)

Fig. 391. *Gyrocoty-loides nybelini* Fuhr-mann, 1931.

Diagnosis: Body elongate, flattened, with smooth margins. Anterior end broad, with deep, weak sucker; posterior end attenuated, cylindrical, containing a tube with powerful distal sphincter and opening dorsally at its anterior end. Cuticle lacking spines. Testes numerous, lateral, preovarian. Ventral cirrus pore opens into preequatorial, submedian atrium anterior to level of vaginal pore. Ovary median near posterior end of broad portion of body. Vitellaria? Vaginal pore dorsal, behind level of cirrus pore. Uterus nearly straight, median, preovarian, with large distal sac. Uterine pore midventral, behind level of vaginal pore. Eggs operculate, unembryonated when laid. Two excretory pores near anterior end of body. Parasites of Holocephali. Locality unknown.

Type species: G. nybelini Fuhrmann, 1931.

GLOSSARY OF TERMS USED IN THIS BOOK

Acetabulum—a muscular sucker.

Acini—saccular glands comprised of a few cells grouped together, possessing a common duct.

Acoelous—lacking a body cavity (coelom).

Acraspedote—condition when an anterior proglottid does not overlap the next posterior one.

Alveolar hydatid—the larval form of *Echinoccocus multilocularis,* characterized by being subdivided into many compartments containing protoscoleces and by an exogenous, infiltrative type of growth.

Anapolytic—condition when terminal proglottids become gravid before detaching.

Androgyny—type of maturation when the male organs develop before the female organs do.

Anoperculate—absence of an operculum on an egg.

Apical disk—a flattened knob on the apex of a scolex.

Apolytic—condition when the terminal proglottids detach before becoming gravid.

Atrium—a sunken chamber into which open various reproductive ducts.

Bilateral symmetry—type of symmetry when each lateral half is the mirror image of the other.

Blastocyst—a bladder at the posterior end of a plerocercus, into which the rest of the body can withdraw.

Bothridium—a muscular holdfast organ, of various shapes, on the scoleces of the Tetraphyllidea, Diphyllidea and Trypanorhyncha.

Bothrium—a dorsal or ventral, longitudinal groove in the scolex of pseudophyllideans.

Brood capsule—an attached cyst inside a hydatid, containing protoscoleces.

Cephalic peduncle—an elongated portion of a scolex posterior to the suckers, bothria or bothridia.

Ceromer—a knob-like appendage, often bearing the hooks of the oncosphere, on a larval tapeworm.

Chainette—an externo-lateral, longitudinal row of hooks on the tentacles of some Trypanorhyncha.

Cirrus—the male copulatory organ.

Cirrus pore—the opening through which the cirrus is extruded.

Cirrus pouch—a muscular organ containing the introverted cirrus and the ejaculatory duct or internal seminal vesicle.

Coenurus—a larval form of *Taenia* with a few to several scoleces but no brood capsules or daughter cysts.

Coracidium—a ciliated oncosphere, found in the Pseudophyllidea and Trypanorhyncha.

Cortex—region exterior to the outer longitudinal muscle bundles.

Craspedote—condition when an anterior proglottid overlaps the next posterior one.

Cysticercoid—a larval form of tapeworm developing from an oncosphere, with a solid body, lacking a bladder.

Cysticercus—a larval form of some *Taenia* developing from an oncosphere, possessing a fluid-filled bladder and a single scolex.

Daughter cyst—a bladder containing fluid and protosceleces which has formed by endogenous or exogenous budding of the germinal epithelium of a unilocular hydated.

Decacanth—the ten-hooked larva that hatches from the egg of a cestodarian. Also called lycophore.

Definitive host—the host in which a parasite attains sexual maturity.

Dioecious—condition where male and female gonads are found in separate individuals.

Egg capsule—a structure containing one or more eggs of a tapeworm, in the absence of a uterus.

Ejaculatory duct—that portion of the vas deferens enclosed within the cirrus pouch.

Endogenous budding—inward proliferation of germinal epithelium of a hydatid, resulting in a brood cyst or daughter cyst.

Exogenous budding—proliferation of germinal epithelium of a hydated outward through the cyst wall, often resulting in a daughter cyst.

External seminal vesicle—a dilation of the vas deferens before it reaches the cirrus pouch, which stores sperm cells.

Extravascular—lateral to the osmoregulatory canals.

Fimbriate—with finger-like projections.

Flame cell—an excretory cell with a tuft of cilia extending into a fine efferent tubule.

Fossette—a ciliated, sensory pit.

Genital atrium—a sunken, pit-like structure into which the genital ducts open.

Gonochoristic—dioecious, having the sexes separated into different individuals.

Gonoduct—a duct of a reproductive system.

Gonopore—genital pore, exterior orifice of a reproductive tract.

Gravid—filled with eggs.

Gynandry—condition when the female reproductive system matures earlier than the male system.

Heteracanthus—hook arrangement on a trypanorhynchan tentacle in which there is no chainette and the hooks are in alternating oblique rows extending from the internal to the external surfaces. The hooks may be similar in size and shape (homeomorphus) or dissimilar (heteromorphus).

Hexacanth—the larva that hatches from the egg of the Eucestoda, bearing six hooks.

Homeoacanthus—hook arrangement on a trypanorhynchan tentacle in which the hooks are approximately alike in size and shape and are arranged in spirals or quincunxes.

Hydatid—a complex cysticercus in *Echinococcus* which normally contains a great number of protosceleces, and buds daughter and brood cysts by endogenous or exogenous proliferation of germinal epithelium.

Hydated sand—free protosceleces in a hydated cyst.

Hypodermic impregnation—sperm transfer by forcefully piercing of the body wall by the cirrus.

Intermediate host—a host in which development of a parasite occurs but sexual maturity is not accomplished.

Internal seminal vesicle—a dilation of the ejaculatory duct within the cirrus pouch, that serves to store sperm cells.

Intervascular—medial to osmoregulatory canals.

Introvert—an organ capable of being withdrawn into the body or scolex.

Koilon—the horny, acellular lining of a birds gizzard.

Loculum—a shallow cavity.

Lycophore—the ten-hooked larva that emerges from the egg of a cestodarian.

Medulla—interior to the outer longitudinal muscle bundles.

Mehlis' glands—unicellular glands surrounding the oötype which contribute a thin membrane around the zygote and its accessary materials.

Metascolex—the posterior portion of a divided scolex.

Monoecious—hermaphroditic, containing gonads of both sexes within a single individual.

Monozoic—not strobilated, the entire body consisting of a single unit.

Multilocular hydated—the specialized cysticercus of *Echinococcus multilocularis,* in which much exogenous budding occurs resulting in infiltration of host tissues.

Myzorhynchus—a slender, muscular stalk arising from the apex of the scolex in some Tetraphyllidea.

Neck—the unsegmented zone between the scolex and strobila of many tapeworms.

Neoteny—the occurrence of sexual maturity in an otherwise juvenile form.

Oncosphere—a hexacanth, the six-hooked larva that emerges from the egg of a eucestodan.

Ootype—the area where the oviduct, vitelline duct and uterus join.

Operculum—a lid-like covering of the opening of an egg shell.

Osmoregulatory canals—the main canals of the excretory system, usually longitudinal with transverse anastomoses but occasionally reticular.

Osmoregulatory system—the excretory system of tapeworms, mainly used in water balance.

Ovary—the female gonad, the origin of ova.

Oviduct—a tube extending from the ovary to the ootype.

Ovicapt—a muscular sphincter on the oviduct.

Parasitologist—a harmless drudge who peers into dark places.

Paratenic host—a host in which a larval stage of a parasite may successfully maintain itself but cannot further develop. Often serves as an ecological bridge between intermediate and definitive hosts.

Parenchyma—a loosly organized mass of cells and fibers.

Pars bothridialis—region of scolex of Trypanorhyncha from apex to posterior margins of bothridia.

Pars bulbosa—region of scolex of Trypanorhyncha occupied by the tentacle bulbs.

Pars postbulbosa—any extensive region of the scolex of a trypanorhynchan posterior to the pars bulbosa.

Pars vaginalis—region of scolex of Trypanorhyncha traversed by tentacle sheaths.

Paruterine organ—a fibrous appendage to the uterus which receives the eggs and retains them in a sac at one end, while the uterus degenerates.

Plerocercoid—the third-stage larva of pseudophyllidean and proteocephalan cestodes, characterized by a solid body.

Plerocercus—the third-stage larva of some Trypanorhyncha, characterized by a posterior bladder (blastocyst) into which the rest of the body can withdraw.

Poeciloacanthus—hook arrangement on a trypanorhynchan tentacle in which a chainette or longitudinal band of small hooks is present on the externo-lateral surface.

Polyzoic—condition when the body is formed of two or more proglottids.

Prebulbar organ—a small organ, often red, of unknown function located anterior to a tentacle bulb in certain trypanorhynchans.

Procercoid—the second-stage larva of several orders of tapeworms. It usually bears the hexacanth hooks near the posterior end.

Proglottid—a tapeworm segment.

Proscolex—the anterior portion of a divided scolex.

Protandry—condition in a monoecious cestode when the male reproductive system matures first.

Protogyny—condition in a monoecious cestode when the female reproductive system matures first.

Protonephridium—see flame cell.

Protoscolex—the scolex of a larval tapeworm. It may have the same dimensions and armature of the adult.

Pseudoscolex—a holdfast made of distorted anterior proglottids, in the absence of the true scolex.

Quincunx—an arrangement of five objects such that four form a rectangle with the fifth in its center.

Scolex—the holdfast and locomotor organ of a tapeworm, usually considered to be at the anterior end.

Seminal receptacle—a dilation of the vagina which receives and stores sperm from the male system.

Sparganum—a plerocercoid whose identity is unknown.

Strobila—the body of a tapeworm.

Strobilization—the process of budding new proglottids, usually in the neck region. (But see *Haplobothrium*).

Strobilocercoid—a cysticercoid that shows strobilization.

Strobilocercus—the cysticercus of *Taenia taeniaeformis* which bears an immature strobila anterior to the bladder.

Testis—the male gonad, the origin of sperm.

Tetrathyridium—the cysticercoid of *Mesocestoides* which has a solid body and a scolex not surrounded by special membranes.

Unilocular hydatid—a specialized cysticercus found in most species of *Echinoccocus,* bearing a great many protoscoleces internally and budding daughter cysts endogenously and rarely exogenously.

Uterine pore—the opening through which eggs escape from the uterus. It may be preformed or appear spontaneously upon disintegration of the gravid proglottid.

Uterovaginal canal—a canal into which both uterus and vagina open.

Uterus—the organ receiving eggs from the oviduct. It may hold them until their release or be replaced by egg capsules or paruterine organs.

Vagina—the duct leading from the exterior to the oviduct, through which the sperm travel to reach the ova.

Vaginal pore—the external opening of the vagina.

Vas deferens—the duct receiving sperm from the vasa efferentia and through which they move toward the cirrus pouch.

Vas efferens—a delicate canal extending from a testis to the vas deferens.

Velum—the overlapping portion of a craspedote proglottid.

Vitellarium—the organ which provides cells and materials used for eggshell formation.

Vitelline duct—the canal through which vitelline cells and products move from the vitellarium to the ootype.

Vitelline reservoir—an enlarged portion of vitelline duct which stores vitelline products until used.

Zerney's vesicle—a saccular diverticulum arising from the point where the seminal vesicle joins the cirrus pouch.

BIBLIOGRAPHY

Selected references, including keys mentioned in text

ABULADZE, K. I. 1964. Essentials of Cestodology. Vol. IV. Taeniata. Akad. Nauk SSSR, Moscow. 530 p. (In Russian).

ARTYUKH, E. S. 1966. Essentials of Cestodology. Vol. VI. Davaineata. Akad. Nauk SSSR, Moscow. 511 p. (In Russian).

BAER, J. G. 1948. Contributions à l'étude des cestodes de sélachiens. I-IV. Bull. Soc. Sci. Nat. Neuchâtel 71: 63-122.

CALENTINE, R. L., and J. S. MACKIEWICZ. 1966. Monobothrium ulmeri n. sp. (Cestoda; Caryophyllaeidae) from North American Catostomidae. Trans. Am. Micr. Soc. 85: 516-520.

CALENTINE, R. L., and M. ULMER. 1961. Khawia iowensis n. sp. (Cestoda: Caryophyllaeidae) from Cyprinus carpio L. in Iowa. J. Parasit. 47: 795-805.

CHANDLER, A. C. 1948. New species of the genus Schistotaenia with a key to the known species. Trans. Am. Micr. Soc. 67: 169-176.

DEBLOCK, S. 1964. Les Hymenolepis de Charadriiformes. (Second note à propos d'une vingtaine d'autres descriptions dont deux nouvelles). Ann. Parasit. 39: 695-754.

DOLLFUS, R. Ph. 1942. Études critiques sur les tétrarhynques du Museum de Paris. Arch. Mus. Hist. Nat. 19: 1-466.

DOLLFUS, R. Ph. 1957. Miscellanea helminthologica maroccana. XXI. Quelques cestodes d'Otidiformes, principalement d'Afrique du Nord. Repartition géographiques des cestodes d'Otidiformes. Arch. l'Inst. Past. Maroc. 5: 329-402.

FREEMAN, R. S. 1959. On the taxonomy of the genus Cladotaenia. The life histories of C. globifera (Batsch, 1786) and C. circi Yamaguti, 1935, and a note on distinguishing between the plerocercoids of the genera Paruterina and Cladotaenia. Canad. J. Zool. 37: 317-340.

FRESE, V. I. 1965. Essentials of Cestodology. Vol. V. Proteocephalata. Akad. Nauk SSSR, Moscow. 538 p. (In Russian).

FUHRMANN, O. 1930. Dritte Klasse des Cladus Platyhelminthes. Cestoidea. In Kükenthal's Handbuch der Zoologie. Vol. 2. pp. 141-416.

FUHRMANN, O. 1932. Les Ténias des Oiseux. Mem. Univ. Neuchâtel. Vol. 8. 381 p.

FERNANDO, C. H., and J. I. FURTADO, 1963. A study of some helminth parasites of freshwater fishes in Ceylon. Z. f. Parasitenk. 23: 141-163.

Helminthological Abstracts. 1934—   Commonwealth Agricultural Bureaux. Herts, England.

HOFFMAN, G. L. 1967. Parasites of North American Freshwater Fishes. Univ. California Press, Berkley. 486 p.

HUGHES, R. C. 1941. A key to the species of tapeworms in Hymenolepis. Trans. Am. Micr. Soc. 60: 378-414.

HYMAN, L. H. 1951. The Invertebrates. Vol. II. Platyhelminthes and Rhynchocoela. The Acoelomate Bilateria. McGraw-Hill, New York. 550 p.

Index-Catalog of Medical and Veterinary Zoology. Authors: 1934– U.S. Dept. Agr., Beltsville, Md.

JOYEUX, C., and J. G. BAER. 1936. Cestodes. In Faune de France. Vol. 30. 613 p.

JOYEUX, C. and J. G. BAER. 1961. Classe des Cestodes. Cestoidea Rudolphi. In Traité de Zoologie. Vol. IV. Masson, Paris. 944 p.

KENNEDY, C. R. 1965. Taxonomic studies on *Archigetes* Leuckart, 1878 (Cestoda: Caryophyllaeidae). Parasitology 55: 439-451.

MATHEVOSSIAN, E. M. 1963. Essentials of Cestodology. Vol. III. Dilepidoidea. Akad. Nauk SSSR, Moscow. 687 p. (In Russian).

MEGGITT, F. J. 1924. Cestodes of Mammals. London. 282 p.

METTRICK, D. F. 1958. Helminth parasites of Herfordshire birds. II. Cestodea. J. Helminth. 32: 159-194.

METTRICK, D. F. 1963. Some cestodes of the subfamily Paruterininae Fuhrmann, 1907 from birds in Central Africa. J. Helminth. 37: 319-328.

OLSEN, O. W. 1939. *Tatria duodecacantha,* a new species of cestode (Amabiliidae Braun, 1910) from the pied-billed grebe (*Podilymbus podiceps podiceps* Linn.). J. Parasit. 25: 495-499.

OLSEN, O. W. 1967. Animal Parasites: Their Biology and Life Cycles. 2d. Ed. Burgess, Minneapolis. 346 p.

SCHULTZ, R. L. 1940. Some observations on the amabiliid cestode, *Tatria duodecacantha* Olsen, 1939. J. Parasit. 26: 101-103.

SINGH, K. P. 1959. Some avian cestodes from India. II. Species belonging to the family Dilepididae. Indian J. Helminth. 11: 25-42.

SINGH, K. S. 1948. On a new cestode, *Gangesia lucknowia* (Proteocephalidae) from a freshwater fish, *Eutropiichthys vacha* Day, with a revised key to the species of the genus. Indian J. Helminth. 1: 41-46.

SINGH, K. S. Parasitological survey of Kumaun. Indian J. Helminth. 14: 1-5.

SOULSBY, E. J. L. 1965. Textbook of Veterinary Clinical Parasitology. Vol. I. Helminths. Davis, Philadelphia. 1120 p.

SOUTHWELL, T. 1925. A Monograph on the Tetraphyllidea. Liverpool Univ. Press, Mem. II. 368 p.

SOUTHWELL, T. 1930. Cestoda. In Fauna of British India, Including Ceylon and Burma. Taylor and Francis, London. Vol. I, 391 p. Vol. II, 262 p.

SPASSKY, A. A. 1951. Essentials of Cestodology. Vol. I. Anoplocephalata. Akad. Nauk SSSR, Moscow. 783 p. (English translation available from U. S. Office of Technical Services, Department of Commerce, Wash. D. C.)

SPASSKY, A. A. 1963. Essentials of Cestodology. Vol. II. Hymenolepididae. Akad. Nauk SSSR, Moscow. 418 p. (In Russian).

SPASSKAYA, L. P. 1966. Cestodes of Birds of SSSR. Akad. Nauk SSSR, Moscow. 698 p. (In Russian).

TENORA, F. 1964. On the systematic situation of tapeworms of the family Catenotaeniidae Spassky, 1950. Zool. Listy. Brno. 13: 333-352.

WARDLE, R. A., and J. A. McLEOD. 1952. The Zoology of Tapeworms. Hafner, New York. 780 p.

WILLIAMS, H. H. 1966. The ecology, functional morphology and taxonomy of *Echeneibothrium* Beneden, 1849 (Cestoda: Tetraphyllidea), a revision of the genus and comments on *Discobothrium* Beneden, 1870, *Pseudathobothrium* Baer, 1956, and *Phormobothrium* Alexander, 1963. Parasitology. 56: 227-285.

WILLIAMS, H. H. 1968. The taxonomy, ecology and host-specificity of some Phyllobothriidae (Cestoda: Tetraphyllidea), a critical revision of *Phyllobothrium* Beneden, 1849 and comments on some allied genera. Phil. Trans. Roy. Soc. London 786: 231-307.

YAMAGUTI, S. 1959. Systema Helminthum. Vol. II. The Cestodes of Vertebrates. Interscience, New York. 860 p.

INDEX